PSYCHOLOGICAL ASPECTS
OF PHYSICAL SYMPTOMS

**APPLETON
PSYCHIATRY
SERIES**

edited by

**THOMAS F. DWYER, M.D.
FRED H. FRANKEL, M.D.
MICHAEL T. McGUIRE, M.D.**

**Department of Psychiatry
Massachusetts General Hospital
Boston, Massachusetts**

APPLETON-CENTURY-CROFTS
Division of Meredith Corporation
NEW YORK

PSYCHOLOGICAL ASPECTS OF PHYSICAL SYMPTOMS

A Dynamic Study of Forty-five Hospitalized Medical Patients

SAMUEL SILVERMAN, M.D.
Assistant Clinical Professor of Psychiatry,
Faculty of Medicine, Harvard University

CONTENTS

PART ONE   *Introduction*

Goals of This Study   3

Basic Concepts of the Mind-Body Relationship:
Historical Review   5

Psychological Stress and Somatic Reactions   22

Methods and Material Used in This Study   31

PART TWO   *Case Histories*

1.   Stomach Complaints: Psychological Significance
      of Associated Sensory Perceptions   41

2.   Fever and Critical Loss of Human Relationships   48

3.   Pruritus Ani and Mouth Lesions in a Markedly
      Infantile Patient   59

4.   Shifting Gastrointestinal and Respiratory Symp-
      toms during Prolonged Emotional Tension   67

5.   Painful Joints and Disguised Psychological Stress   77

6.   Hematemesis, Abnormal Electroencephalogram,
      and Psychotic Episode   85

7.   Lower Extremity Pain Related to Multiple Psy-
      chological Factors   96

8.   Cough and Depression   104

9. Vertigo in Gastrointestinal Disease: Somatic Equivalents of the Affects   111

10. Itching Ears: Adaptive Processes in Chronic Illness   121

11. Sore Legs, Alcoholism, and Secondary Gain   128

12. Epigastric Pain and Indigestion: Symbolic Aspects   138

13. Dyspnea Related to Anniversary Stress   144

14. Stomach Pain: Psychological Aspects of Clinical and Laboratory Procedures   151

15. Cerebral Embolism in an Uncommunicative Patient   158

16. Sore Throat: Symbolism of Body Organs   159

17. Stomach Pain and Depression   164

18. Nausea, Flank Pain, and Recurrent Psychological Losses   169

19. Gastrointestinal Symptoms in a Loss-sensitive Patient   180

20. Chronic Epigastric Discomfort: The Stomach as Target Organ   186

21. Stomach Pain in Remission with Rapidly Shifting Psychological Defenses   193

22. Gastrointestinal Complaints: Patient's Need for Diagnosis of Organic Illness   198

23. Pain in Back and Extremities Related to Psychological Stress   205

24. Chest Pain, Alcoholism, and Resistance to Psychotherapy   213

25. Chronic Ulcer Symptoms: Difficulties in Following Medical Advice   220

26. Anorexia in a Patient with Markedly Unstable Psychophysical Equilibrium   227

27. Eye Trouble, Endocrine Dysfunction, and Psychotic Episode   232

28. Epigastric Distress, Surgical Intervention, and Chronic Neurosis   241

29. Emotional Conflict Associated with Endocrine Dysfunction   247

30. Chills and Fever in a Markedly Neurotic Patient   254

31. Hazy Vision, Recurrent Stress, and Physical Crises   262

32. Chest Pain Related to Psychological and Bacteriological Factors   273

33. Back Pain: Psychological Aspects   280

34. Constipation, Backache, and Somatic Identification   287

35. Itching, Nausea, and Generalized Malaise: New Symptoms (Readmission of Case 28)   296

36. Pain in the Back, Multiple Stress, and the Effect of Certain Medical Procedures   302

37. Chest Pain in a Highly Narcissistic Patient   310

38. Dyspnea, Somatic Identification, and Multiple Psychophysical Vicissitudes 316

39. Sore Throat in the Presence of Acute and Chronic Stress 323

40. Feverishness and Headache: The Role of Environmental Factors 329

41. Abdominal and Back Pain: Influence of Somatic Identification 333

42. Biliary Symptoms, Syncope, and Psychological Stress 340

43. Episodes of Weakness in a Patient with Severe Neurosis 348

44. Throat and Stomach Symptoms as Symbolic Expressions of Emotional Tension 355

45. Back Pain in an Accident-prone Patient 361

46. Abdominal Cramps Associated with Marital Crisis 366

PART THREE *Discussion*

Results 377

Theoretical Implications 414

Some Clinical Observations 419

Bibliography 431

Author Index 441

Subject Index 445

PSYCHOLOGICAL ASPECTS OF PHYSICAL SYMPTOMS

PART ONE

Introduction

Goals of This Study

This work was undertaken in order to add a new dimension to the study of the relationship between psychological factors and physical symptoms. Hopefully, it will be of use to all who are interested in this problem, be they psychiatrists or not. Its substance is the reporting of objective, considerably detailed raw data of psychiatric interviews done under standardized conditions and unbiased with regard to diagnostic category, duration, or severity of illness, in a series of 30 to 31-year-old males consecutively admitted to the medical wards of a general hospital over a period of four months. This kind of material has not been available hitherto in the psychosomatic literature. It provides a unique reservoir from which inferences can be drawn concerning the role of psychological factors in the development, exacerbation, and remission of physical symptoms in patients with and without physical disease. Furthermore, the study illustrates how the gathering of such information about any given patient on a medical (or surgical) ward may be accomplished in an economical, meaningful way and documents how this can then be translated into relevant psychodynamic formulations which have both research and clinical application. Interviewing technique, setting of interviews, choice of population, and other aspects of the methodology employed can be replicated. In each case a final summary of the physical findings is presented, but the psychological data are explored in detail for a number of explicit variables. These include overt and hidden indicators of psychological stress, shifts in psychological equilibrium, affective responses, psychological mechanisms of defense, processes of somatic identification, psychological sensitization or conditioning of organ systems, and recurrent sensorimotor patterns. The last three variables are relatively less well known than the others. None, however, have been investigated in the past either singly or in multiples by the methods to be presented in this work. Further definition and elaboration of the variables are given later. In each case, in addition to a tabulation of these dynamic factors, there is a discussion of pertinent clinical and theo-

3

retical points relevant to the particular kind of illness under consideration. There are also references to the work of others on the psychological aspects of the principal symptoms and diagnostic categories involved. In a separate section, the overall findings are reported in terms of each psychological variable and its theoretical implications. The role of different combinations of psychological variables in the development of physical symptoms in organic and nonorganic illness is also considered and compared with studies in the same area by other investigators, whenever available. In addition, the possibility of using the variables both as predictive factors and in further research on organic disease is explored. Finally, the usefulness of these psychological factors for application in clinical practice is discussed in some detail.

Basic Concepts of the Mind-Body Relationship: Historical Review

The relationship between mind and body has stimulated man's curiosity, inquiry, and speculation for many centuries. It will be useful to review earlier concepts dealing with this general problem, and then survey more specifically modern psychiatric studies of patients with physical disease. Alexander (1962), in his historical overview of psychosomatic medicine, points out the centuries' long conflict between the animistic concept of nature and the discoveries of physical causality. Primitive man's psychology developed from subjective and introspective experiences. His actions were undoubtedly related to his emotions in a simple fashion. Fear made him run; anger made him attack. In turn, he most likely projected such motivations to all natural events, there being no scientific explanations then available to him. These primitive notions fostered the development of demonology which exerted a far-reaching adverse effect on all subsequent psychology, causing suspicion to be cast even on those observations which were rational and empirical. Nevertheless, the search for materialistic explanations through the periods of the Greek and Roman civilizations did not eradicate the concept of the psyche. When these cultures passed, there was a return of demonological influence which lasted through the Middle Ages. With the advent of the Renaissance and the growing domination of the scientific approach there was a concomitant recession of interest in psychological phenomena. However, emotions are so closely associated with physiological processes and bodily disease that the relationship could not be altogether ignored. In the seventeenth century, which saw great triumphs in physics, astronomy, and human anatomy, what we now refer to as psychosomatic medicine was anticipated by the two most famous physicians of the times, Thomas Sydenham and William Harvey. In the works of the former, one finds the stated belief that almost any of the manifestations of physical illness may be simulated by hysterical symptoms. Harvey likewise

5

recognized the many bodily changes associated with aroused emotions, referring particularly to cardiac dysfunction. Despite these observations, the persistent progress and accumulation of knowledge in the natural sciences relegated the subject of psychology mostly to the poets and philosophers until well into the nineteenth century.

Stainbrook (1952), in his survey of psychosomatic medicine in the nineteenth century, notes that there were two basic and conflicting philosophical approaches to the problem of the relationship between mind and body. Descartes postulated an interactionism in which psyche and soma were considered distinct entities, although reacting upon one another. On the other hand, Spinoza's doctrine of parallelism held that mind and body were coexistent aspects and manifestations of a single fundamental substance. Two other basic but also opposite concepts about the mind-body problem came from the emerging medical thinking of those times. One was a denial that mental processes could cause or affect brain processes, as epitomized in the physiologist Moleschott's "Kein Gedanke ohne Phosphor." This focus on the physicochemical aspects of the mind-body problem was especially championed by Griesinger and echoed by Kraepelin. The other was the effect of Mesmerism in propounding the influence of mind on body. According to Margette (1950), the first person actually to use the term *psychosomatic* in medicine was Johann Christian Heinroth in his treatise "Lehrbuch der Stoerungen des Seelenlebens." His thinking was representative of the trend toward excess speculation and generalization which lent a romantic tinge to the ideas about the relationship of mind and body. He considered that the body is the somatic abode of the soul, that sin causes disease which affects the soul and, in turn, the body. It should be noted, however, that in some of these romantic concepts could be found precursors of later ideas about the unconscious. In the latter part of the century there was a considerable gathering of material relating emotional disturbance to physical disease, but with better controlled and more reasoned observations. The work of the eminent French physician Féré is illustrative of the keen appreciation by many physicians of the existence of these phenomena, even though these were set forth on an ancedotal, descriptive level and limited by the actual medical knowledge of the times.

Excerpts from Chapter VI of Féré's book *The Pathology of Emotions*, published in 1899, are here quoted for the purpose of illustrating the scope of these observations:

Although the proposition may not be one of absolute exactitude, one can say that in general the local effects of an emotion are always the same in an identical person and manifest themselves toward the organ which

offers normally a congenital or acquired defect. . . . They are most frequently the sad emotions which have pathological effects. . . .

No one doubts that violent and repeated emotions can influence in
a prejudicial manner, organic diseases of the heart and large vessels . . . can
provoke troubles of the peripherical (peripheral) circulation . . . ruptures
of altered vessels, various hemorrhages. . . . Amenorrhea is frequently the
consequence of painful emotions. . . . The moral emotions frequently affect
the respiration: anger can kill by suffocation. . . .

J. Weir appears to be the first who has reported scurvy arising under
bad moral conditions . . . especially the sad affections, nostalgia and the dis-
couragement of defeat . . . (they are) as great as the influences of the physical order: cold, humidity, obscurity, alimentation (which is) insufficient
and of bad quality, etc. . . . In gout . . . the depressing emotions act by
diminishing the elimination of organic wastes which produce accumulation
of uric acid salts. . . . The emotions act not less effectively upon diabetes.
They provoke an exaggeration of glycosuria. . . . The painful moral affections have often provoked the apparition of skin troubles. . . . The fall of
the hair is also common after prolonged anxiety: sometimes . . . in some
hours after the acute emotions. . . . If the tonic emotions facilitate digestion,
as Descartes has already remarked, the painful emotions act in an inverse
sense . . . and are capable of drying the secretion of gastric and intestinal
juices. . . . The sad emotions, especially when they are prolonged, can favor
the formation of biliary calculi, it may be primarily, by the delayed nutrition which they provoke; it may be secondarily by determining an exalta-
tion of brain activity which associates itself to an excess of production of
cholesterine. . . . The acute emotions provoke very often hepatic colics, it
may be by increasing the quantity of bile flowing into the biliary passages,
it may be by the spasmodic contractions of their walls.

A moral emotion can suspend the secretion of milk . . . Convulsions
of infancy can have their cause in an anger or violent chagrin of the nurse.
. . . A much more common accident, but which might have equally grave
results, is diarrhea. . . . We have seen that the emotions can provoke in the
psychological state, modifications in the urinary secretion and excretion. In
general, polyuria is induced. . . . The influence of the violent emotions upon
the contraction of the uterus muscle, and upon the premature expulsion of
the foetus, has been long known.

Cullen admitted that the sad emotions favour the contagious diseases,
and particularly the plague. . . . Ancient authors make the emotions figure
largely in most of the eruptive fevers. . . . The emotions play also a role in
the evolution of surgical maladies, and especially in their infectious complications. . . . It is admitted that dilatation of smaller vessels favours . . .
phagocytism. . . . In the asthenic emotions, upon the contrary, the inverse
phenomena entail a diminution of circulation . . . bring about a diminution
of the calibre of the vessels, and diminished circulation, and consequently
a condition unfavourable to the issue of the white globules, and to phago-

cytism. The asthenic emotions realize, from this point of view, the same conditions as the traumatisms, fatigue, cold, inanition, blood losses, nerve sections. The conditions of the vessels are not the only ones to change: the phagocytes, and the white globules especially are modified in their vitality, their chimiotaxie, their property of being attracted or repelled by microbes; or their products of secretion vary under the same circumstances. . . .

The genetic and dynamic meaning of the emotional states associated with all these illnesses had to wait on the developments of the twentieth century. Freud's genius created the investigative means to study empirically the effect of unconscious mental processes on bodily function. Psychoanalysis made possible a deeper scientific exploration of the psychological aspects of psychosomatic medicine.

From the very beginning, psychoanalysis postulated that all mental phenomena are derived from an organic substrate. The instinctual drives that are so intimately involved with mental activity are considered to have a somatic origin, though their psychological representations are in the form of perceptions, apperceptions, thoughts expressed by verbal and nonverbal communication, feelings, and behavior. The instinctual force first studied in great detail was the libido which comprises the sexual drives. An electrodynamic or hydrodynamic model was utilized in the early psychoanalytic formulations. Thus sexual energy under repression was considered as flowing from its normal somatic outlet into other bodily areas and so affecting them that they became critical points for the development of symptoms. The blocked libido was thereby thought to be transformed into somatic manifestations in the form of conversion symptoms. These physical symptoms associated with hysteria were early principal objects of psychoanalytic inquiry.

Ferenczi (1919), in addition to noting hysterical disturbances of skeletal musculature, skin, and mucous membrane surfaces, focused on another large group of symptoms found in the hysteric. These he considered to be related to changes in circulatory and glandular functions as well as in processes concerned with "the nourishment of tissues." He also thought that similar dysfunction could be evoked by hypnotism and suggestion in subjects who did not have hysteria. In cases of globus hystericus he postulated that anesthesia of the pharynx and upper esophagus were related to the activation of repressed sexual fantasies dealing with fellatio, cunnilingus, and/or coprophagia, resulting in a symbolic "genitalization" of the mucous membranes of those areas. However, anesthesia was considered to be a "negative expression" of the forbidden fantasies, while the development of globus hystericus would be the "positive expression." He stated that in the latter instance the contractions of circular and longitudinal esophageal muscles actually produced a lump. This, in turn, assumed erotic significance, e.g., possibly the expressed wish for fellatio, though this meaning would be outside the individual's awareness. Ferenczi proposed a special name for this type of symptom formation, calling it a "materialization phenomenon, since its essence consists in the realization of a wish . . . out of the material in the body . . . by a plastic representation. . . ."

However, conversion symptoms, considered derivatives of specific repressed sexual fantasies expressed in symbolic body language, were found not to be the sole explanation of all somatic manifestations related to psychological factors. Freud (1924), writing on "Psychogenic Visual Disturbances," pointed out that unconscious psychological forces may also influence the physiological functions of an organ or body part without the resultant physical manifestations necessarily having a specific or definite psychic meaning. Fenichel (1945) suggested that this kind of physical symptom be called "organ neurotic" in contrast to the conversions.

The physical changes in organic disease also eventually came under psychoanalytic consideration and were first extensively described by Groddeck (1917, 1928) as being greatly influenced by unconscious psychological factors. He made rather dramatic and extreme claims about his successes in using psychoanalytic methods to improve and cure severe physical illnesses, among which were included tuberculosis, gout, scleroderma, and goiter.

Psychoanalytic literature, however, did not contain the term psychosomatic until it was first introduced therein by F. Deutsch in 1927. Some years later (1935), a massive compilation of studies—both analytic and nonanalytic—on the mind-body relationship appeared in the first edition of Dunbar's *Emotions and Bodily Changes*. In 1939 the *Journal of Psychosomatic Medicine* was founded.

Meanwhile, an approach to understanding the interaction of psyche and soma which did not adhere to basic psychoanalytic theory was being developed by A. Meyer (1951) in his school of psychobiology. He pointed out prevailing misconceptions about the mind and body:

More and more we realize that what figures to our mind as matter is much better expressed in terms of combinations of electrons, if not simply of energies, which throw off many of the forbidding and restrictive features of those masses which form the starting point of our concept of inert matter, which is practically sufficient for most demands of ordinary physics, but a hindrance to a better conception of the more complex happenings of biochemistry. Mind, on the other hand, is a sufficiently organized living being in action; and not a peculiar form of mind-stuff. A sufficiently organized brain is the central link, but mental activity is really best understood *in its full meaning as the adaptation and adjustment of the individual as a whole, in contrast to the simple activity of single organs such as those of circulation, respiration, digestion, elimination, or simple reflex activity.*

Meyer attached much importance to the consideration of multiple factors, not only the physical and specifically sexual, but also the socioeconomic and environmental. Data were obtained from carefully taken longitudinal life histories of each patient, but in the compilation and interpretation of the psychological factors, the theory of the unconscious was replaced by the concept of a "more or less conscious."

This psychobiologic approach may be contrasted with studies of psychosomatic problems in which psychological factors were considered to be the basis of specificity for a particular physical disease. Dunbar (1943) postulated the concept of the personality profile, defining it as a characteristic complex of behavioral, ideational, and affective patterns derived from many experiences involving child-mother relationships and later more widespread interactions with people. The patient's life history as described by him and supplementary information from other people who knew the patient constitute the data from which the type of profile is determined. It was assumed that the personality profile can be specific enough to be correlated with definite diseases such as hypertension, peptic ulcer, ulcerative colitis, rheumatoid arthritis, and so on. However, the profile is based on data which are obtained from conscious and superficial recall by the patient and the unavoidably subjective and distorted impressions of those close to him. The concept is static, introduces diffuseness, and does not allow for the interplay of psychological, physical, and environmental forces. Consequently the profile is actually not specific and does not account for the existence of multiple factors.

Interest in the triad of life situations, emotions, and a particular physical disease began to be manifest in the work of various investigators, especially in the early fifties. Holmes et al. (1951) found that a life situation involving conflict and anxiety could increase the intensity of symptoms of rhinitis and sensitive mucous membrane response which may already be present. The responsiveness of nasal tissues to pollens was greatly increased under such circumstances through parasympathetic neural impulses. Reiser et al. (1951a) studied many patients with arterial hypertension and felt their observations demonstrated that the course of the disease was adversely affected by emotionally stressful life situations. They emphasized that the external event has to have a special (traumatic) significance for the individual involved. In 12 representative patients with malignant hypertension (1951b) there were close temporal correlations between onset of the illness and life situations, but the data did not indicate any specificity either of personality structure or conflict situations, nor did it clarify why this particular organ system was affected. It was postulated that an additional factor such as a predisposing renal lesion in patients with coexistent renal disease, but not known as patients with hypertension, was involved.

Hinkle et al. (1951a, 1951b) reviewed the principal observations made on the importance of life experiences in diabetes mellitus, going as far back as three hundred years ago to Thomas Willis. They noted that, beginning with W. C. Menninger in 1935, there had accumulated an increasing amount of evidence for these observations in the work of Daniels, Dunbar, Mirsky, Bruch, Fischer and Dolger, Halliday, and Rosen and Lidz. However, experimental evidence of the relationship between life situations, emotions, and metabolic changes in the diabetic had been less abundant. Mirsky (1946) demonstrated that hyperglycemia and glycosuria could be precipitated in diabetics during psychiatric interviews. Meyer, Bollmeier and Alexander (1945) reported correlations between amount of urinary sugar and attitudes and emotional response of two patients with diabetes mellitus during psychoanalysis. Hinkle et al. (1951a, 1951b), studying three cases chosen from 50, also noted the triggering effect of serious life stress but observed that this in itself was not the cause, since many persons encounter such stress without developing diabetes. The authors pointed to early training, perhaps constitutional factors that might make the stresses specifically meaningful. More detailed influences might be an overly conditioned relationship between an intense need for maternal love and desire for food, especially carbohydrates. Real or symbolic deprivation of maternal love causes great craving for food, leading to obesity, followed later by weight loss, polyuria, thirst—symptoms of the onset of diabetes. Hinkle et al. (1951b) conclude that diabetes mellitus is a disorder of adaptation resulting in reactions to various life stress with a physiological response appropriate to starvation, but ineffective in dealing with the stress.

Duncan et al. (1950) studied 26 unselected cases of paroxysmal arrhythmias, 50 per cent with structural heart disease, and found that the cardiac irregularities occurred during periods in life when the patient was under stress but basic rigidity made adjustment difficult. The personalities of the patients showed no constant or specific pattern, though there were certain recurrent traits, among them unexpressed or inadequately expressed hostility, compulsion, unusual ambition, and long-standing anxiety. Arrhythmia is seen as an adaptational failure since in itself it is purposeless and often more or less disabling. Lidz and Whitehorn (1950) found that when the more subtle manifestations of emotional disturbance are noted, emotional stress will precede the onset of hyperthyroidism in over 90 percent of cases. These traumata are usually not simple, brief, or accidental, but rather continuous, involving important interpersonal relationships. Ripley and Wolff (1950) studied 18 patients with glaucoma and noted that the development and exacerbation of symptoms appeared temporally related to stressful life situations. Important in exacerbation of glaucoma symptoms was emotional tension which found no satisfactory discharge other than actual weeping or lack of tears. It was postulated that both conscious and unconscious psychological forces were related to an imbalance between the sympathetic and parasympathetic divisions of the autonomic nervous system, with accompanying vasomotor responses reflected in variations of blood pressure and intraocular pressure. Holmes and Wolff (1952) found in 65 subjects with backache and 10 without backache that those patients who exhibited the backache syndrome were reacting to security-threatening situations which evoked a variety of affects including anxiety, hostility, and guilt. These subjects showed patterns of skeletal muscle hyperfunction which seemed to be an integral part of "action" type of behavior involved in attempting to adjust to interpersonal and social relationships.

Wolff (1950) emphasized life situations as stresses which exert an influence on many body organs, causing them to react in characteristic, stereotyped ways. It is the occurrence of the external event which is considered to be of primary importance rather than the special, symbolic meaning it may have for the particular person. In other words, X stress causes a stereotyped somatic response in anyone. In a particular individual only one or, at the most, several organ systems will respond to the stress. Persistence of stress results in chronic bodily reactions which in time will produce actual tissue changes. Wolff (1953) states in the preface of his book Stress and Disease:

The common knowledge that man gets sick when life circumstances are adverse, and is healthy when they are propitious has been extended here by precise measurements of bodily functions before, during and after periods of stress.

It is true that Wolff's data are rich in physical details which have been carefully worked out. However, the first part of the quoted statement is highly questionable and, in any event, a most oversimplified presentation of the problem. He does not deal with the below-the-surface psychological responses of the individual. The influence of unconscious mental processes and their complicated hierarchical arrangements and shifts are not taken into account in compiling the psychological data.

Hinkle et al. (1958) studied two groups of Chinese who had come to the United States in pursuit of educational or professional careers. These were selected on the basis of the numbers of episodes of illness they experienced, members of one group being frequently sick, members of the other rarely. The family histories showed no special differences either in health or longevity of kin. Many of the disorders occurring in those frequently sick were of the "familial type:" migraine, allergic rhinitis, myopia. Both groups had experienced many different life experiences. It appeared that the determinants of general susceptibility to illness were both genetic and environmental. However, the life situations themselves were less important than the way in which they were perceived by the individual. In general, those persons more frequently ill found their life experiences to be conflict-laden and, in turn, reacted with greater somatic and psychological dysfunction in their attempts to adapt to the greater number of perceived challenges.

Solomon and Moos (1964) in their theoretical integration of the relation between stress, emotions, immunity, and illness in general, refer first to the findings in a particular disease entity, rheumatoid arthritis. In its pathogenesis an autoantibody to γ-globulin, rheumatoid factor, is considered to be often present. Their thesis is that this illness and others associated with immunological dysfunction (systemic lupus erythematosus, idiopathic thrombocytopenic purpura, thyroid disease, dermatomyositis, polymyositis, scleroderma, ulcerative colitis, myasthenia gravis, and still others) may be influenced at various stages of development by emotions. This may be through CNS-controlled hormone changes. The basic theoretical point presented is "that autoimmunity may be related to relative immunological incompetence and that such immunological incompetence in turn might be related to emotional stress and both anxious and depressive affect, which are associated with elevation of adrenal cortical steroid hormones." They further point to "evidence that host resistance is important in the growth and spread of cancer via immunological mechanisms." It is postulated that a relationship exists between stress, emotions, adrenal corticosteroid levels, immunity, and disease. The article is admittedly highly speculative and the references to personality factors and emotions are quite generalized, largely descriptive, and overshadowed by the emphasis on physiological investigations.

Psychoanalytic concepts make it possible to investigate in depth psychological processes of the individual and provide an operational tool for studying the less obvious or hidden and symbolic significance of stress situations for each person. One very influential pioneer in extending this approach to the study of organic disease and formulating broad concepts in the psychosomatic field was F. Alexander (1950). He introduced the idea of concomitant innervation which states that, if expression of a particular emotional need is blocked, there is prolonged, excessive innervation of the organ associated with such need. This occurs through continuing activity of the autonomic nervous system. The unconscious wish rather than the compensatory conscious opposite reaction (e.g., desire for being taken care of rather than compensatory aggressivity) is used in making the correlations between the stressful emotion and the organ dysfunction. If the repression of this particular emotional need continues a sufficiently long time, chronic innervation of the associated organ or organ systems will result in morphological change and disease.

Alexander also postulated a vector concept for understanding the so-called organ neuroses. He suggested measurement of the participation of the three basic directions which might be taken by the organism in coping with the external environment: reception, elimination, and retention. Their investigation is called vector analysis. Emotional conflict which is reflected in overcompensatory aggressiveness is mediated through the sympathetic nervous system; the resultant smooth muscle constriction is involved in hypertension and the skeletal muscle spasm in rheumatoid arthritis. When conflict is basically expressed in marked passive-receptive tendencies, then the parasympathetic nervous system—linked with storage and retention—is involved, and the compliant organs such as lung and bowel will be affected, resulting in asthma and constipation.

The seven diseases studied by Alexander and his colleagues which led to the so-called specificity hypothesis are duodenal ulcer, ulcerative colitis, asthma, essential hypertension, rheumatoid arthritis, thyrotoxicosis, and neurodermatitis. Characteristic patterns in terms of different constellations of psychological conflict rather than personality profile were described for these seven diseases. For example, French and Alexander (1941) postulated that, in asthma, the conflict centered around marked unresolved dependence on the mother, to such an extent that situations involving or representing a threat of separation from her would precipitate an attack, symbolizing a suppressed cry for her. They felt that a combination of allergen sensitivity and activation of the specific emotional conflict produced the physical symptoms. Later (1962), Alexander maintained that the reference to specificity had been misinterpreted. He pointed out that the characteristic patterns in the seven aforementioned diseases could also be found in patients who did not have physical disease. This can be explained on the basis of multicausal factors. An "X" factor, i.e., a specific organic vulnerability, either genetic or environmentally acquired, is necessary for the development of the organic manifestations in response to particular psychological stress.

However great Alexander's influence has been in psychosomatic investigation, many criticisms have been raised about his theoretical approach. Some of these include omission of other variables, particularly the role of the ego, the great resemblance of psychological constellations described for organic diseases which are unrelated to each other, the insufficiency of a

sympathetic, parasympathetic dysfunction in explaining the difference between diseases, and failure to include the role of the central nervous system,
particularly the limbic and reticular activating systems.

The limited usefulness of stereotypy, specificity, and one-to-one relationships in the study of psychosomatic problems is underscored by Grinker
and Robbins in their *Psychosomatic Case Book*, published in 1954. They
emphasize that rarely has there been an approach to the psychosomatic
field from the standpoint that it is indeed a field, even though many investigators pay "lip service to multiple causality." Their thesis is that the
field should be treated truly as one in which "multiple cyclic, self-corrective
or spiraling transactions occur." The psychosomatic field extends in time
from birth to the end of life. It encompasses all aspects of the study of
living man. Everything happening within or outside the organism influences
both psyche and soma.

The Grinker and Robbins concept of field theory used in considering
the relationship of parts to the whole in the human organism is borrowed
from physics:

*This organization, although constantly in the process of change, has a sta-
bility in its "part-whole" relationships. Viewed during a short time segment
along a spatial dimension it appears as a structure. Viewed as a process in
time during change it is a function. Thus the living organization is a structure-function of which special aspects become accentuated depending on
the position of the observer.*

Structure-function may be called either an organization or a field whose
parts are not independent, self-acting entities. Each part, in addition to its
own reactions, also interacts with other parts of the whole. In this way the
parts of an organization are able to maintain the whole, not in terms of an
added total, but *via integrated transactions*. The whole, in turn, influences
the parts through variable integrational and organizational forms. The field
is constantly involved in *transitional* and corrective activity. Physical, psychological, socioeconomic and cultural processes are involved in the transactions. Each of these can be studied more or less minutely. However,
"two-variable" correlations e.g., specific life stress and bodily reaction, are
by themselves considered to be of little value.

Grinker and Robbins further point out that the global responses of
the very young to external and internal stimuli are succeeded in the older
individual by increasingly differentiated reactions. Conditions which favor
regression in the adult will activate these infantile responses, and quite
regularly under such circumstances one may note the return of manifestations of a psychological triad comprising dependency, frustration, and

hostility, which have very early origins. In addition, most psychosomatic disturbances precipitated by the individual's particular life stress are characterized by another triad—physiological in nature—of hypersecretion, hyperemia, and hypermotility. Together with such common, general psychologic and physiologic responses there are also present the bases for individual differences. One of these is innate heredity, either genotypic and constitutional, or else influenced by intrauterine development. Subsequently during childhood there is also a period of great significance for psychosomatic variability. During this interval there develop learned psychologic and physiologic patterns which are influenced by maturational processes and special environmental viscissitudes. These constellations are then integrated into a new personal and highly individualized system. The early patterns of functioning which involve primitive affects expressed through visceral pathways become latent but not extinct. Regression leads to their reactivation. The genetic aspects of transactions in the field are emphasized because they contain the *locus minor resistentiae* for the development of later regressions associated with the stresses to which the growing and grown individual is exposed. According to Grinker and Robbins, the individual's past experiences can be reconstructed only from current psychological and behavioral responses by the use of psychoanalytic techniques.

Schur (1955) likewise has stressed the need to understand an individual's emotional and somatic responses in terms of his "total condition—all innate and environmental factors in their intricate interdependency." He, however, felt that the expression of this in the total-field concept of Grinker and Robbins offered no apparent advantage in further clarifying these phenomena. In addition, he considered that the results of Cannon's animal experiments, demonstrating the effect of the major emotions on the soma, had been applied in an oversimplified way to the formulation of psychosomatic hypotheses, especially by Alexander and his colleagues. One such reference, for example, was to the role of repressed hostility leading to a damming up of aggression and "chronic stimulation of the sympathetic nervous system, resulting in a constant state of preparedness for flight or fight," without consummation. The basis of Schur's criticisms is that any attempt to apply to human psychophysiology results from animal experimentation in the field of emotions would fail unless the complex facets of ego functions are included. It is the presence of this most intricate mental structure—the ego—which distinguishes man from animal. In order to understand the influence of affects, such as anxiety and hostility, on bodily function in humans, one must study how these are controlled by the functions of the ego rather than just considering them from a simple quantitative point of view. K. Menninger's concept of the homeostatic function of the ego incorporates this difference in approach, but Schur preferred to use a more specific physiological model, referring to the ego as an organ of adaptation (after Selye, 1946, 1950).

Viewing anxiety as an ego function—a reaction to danger, present or anticipated—Schur considers the following to occur as the individual matures: Anxiety has a phylogenetic origin in a biological response and has an innate character in the newborn. It is manifested in the infant by a tendency to diffuse discharge phenomena, lack of coordination in motor response, and easily disrupted homeostasis leading to still greater disturbance. As development progresses, there is parallel maturation and interdependence of the central nervous system and the motor apparatus, stabilization of homeostatic processes, and emergence of a capacity for increasingly logical and realistic thinking (secondary thought process) as an essential part of ego formation. The net effect is for reactions to certain excitations to become more and more desomatized. Schur speculates that reestablishment of homeostasis may be the model for what subsequently becomes the ego function of neutralization, thus representing one of the earliest barriers against physiological disturbance. It would follow that children with innate or early acquired abnormalities of homeostatic mechanisms would tend to have greater disturbance in the ego function of neutralization. This term derives from a concept advanced by Hartmann et al. (1949) that instinctual destructiveness can be mitigated through a process (deaggressivization) that is a counterpart of the desexualization of sexual drives. The result is creation of sources of energy available for other purposes of the mental apparatus. Schur's hypothesis thus assumes, on the one hand, that desomatization of responses is dependent on the ego's continuing ability to replace action by logical thinking and to neutralize instinctual drive energy. On the other hand, resomatization of responses occurs when these capacities are interfered with and diminished.

Referring to his lengthy study of the dermatoses, Schur also contributes some further reflections on secondary or pathoneurotic manifestations and chronicity in organic disease. He notes that once a symptom or lesion has been established, then, even if the original precipitating stress was specific, subsequently, many nonspecific factors can cause similar specific response.

The importance of the ego as a regulative agency has been emphasized by K. Menninger (1963). In his book, The Vital Balance, he presents a point of view which emphasizes a unitary concept of mental illness and elaborates on a "dynamic, process-oriented genetic" approach toward the understanding of disease. Adaptation, homeostatic processes, and the controlling aspects of the ego receive considerable attention. Included among the pressures which this agency of the mental apparatus mediates are those deriving from physiological processes. The principle that organisms react to external changes in such a way as to maintain a relatively constant milieu has, of course, been known for several centuries. Menninger gives a brief historical outline of the thinking on this matter: Maupertius (1678-1759) is thought to have formulated the principle of least action; Bernard in 1865 referred to the maintenance of a relatively constant internal milieu; Fechner (1873) postulated that maximum stability for stationary systems means maximum utilization of energy; LeChatelier (1888), concerned with chemical equilibrium, suggested that systems tend to change in order to minimize external disruptions; Cannon (1939) referred to constant conditions maintained in the body as equilibria and described the complexity of the physiological processes which maintain steady states or homeostasis; von Bertalanffy (1950) preferred the term "steady state." Menninger raises the question of whether long-term processes such as growth, maturation, and decline can be encompassed solely by the principle of homeostasis. He suggests a hierarchy of homeostatic levels, and the possibilities of growth and decline of the homeostatic mechanisms. He also postulates an entirely different principle, that of *heterostasis*. This represents a tendency to move away from the *status quo* and to search for new and unsettled states, and is in sharp contrast to the tendency to automatically seek the former, tension-free state of balance. The dynamic balances that develop between these two principles are of vital importance to the organism.

Although the ego is the name for a group of psychological functions which are intimately involved in regulating the activities of the human organism, it is also "thing-like" because of its close connection with the body. Maintenance of the physiopsychosocial balance is a principal and most intricate function of the ego which cannot be overlooked in the search for better understanding of mind-body relationships. The ego is concerned with the processes of adjustment, adaptation, and accommodation to internal and external stresses and may be considered as having a very close association with the physical apparatus for these purposes.

F. Deutsch was another pioneer in the application of psychoanalytic principles to a more comprehensive understanding of bodily dysfunction. In 1959 he culminated many years of work in psychosomatic medicine with a theory of mind-body relationships which considered the psychological mechanism of conversion to be a greatly expanded process lasting throughout life from the earliest phases of development. This concept challenged the hitherto limited significance of conversion as a mental mechanism found in persons ill with hysteria and attempted to apply it to an understanding of all psychophysiological responses. According to Deutsch, the first manifestations of the conversion process can be noted in the newborn child. The infant, through his sensory apparatus, is at first aware of only one reality, his body, which he cannot differentiate from his contacts with his nursing parent and his primitive perceptions of the external environment. The ability to differentiate himself from objects in the outside world develops from the child's reactions to a series of absences and deprivations, which he inevitably has to experience early in his growth. It is postulated that these losses are experienced by the infant as though he had lost part of himself. He then attempts to regain the lost object by the mental process of imagining or hallucinating it. Each such occurrence of loss and restoration of the lost object, together with the underlying physicochemical processes associated with the experience, is linked with the perceptions of body and external world, especially the human beings caring for the child. These perceptions are primitive, multiple, and varied: erogenous-zone sensations, interoceptive sensations, exteroceptive sensations of touch, pain, and temperature, and the special sense perceptions of smell, taste, hearing, and vision. In time, psychophysiological configurations develop, involving these elements and representing the original emotionally significant objects. This process is termed "symbolization." Later, when the individual experiences the loss of a person important in his emotional life, there may be a recreation (called retrojection) of the psychophysiological Gestalt associated with this person. This represents an attempt to regain the lost object. It may take a pathological turn with the manifestations occurring in ideational form or as physical symptoms, with or without actual changes in the organ system involved.

These hypotheses have been challenged in turn by Rangell (1959), who asserts that the conversion process should not be equated in a total way with psychophysical responses. He agrees that the process of conversion needs to be detached from the concept of hysteria. He believes that it is involved in a much wider range of psychological conditions. Its basic elements are the displacement of energy from psychic to somatic systems and the use of physical innervations for symbolic expression by means of a body language of both the repressed, forbidden instinctual drive and the defense against its direct discharge. Conversion may then express repressed impulses and ideas not just in hysteria but in the whole range of psychopathology, at any level of ego or libidinal development.

While undoing what he considers to have been too rigid a restriction of the concept of conversion, Rangell warns against overextending it in the opposite direction. It is necessary to set limits that distinguish the conversion process from related phenomena. Conversions do not include the *normal*, automatic, continuous flow of psychic energy from soma to psyche back again to soma, which makes the whole organism into a psychobiologic entity. This kind of discharge involves neutralized energy in what is basically a conflict-free sphere of ego functions. Instinctual drives are psychological derivatives with origin in the soma and they discharge their energies through mental and physical pathways. Thus the body may serve

as the object of a drive or as an apparatus executing an ego function involved in a sublimation or purposeful behavior. Conversion should be
limited to being a sequel to psychological conflict and should be considered
to be "an active ego process, in the direction of symptom formation."

Conversion does not include somatic-to-psychic pathways of discharge
and is also to be differentiated from the organ neuroses. The latter are
nonspecific sequelae of psychological tensions, affects which have not been
discharged, and generally what is called the chronic, dammed-up state.
However, overlapping does occur. Psychosomatic syndromes are actually a
combination of the organ-neurotic and the conversion processes. There is
thus disagreement with Alexander, as well as with Grinker and Robbins
who tend to limit conversion to diseases of the voluntary body systems,
whereas organ neurosis is related only to neurovegetative, hormonal functions. Yet symbolic expression may be manifest in visceral organ functions
as well as in the voluntary and skeletal ones. Psychosomatic disease can
affect skeletal and voluntary structures. Rangell favors Schur's comprehensive term "somatization" for those conditions where conversion does not
apply.

Recently, the multifactorial approach to an understanding of all illness
was given great emphasis by Engel (1962b) in a unified concept of health
and disease. The organism as a whole (or organ systems within it) is in
a state of health "when functioning effectively, fulfilling needs, successfully
responding to the requirements or demands of the environment, whether
internal or external, and pursuing its biological destiny, including growth
and reproduction." On the other hand, "Disease . . . corresponds to failures
or disturbances in the growth, development, functions and adjustments of
the organism as a whole or any of its systems." This broad definition of
disease is an attempt to avoid the "substantive assumption that disease is
a thing in itself, unrelated to the patient, the patient's personality, bodily
constitution or mode of life, a concept of antiquity which repeatedly re-
asserts itself even in our language, as when we say that a patient has a
disease or that we treat a disease." The scope of the definition is such that
it allows for conceptualizing disturbances at all levels of organization and
for consideration of their interrelationships. The search for a single cause
of disease had led to a disregard of the multifactorial approach, e.g., a
specific microorganism is the necessary condition for a particular infection
and a special anatomical lesion is a manifestation of a particular illness,
but neither is the exclusive or full explanation of the condition. Nowadays
the onus for such single explanations has been shifted onto ever more re-
fined physical determinations of the biochemical or molecular biological
defect felt to be present. There also remains a tendency to rely on mecha-
nistic concepts for understanding of illness: If peptic ulcer is considered

to be due to overactivity of the vagus nerve, the why of this overactivity may often be ignored. The focus on single-factor etiology has a comforting convenience because it permits the illusion that the responsible cause can be attacked, excised, destroyed, exorcised, or gotten rid of simply, but unfortunately this approach does not allow for a really comprehensive understanding of illness.

Among the multiple factors that need to be considered in the etiology of disease are the genic ones, and these Engel believes are to be understood in biochemical terms. They are highly influential in determining the strengths and weaknesses of the individual's various systems, including the psychological system. He suggests, for example, that the nature of the instinctual drives is in part influenced in this way. One might include the effect genic factors have in determining what innate special characteristics are present in an individual's ego. Another broad group of factors are the developmental ones. Here the extraordinary variety of life experiences and situations and the coping mechanisms, including the psychological, which are utilized to adapt to the environment, also play a basic role in determining whether health or disease prevails. Engel emphasizes that in considering this group of factors, one should include the concept of "critical periods," both somatic and psychological. Response to stress, whether physical or mental, differs at different ages, and consequences that occur later in life as a result of stress will be determined by what the individual's early experience has been as well as by innate factors.

Psychological Stress and
Somatic Reactions

Turning from these general aspects of the mind-body relationship to more specific factors in the etiology of disease, it should be noted that man's psychological relationship to and interaction with his fellowman as an important environmental causal factor in his illnesses has been overshadowed by studies of the influence of his exposure to bacteria, viruses, noxious chemicals, and physical pressures. In recent years, however, there has been increasing interest in the relationship of "psychological stress" to somatic illness, but there is currently no definition of the term on which general agreement exists. K. Menninger (1963) points out a tendency for definitions of stress to be abandoned in favor of classification, e.g.: (1) mild stress—the effects lasting from seconds to hours; (2) moderate stress—the effects lasting from hours to days; (3) severe stress—sequelae continuing weeks, months, or even years. A recent working definition has been proposed by Engel (1962b): "Psychological stress refers to all processes, whether originating in the external environment or within the person, which impose a demand or requirement upon the organism, the resolution or handling of which requires work or activity of the mental apparatus before any other system is involved or activated." Events which constitute psychological stress, however, first must be registered through the perceptual systems.

Furthermore, the term is reserved for the triggering of organismic response, not for the effects produced. Another word—"tension"—is better designated for the internal state of activity and pressure which the stress initiates. Not all stress is noxious. A certain amount of stimulus influx appears to be essential to the well-being of the individual. Sufficient lack of stimulation, as shown by studies in sensory deprivation (Hebb, 1949, Lilly, 1956), may have a deleterious effect on the subject's physical and mental health. As reported by Fox (1960), sensory deprivation is the subject of many investigations which describe the occurrence of hallucina-

22

tions during isolation as well as the decline of intellectual function then and afterwards. When sensory stimuli from the external environment are blocked, the organization of instinctual drives undergoes more primitive expression, and reality testing is impaired. Furthermore, some contact with other human beings, even if it has elements of stress, seems to be necessary, if incapacitating reactions of loneliness and depression are to be avoided. It is possible for some individuals, at great price in terms of warped personality makeup and constriction of their emotional lives, to maintain an isolated existence. There are also certain narcissistic persons whose need for contact with others seems limited, but whose isolation, including that from stress, is only partial, e.g., in the social sphere, but not at work. These individuals may be able to avoid incapacitating symptomatic or characterological disturbances. In any event, it is possible to maintain relatively harmonious somatic function in the absence of physical stress, providing that the mental apparatus is able to deal with psychological stress without invoking bodily defense responses. However, this may be at the expense of smooth psychological and social function and adaptation so that the result is some form of psychopathology. The mechanisms of denial, phobic reaction, isolation, and intellectualization thus may spare the individual from further psychological distress and physical disturbance, but they then limit the individual's full capacity to cope with additional or extended stress situations. In certain instances, even when psychological mechanisms are the principal means of adjustment, they may involve the body in physical stress (alcoholism, drug addiction, accident proneness) or in a conversion reaction which is a somatic response to an underlying repressed conflict. Should all these attempts at adjustment fail, then emergency bodily reactions of even greater scope are mobilized to deal with the stress. In most instances there is considerable overlap between these conditions, i.e., between what would best be called *relatively* compensated and decompensated psychological states.

Psychological stress derives particularly from interaction with other human beings and from reaction to the social, economic, and cultural settings which man has created. If stresses from these sources are sufficiently intense and sustained, it may be assumed that any individual will react strongly. Most stresses, however, are those which are associated with the unpredictable vicissitudes of everyday life and are minor conflicts. Obviously, the source of stress can be manifold, but references to it should designate whether these are superficial or descriptive or psychodynamic in their orientation. Although, in the present study, stress is considered from both points of view, the principal emphasis is on the dynamic aspects. At times, what on the surface appears to be insignificant or trivial stress or is not even considered as a cause of tension by the casual or uninformed observer, may have far-reaching symbolic meaning for the individual in-volved, acting to disrupt his psychophysical equilibrium and perhaps setting the stage for development of illness in which physical symptoms appear prominently.

Whereas recognition (though not necessarily understanding) of psy-chological stress is easy when it is presented by the patient in an unam-biguous and dramatic (even if exaggerated) fashion, on many occasions it is not so unmistakably evident. An obvious trauma, psychological, if not physical, may occur as the result of a car accident and be manifested by immediate anxiety, including somatic equivalents. The situation and its emotional impact will be evident in the individual's awareness and in his recounting of what took place. On the other hand, there may be a de-layed emotional response with physical concomitants, a reaction which the patient less clearly associates with the traumatic event, although the ex-perienced observer may see it quickly. Another clearly evident stress would be the death of a close relative or friend with immediate psychophysical responses involved in the mourning process. The accompanying affective, ideational, or behavioral manifestations would tend to be more readily recognized and linked with the stress, whereas somatic dysfunction, if present, would be so connected less quickly. Thus, under such circum-stances, a depressive affect would be more readily associated with a stressful loss than, say, a persisting gastrointestinal upset. In certain instances, evi-dence of depressive emotion or thinking is masked and delayed, though physical reactions to the responsible stress are present.

There are events which act as stresses and may simultaneously involve many people. This would follow a national tragedy, such as the assassina-tion of the President. The effect would be reinforced by the element of surprise. Many kinds of physical symptoms and dysfunction would be included in the manifold reactions. In this kind of situation the stress involves a figure who represents less a closely-related-to object than an idealized parental image and on this basis fulfills generally identical emo-tional needs for many people.

There are occurrences less dramatic and less obvious than the so-called major psychological traumata. In these the tie between the event and the resultant repercussions in the individual becomes more obscured, particu-larly if the manifestations are largely somatic. The dynamic psychological significance of the event is unknown to the individual, and in a psychiatric interview it may even be overlooked or not given consideration by the interviewer. For example, let us consider the matter of anniversaries. These may serve as stressful times for the individual, whether he remembers the occasion or not, since the dynamic psychological significance may be un-known to him. Many occurrences which at first glance do not appear stressful and are recounted by the individual in a matter-of-fact way may be noted by the interviewer (but not, at first, by the patient) to have a temporal relationship to the onset of physical difficulties. If the interviewer is skillful enough to elaborate their associative connections, these occurrences will turn out to have been stressful, even though the anxiety, hostility, or guilt linked with them had been blocked from awareness and direct expression through mechanisms of denial and avoidance.

The sexual impulse which, for many reasons, becomes associated with anxiety or guilt may act as stress, irrespective of whether it is only anticipated in fantasy or actually carried out. The effects of such stress are often physical, though the cause is frequently unrecognized. Following sexual activity of this kind an individual may feel generally uneasy, tense, or depressed and may connect these aftereffects with the sexual experience, but will often tend to ascribe physical sequelae to other causes. The bodily responses may be further augmented and complicated by insufficient discharge of sexual tension. Masturbation may be followed by abdominal cramps or diarrhea or "neuralgic" pains in the legs; voyeurism by scintillating scotomata or severe migraine-like headaches; fellatio or cunnilingus by globus hystericus or sensations of nausea; unsatisfactory sexual intercourse by frequency of urination or low back pain, to cite only a few examples. Some of these physical symptoms appear to be related to disturbances in the sympathetic-parasympathetic equilibrium which are triggered off by the stressful sexual activity. Others may be connected to shifts in hormonal balance. Still others may represent conversion reactions. In any event, the kind and location of these bodily symptoms is not altogether determined by physical factors but is also influenced to a certain extent by psychological elements.

Then there are the everyday happenings, numerous and protean in their manifestations, which represent lesser, often transient, stresses. Again, repercussions in the form of physical symptoms may not be connected by the individual with the stressful situation, especially if the resulting incapacity is minimal or short in duration, or if it responds quickly to medication, frequently self-administered. To mention only a few such everyday occurrences: differences or arguments with colleagues or boss, friends or relatives; scenes which may be annoying, irritating, or embarrassing—at work or socially; anxious anticipation or review of one's performance or participation in a wide range of everyday activities—again at work or socially —with disappointments and frustrations. Many headaches, backaches, digestive upsets, states of fatigue, palpitations, pains of all kinds in all possible body areas are some of the many physical symptoms reflecting the "tensions of the day."

Not only actual stress but anticipation of stress can provoke physical responses. Included in this category are situations which lie ahead and are seen as tension-producing, or less obviously, mean temptation, aggression, exposure, competition, or seduction, involving spheres of emotional conflict in the individual. Somatic reactions may then appear intermingled with psychological manifestations or by themselves. In the latter case, the connection with the stress-associated future situation may be unrecognized.

A group of events which may not seem to constitute stresses, but which must be included, are successes. There are individuals whose sense of guilt, derived from long-standing emotional conflicts, impels them through the agency of their conscience to constantly atone for their "transgressions." For them, success brings no happiness, only the need for more suffering. This may be expressed not only in terms of a relapse into emotional illness, but may also be manifest through physical decompensation. The psychological manifestations occurring under such circumstances are well known, whereas the physical equivalents and sequelae are not. The latter at times result from the individual's overlooking or needlessly exposing himself to actual hazards, or being driven to physical excesses without being able to take into account the possible consequences. Other persons seem on the verge of success but never reach it because excessive guilt blocks it by activating or exacerbating physical dysfunction. Success may also be stressful because it brings with it the need to maintain or even excel the accomplishment already achieved, and this, in turn, mobilizes anxiety. This will occur especially in individuals whose neurosis involves a deeply ingrained sense of inferiority, which may require constant powerful compensatory psychological defenses to keep it in check. The related anxiety again may not be recognized if it appears in the form of somatic equivalents.

The intensity of psychological stress requires some further consideration. The wide range from major trauma to everyday irritation has already been mentioned. Minor stresses, however, can exert a considerable effect if they are recurrent and if the intervals between them do not allow for sufficient recovery, that is, reestablishment of a more favorable psychophysical equilibrium. In other words, when the individual experiences psychological stress, it may be either in the form of a large stimulus influx or a more gradual, cumulative one. However, in both instances, the individual's adaptive powers will be put under a strain by the more than usual demands made on them. It should be emphasized that the coping mechanisms are psychophysical and that the presence of psychological stress of a less obvious kind may first be manifest in discharge of built-up tensions through physical pathways. The neutralization or modification of stress by medication, favorable incidental and accidental events, or formal and informal psychotherapeutic interventions, will, of course, have to be assessed in determining the actual impact of the stressful event or events.

A particular form of psychological stress has come under much scrutiny in recent years. It has been more or less closely related to the onset or exacerbation of a large variety of physical illness. The stress is associated with the actual or threatened loss of an object emotionally significant for the individual concerned. More is involved than an affective reaction of depression. There may develop an inability to maintain necessary and sufficient object relationships by substitute means. It is postulated that when this culminates in feelings of helplessness and hopelessness, a profoundly negative effect is exerted on bodily processes.

Many observers studying a large variety of organic illness have made reference to this psychological stress. In the thirties Mittelmann (1933) mentioned it in his work on thyrotoxicosis, and French (1939) in his evaluation of psychogenic factors in asthma. In the forties, Lindemann (1945) referred to it in his investigation of psychiatric problems in ulcerative colitis, and Wittkower (1949) in his treatise on tuberculosis. However, it was not until the fifties that the literature began to carry an ever-increasing number of reports on this relationship between real or threatened loss and development of organic disease: in congestive failure, Chambers and Reiser (1953); in tuberculosis, Day (1952) and Kissen (1956); in cancer, Bacon et al. (1952), Kowal (1955), and Renneker et al. (1963); in rheumatoid arthritis, Ludwig (1952); in Raynaud's disease, Millet et al. (1953); in obesity, Hamburger (1951); in ulcerative colitis, Engel (1955); in infectious hepatitis, Papper et al. (1956); in disseminated lupus erythematosus, McLary et al. (1955); in functional uterine bleeding, Heiman (1956).

A definitive study on this problem was carried out by Schmale in 1958. He undertook to work out the incidence of object loss and depressive-like reactions occurring prior to the onset of disease in a medical population of 42 patients unselected except for age. Psychological data were obtained from open-ended, minimal-activity, tape-recorded interviews of up to 90 minutes; in about half the cases there was a brief followup and also an interview with at least one family member. It should be noted that, in collecting the data, there was a specific search for references to past health and significant object changes or loss in the past. Among the 42 patients, actual loss was noted in 5 instances, threat of loss in 9, symbolic loss in 16, no perceived loss of object in 12; however, for the latter group it was possible to make an interpretation of actual, threatened, or symbolic loss in 11. There were 7 categories of affects considered to be reactions to events immediately preceding illness: (1) anxiety, in most patients, but fleetingly; (2) anger in 18; (3) fear in 13; (4) guilt in 5; (5) shame in 12; (6) helplessness in 30; and (7) hopelessness in 10. The latter two affects were considered to be indicative of depression. Time intervals in which significant changes in object relationship preceded onset of disease symptoms varied from 24 hours in 16, within 1 week in 15, in 8 within a month, and in 3 there was an interval of 6 to 12 months. Schmale felt that his evidence made chance or coincidence as a factor unlikely, but suggested that further investigations should be in the direction of longitudinal studies. He also considered that in many of the cases the patient's feeling of helplessness and hopelessness clearly preceded any clinical manifestations of disease. He emphasized that the concept of separation and depression does not establish a cause but rather a setting of the disease. It may be one of the "possible or necessary conditions which allows disease to appear when it does." The feelings of helplessness and hopelessness may be related to "increased biological vulnerability." Schmale concludes: "By knowing the patient's patterns of object relationships, including the kinds of object conflicts which threaten the patient's concept of himself, and the ego processes available to handle such conflicts, it may be possible to predict specific circumstances under which the patient will become sick."

One of the questions that such a study immediately raises is why many patients subjected to previous object loss do not develop physical disease or develop it much later. Greene (1958) approached the problem through the study of a particular disease group—leukemia and lymphoma, but felt that the mechanisms involved could be applied to illness more generally. He introduced the concept of the "vicarious object." Identification with the lost object is accompanied by denial of the affect of grief. At the same time there is a projection of both the significance of the loss and affect onto another figure subjected to the same loss, e.g., mother, if the father died. Concomitantly, the individual would identify with a person experiencing the same loss by comforting him or her, and thus would experience relief. The vicarious object is usually someone in the family, realistically weaker, rarely elderly; sometimes it may be a pet animal. Greene feels that many adult patients have used these proxy mechanisms for transient or long-term successful adaptation to object loss. Then when such mechanisms are no longer possible, this becomes partly responsible for the development of feelings of helplessness and hopelessness which provide the setting for onset of organic disease. The observation of families of patients who have died reveals that different members may respond in different ways with grief, development of physical symptoms such as the dead person had suffered from, or replacement of the lost one by the taking of another member of the family as vicarious object. A family may maintain itself through these mechanisms while working through the loss of the significant object, prior to or after that person's death. In a subsequent article (1959), Greene focuses on the fate of the vicarious object when changes in the vicarious relationship occur. Data were obtained from a study of children who developed leukemia under circumstances when their role as vicarious object for a significant person, usually the mother, changed. They had represented such objects for their mothers principally in a setting where the mother had experienced emotional deprivation preceding and during the pregnancy with the child. Later, as a result of further frustration and disappointment, the mother gave up the child as a vicarious object and frequently developed a depression. Under these circumstances, the manifestations of leukemia appeared in the child. Greene suggests that "an involvement in a vicarious object relation is one common precursor in persons in the population who become ill with leukemia and other 'psychosomatic' disease. Disruption of the vicarious object relation for such persons determines when the somatic manifestations will develop. The particular somatic manifestations are determined mainly by biological rather than psychological characteristics of the individual."

Imboden et al. (1963) undertook to study separation experiences and health records in normal adults particularly because, in their opinion, earlier work on separation in relation to its somatic effect had been uncontrolled, retrospective, and not designed to minimize unconscious observer bias. A group of 455 ostensibly normal, actively working individuals were asked to report whether or not within the previous year there had been a death of a relative, separation or divorce from spouse, and whether there was illness in the family at the time of inquiry. A comparison of the individuals so reporting was made with those who did not, by using Cornell Medical Index series, Minnesota Multiphasic Personality inventory scores, and frequency of dispensary visits for symptomatic complaints during a subsequent 18-month period. Of this total, 117, or 25.7 percent, had experienced some form of separation: family member currently ill—62; death of family member—40; both death and current illness in family—12; marital separation, divorce—3. Of the 338 subjects reporting no separation, 100 were drawn for comparison. The mean age of both groups was 35 years, about 90 percent male, about 80 percent married, about 90 percent white, about 50 percent with college or higher education. Only the college-educated in both groups were compared in terms of a number of variables. The most striking finding is that about 25 percent of *ostensibly normal* adults reported recent deaths and presently existing illness in their families. This compares with the 33 percent of *patients* admitted to a medical service who reported actual or threatened separations in Schmale's study (1958). Furthermore, Imboden's study showed that the frequency with which groups reporting separation visited the dispensary for symptomatic complaints did not differ significantly from those reporting no separation experiences. Imboden and his co-workers felt that the reference to object loss as constituting "a necessary but not sufficient condition" for development of disease (Engel, 1955) was open to question. They reiterated the observation made by others that many factors are invariably connected with the development of illness. They felt that in the absence of what they considered adequate control, the association of separation-somatic disease may be "a characteristic of the human condition rather than a characteristic unique to the clinical entity being studied." Even if it has been shown that such association exists, its significance needs careful interpretation. If the subject is seriously ill at the time of being interviewed about his past, his responses may be different from those elicited if he is in good health. Such "reporting characteristics" are considered to be quite influential in determining the kinds of recollections and psychological data elicited. However, Imboden and his colleagues do not rule out the possible importance of antecedent separation experiences with emotional and physiological sequelae in the etiology of physical illness.

While it is true that separation and object loss are followed by a variety of consequences, these different outcomes, be they psychological or physical, minimal or maximal, in the range of normality or pathological, depend on many factors, each of which needs to be investigated in a more detailed way. In turn their hierarchical arrangements, interactions, and shifts also will have to be further explored. It is the intent of this work to subject one such group of factors—the psychological—to closer scrutiny.

Methods and Material
Used in This Study

Clinical material from a series of consecutive admissions to the medical service of a one-thousand-bed general hospital was collected to provide the basis for this study. The project was formulated in the following manner: A period of four months was allotted for the collection of data. It was ascertained that if patients, aged 30 or 31, admitted to the male medical service were the only ones selected consecutively within the designated time period, then approximately 50 cases would be included. This number was considered to be a suitable sample. Actually, 49 patients in that very narrow age range were admitted during the four-month period. Of these, one was unable to speak because of a cerebrovascular accident, and three left the hospital before an adequate study could be made. Accordingly, the sample finally consisted of 45 (one readmission) cases in which the necessary data could be obtained. It was expected that all the patients would present physical symptoms of one kind or another. However, it was further anticipated that not all of the patients would turn out to have organic disease; actually 17 cases had a diagnosis which excluded physical disease.

The patients were all white men who had been in military service, though not necessarily overseas or in combat duty. All came from the lower-middle or working classes. They were generally concerned, if married, with the problems of raising a family and maintaining a home; if single, with finding the right girl to marry, or fitting as comfortably as possible into a bachelor's existence. Some faced difficulties in keeping their jobs; others were concerned with advancing themselves at work or academically. In a number of cases, the factor of pension payments and its effect on secondary-gain process influenced the overall response of the patient. Some patients saw the physicians in an authoritarian light, but attenuated in comparison with their former reactions to military personnel.

31

Within 24 to 48 hours after admission, each patient, if ambulatory, was seen in a special recording room for an interview by the same interviewer, the author. Each such interview was recorded on tape. The patient was simply told that the interviewer was a member of the hospital staff and that the interview was a part of the patient's general work-up. In some instances where the patients were too ill to leave their beds, the interview was recorded in longhand as it proceeded. Each interview lasted approximately one hour, except in those instances where the patient was seriously ill. The interviewer had no information about the patient's illness before seeing him.

The interviewing technique was a modification of the associative anamnesis which was first developed by F. Deutsch in 1939. The associative anamnesis has been referred to not only as a method of interviewing but also as a way of doing psychotherapy. It should be clearly understood that it is used in this study exclusively as an interviewing instrument. The associative anamnesis has been described, illustrated, and explained in a very detailed way by Deutsch and Murphy (1955). Only a brief outline of the procedure used will be given here. Each interview was begun with exactly the same question, after the brief formalities of introduction, namely, "What are your symptoms?" The associations to this first verbal stimulus then became the initial leads and indicators for the conduct of the remainder of the interview. In this way, a particular direction could be developed for exploring the patient's unconscious from the starting point and orientation provided by his symptoms, and could be expected then to lead to the development of a macrosample of the unconscious processes, insofar as it was possible to do so in the presence of resistances. This sample was derived from material associatively connected with the presenting symptoms. Elaboration of associative chains proceeding from these symptoms was sought for, but no extraneous stimuli were introduced; only the patient's associations were used for the purpose of eliciting more response. Not only ideas and feelings but sensory perceptions were recorded. Significant omissions in any of these areas were also noted. When sufficient material had been elicited for recurrent patterns of psychological response to be discerned, these were in turn further explored, not only as they might be reflected in the patient's present life, but as they occurred earlier in his development. A benevolently neutral attitude was maintained by the interviewer. The interview was stopped promptly at the end of the hour, irrespective of the point reached at that time. No attempt was made to conduct the interview so as to obtain data for a complete formulation of the patient's emotional problems. No leading questions were asked at any time. Every effort was made to structure the interview situation so that it would be relatively uniform for every patient.

The reactions of the individual patients to the interview varied, although none were intense. Some patients asked what kind of doctor the interviewer was, shortly after an area emotionally significant for them had been touched upon. A lesser number waited until their return to the ward and then asked nurses or fellow patients about who the interviewer was and what the purpose of the interview might be. Such questions came principally from individuals who had had previous contact with a psychiatrist. Others inquired at the end of the interview about what kind of illness they had and/or what could be done for them in the way of treatment. Several minimized the significance of their symptoms and hospitalization. A few were mildly suspicious (especially if pension payments were involved). About one third made no comment at all about the interview nor inquired further about their illness.

After completion of the interview, it was transcribed (if recorded) and a psychodynamic assessment of the data was made before any other information relevant to the particular case was seen. Since this psychological material was to be correlated with the physical symptoms and the presence or absence of organic disease in each case and not with any detailed medical data (including laboratory findings), the medical material is presented only in broad outline to provide a physical background for the cases. For this purpose a final summary, routinely compiled by the doctor in charge of the case and included as part of the official record, was obtained for each case. This summary consisted of the physical findings, course in the hospital, and final diagnosis. These are presented just as they are recorded, without discussion of their medical content, since such critical evaluation was not planned as part of this study. In approximately one fourth of the cases data were obtained about further hospitalization and clinic visits that occurred within a period covering as much as twelve years after the hospital admission originally reported. It was thus possible to describe the further course of the patient's health and its relationship to his particular life situations as they developed in this interim period.

The 45 cases are presented in accordance with a design which makes each one a source of research data dealing with the psychodynamic aspects of physical symptoms. Verbatim interview material is followed by psychodynamic impressions which provide an interpretive explanation of the meaning of the interview. The physical data in the final summary are listed next. The section devoted to comment includes both theoretical and clinical points relevant to the particular symptoms and illness under consideration and references to the work of others in the diagnostic category involved. After each case an outline is provided which lists the chief presenting symptom, the psychological variables being studied, the diagnosis, and a summary of the pertinent data elicited for each of these categories.

Some brief remarks about the sections into which each case presentation is divided will be helpful in further clarifying their purpose.

CHIEF PRESENTING SYMPTOM

The first question asked of each patient was, "What are your symptoms?" This was done in order to expose each patient to a uniform initial verbal stimulus. There was considerable variety of response. Often the patient gave a single symptom with little or no elaboration. When several different symptoms with more extensive associations followed, the dominant symptom—the one to which the patient referred most often—was selected as the chief one. In a number of instances, the chief symptom presented to the psychiatric interviewer differed from that presented to the internist. For example, in Case 1 it is "tightness in the stomach" as compared with "exhaustion." In Case 6 it is "nervousness" as compared with "vomiting and loss of consciousness." This difference occurred when multiple symptomatology was given initially; the chief symptom then was selected by the interviewer on the basis of the dominance already referred to. Here, the patient's actual physical condition and immediate sensorimotor experiences, the events to which he was recently exposed, and his emotional reactions to the interviewer were all factors in determining which one of multiple symptoms was emphasized by him or at times suppressed and/or repressed.

BASIC ANAMNESTIC EXCERPTS

As already indicated, the interviewing technique used in each case was the associative anamnesis. The complete interview could not be reproduced because of the extremely large amount of space that would be required for 45 cases. However, all the material in each given interview was not necessary or relevant for the purpose of the study. Some of the data was obtained only after certain verbalized resistances were modified or bypassed; the material is presented without including the connecting or intermediary associations which were felt to be noncontributory to an understanding of the basic dynamic material. In all instances, wherever possible, the general direction of the associations and the principal psychological themes are indicated in the order in which they first appeared and then might have recurred. Verbatim material from the interviews is quoted liberally to illustrate the actual associations brought up by the patient. In some instances, because the patient was too ill to respond to a lengthy interview, the material is presented in a form which also contains the dynamic impressions that were developed.

PSYCHODYNAMIC IMPRESSIONS

The associative anamnesis makes it possible to obtain a great deal of information and arrive at a meaningful estimate of the patient's psychological state, using his presenting symptoms as a starting point for the interview.

While such estimates are not infallible, they have sufficient validity, proven by repeated experience and checks, to be accepted as reliable general indicators of the patient's current emotional problems and antecedent neurotic patterns. It is then possible to identify basic personality traits and prominent psychological defenses as well as changes in defensive alignments, including regressive or decompensatory shifts. The material also permits an assessment of the patient's relationship to and identification with the significant objects, past and current, in his environment. In most instances some estimate could be made of the kind of superego structure present. Furthermore, reference to stress and its relationship to the onset or exacerbation of symptoms or disease is detailed from a dynamic standpoint. Sensorimotor configurations are also noted, especially in terms of their linkage with symptoms and with people emotionally significant for the patient. The patient's emotional responses, the particular kind, estimated intensity in a scale ranging from $+$ to $+++$, and pathway of expression, whether affective only, or ideational, behavioral, or somatic, are included.

PHYSICAL HISTORY, PHYSICAL EXAMINATION, LABORATORY DATA, ROENTGENOGRAMS, HOSPITAL COURSE, AND DISCHARGE DIAGNOSIS

These sections are included in the final summary obtained for each case. These summaries were not done by any one individual since the patients were primarily admitted for treatment (and not research) and were routinely assigned to the different medical residents on service. Workups included consultations with senior house and attending medical staff. Before becoming part of the official records the final summaries were approved by a senior staff physician.

COMMENT

In this section it was possible to discuss a wide variety of topics related to the psychodynamic aspects of physical symptoms. These include further pertinent clinical and theoretical observations and comparisons with other cases. There is also reference to the work of others on the psychological aspects of the principal symptoms and diagnostic category involved.

FOLLOW-UP DATA

In about one fourth of the cases it was possible to obtain data about the patient's physical condition and life circumstances as long as 12 years after the original hospitalization. In several instances the patient had died and the postmortem findings were available.

SUMMARY OF VARIABLES

After a general review of all the data the following variables were listed at the end of each case:

1. CHIEF PRESENTING SYMPTOM.

2. SENSORIMOTOR CONFIGURATIONS: particularly as they link the patient's symptoms with his affects and behavior, and in turn with the people emotionally significant for him, both in the present and past. Even in earliest infancy, sensory perceptions and reactive movements should not be considered from an exclusively physiological standpoint. They have psychological significance also and this is reflected in the development of the ego, which is first a body ego. As differentiation of self from outside world occurs, objects in the environment become known through sensory configurations specific for each of them and mediated through the perceptive functions of the ego. These complexes are fused with similar perceptions of one's own body and linked with reactive movements once experienced in oneself. With further development these sensorimotor configurations are built up hierarchically with varying degrees of complexity. Thus the individual's early cognition of and reaction to the significant objects in his environment may under certain circumstances (regression) later in his life be expressed bodily through reactivation of these sensorimotor configurations.

3. SOMATIC IDENTIFICATION: refers to resemblances between the patient and emotionally important figures, expressed in physical terms: symptoms, illness, or malfunctioning body organs, areas, or systems. If the same body part is organically involved in the patient as in the relative (or significant object) and the associative connections are undisguised, the somatic identification is called "direct, with constitutional components." If the same body part is physically involved in the relative but only symptomatically referred to in the associations as being present in the patient, the somatic identification is referred to as "direct." If there is no direct connection expressed in physical terms between involved organ system in the patient and the emotionally significant person, but there are suggestive, though disguised, associations, then the somatic identification is called "indirect."

4. SENSITIZED ORGAN SYSTEM: refers to a conditioned reactivity of a particular organ or organ system to current stress with resultant dysfunc-

tion. This conditioning is related to past physical involvement (single or multiple) of the organ, occurring in a particular emotional setting determined by the individual's psychological state at the time, especially his reactions to people and events emotionally significant for him.

5. STRESS *—SURFACE MEANING: derived from conscious recall only and does not, therefore, include the deeper psychological significance of the stress.

6. STRESS †—DYNAMIC SIGNIFICANCE: refers to the deeper meaning of the stress as derived from an interpretive psychodynamic evaluation of the anamnestic material and expressed here in concise form.

7. PSYCHOLOGICAL DEFENSES: including those intrapsychic processes outside of the patient's awareness, but derived from the anamnestic material.

8. AFFECTS—INTENSITY AND PATHWAYS: the major affects of anxiety, depression, and hostility are listed. Their intensity is expressed in a range of mild (+), moderate (++), and marked (+++). Pathways are noted as affective (overt emotional response), ideational (content of the patient's thinking), behavioral (facial and postural expression), somatization (concomitant associated physical symptoms).

Anxiety is defined as the reaction to danger, present or anticipated, realistic or neurotic. Dynamically it is considered a psychological signal, warning the individual of such danger and in this sense expressing a function of the ego. If the danger does not actually exist in the environment, but only in the mind of the individual and is therefore a distortion of reality, the anxiety is pathological. Under these circumstances anxiety may be experienced as a result of repressed sexual and aggressive pressures, especially when the customary defenses against them become insufficient. Anxiety also develops when expression of these drives is opposed by a strict conscience, or external disapproval is expected for a projected act. Specific manifestations of anxiety include a sense of foreboding, dread, shame, restlessness, uneasiness, irritability, difficulty in concentration, direct or indirect (symbolic) reference in content to inferiority or inadequacy feelings, anticipation of emasculation, and many concomitant, associated somatic equivalents.

Depression is considered to be a complex psychological state involving marked dependency on and ambivalence toward emotionally important persons, with reactions of grief or intense sadness to possible or actual loss of these objects. Attempts at regaining them or substitutes are accompanied by pathological mechanisms of introjection, hostility turned inward,

---

* Only a brief reference is noted here, since a full definition and discussion of this variable has already been given in the Introduction.

† Ibid.

loss of self-esteem, culminating in ego states of hopelessness and helplessness. Overt manifestations include crying, psychomotor retardation, facial expressions of sadness, direct or indirect references in content to guilt, need for support, imminent, actual, or symbolic loss of important persons, finances, job, prestige, reputation, body part, as well as loss of self-esteem, and various concomitant and associated somatic equivalents.

Aggression is defined as encompassing many, but not all aggressive reactions to frustration or danger and including by-products of self-preservation and self-expansion or of sexual expression. The remainder of aggressive phenomena might be called essential destructiveness (Waelder, 1960). Overt affective responses include irritation, annoyance, anger, related postural and facial expressions, direct and indirect reference in ideational content to hostile attitudes and thoughts, and accompanying somatic equivalents.

9. OTHER FACTORS: refers to any other relevant psychological data noted in the anamnesis.

10. HOMEOSTATIC SHIFT: outlines the basic psychophysical changes as determined from a survey of all the material in each case. (A preliminary discussion of this variable has already been presented in the Introduction.)

In the last section of the book, the cases are divided for purposes of comparison into those with organic and with nonorganic illness. The findings for each of the psychological variables studied are listed and then discussed in depth. Principal consideration is given to their role in causing dysfunction of organ systems with resultant development of physical symptoms. The findings of other investigators and their interpretations are included wherever these are pertinent. An attempt is made to develop a more meaningful and systematic approach to an understanding of the psychodynamic aspects of physical symptoms.* It should be emphasized, however, that the basic purpose of the study is suggestive. It is not intended that the results or recommendations be considered as representing final determinations. Rather, it is hoped that these findings will contribute to improved clinical evaluation and treatment of the patient with physical symptoms and suggest leads for further research into the psychophysical aspects of illness.

---

* A separate chapter is devoted to some recommendations and suggestions for better comprehension and management of physical illness in light of the findings.

PART TWO

Case Histories

case 1
Stomach Complaints: Psychological Significance of Associated Sensory Perceptions

CHIEF PRESENTING SYMPTOM

Tightness in stomach.

BASIC ANAMNESTIC EXCERPTS

The patient does not talk freely. His verbal responses are brief, interspersed with frequent pauses. His emotional and postural attitudes reflect uneasiness and tension. The basic affect noted is anxiety.

The first associations to the presenting symptom involve references to tiredness and nervousness. Tiredness is connected with a feeling of depletion. Nervousness refers to a general concern about the present and future. The symptom of tightness in stomach is aggravated by eating and relieved by walking. These variations are reflected in interoceptive sensory perceptions detailed in pairs of opposites: tight–loose, and knotty–relaxed. In turn, this sensory cluster is directly linked with increase and decrease of anger and worry about "everyday matters."

The patient's anxiety is both denied and then revealed in the next associations: "I don't suppose it's anything serious. It can't be ulcers; they come from eating trouble. I generally eat everything and am not fussy. ... This is the first time I've been in a hospital as a patient; it makes me nervous." He used to work in a military hospital as a medical corpsman, giving injections for venereal disease. Appetite then was quite finicky due to tensions he felt in his work. He is now particularly concerned about job and family responsibilities, especially in the past few months.

Further and more specific associative links to the sensation of stomach tightness are elicited: "I'm on an assembly line. There's been so much work in the past year and so little time to do it. You can't even go to the toilet when you have to. My wife thinks the pressure up there is making

41

me like this, and she wants me to get another job where things aren't so tight." Further references to his wife include her irritation and disgust because the patient, home from work, eats and then often almost immediately falls asleep. The two children—boys—are wild and fresh, frequently angering the patient: "I get mad at the kids, can't handle them like a woman can. Where do they find all the energy? I try to keep them quiet— but it's hard to do." Hostility is openly expressed.

The patient recalls his own childhood and eating problems: "There was always plenty of food then; all I wanted. Now you look in your own refrigerator and don't see the things you want. Mother was a good cook, but I was fussy, crying and upset, had stomachaches, and wouldn't eat fish and certain things. She would have to cook something special. Now that I have my own family, I realize I can't be so fussy. I was thin as a kid—like my older brother who got killed in combat. I used to wear his clothing, and he'd gripe. My other brothers and sisters were healthy as were my mother and father, until he injured his back a couple of years ago while working on big sewer pipes and cesspools."

Further reminiscences about the past turn to the theme of control: "I never looked for fights, tried to be nice about things and to be reasonable. If things get wild, anything's liable to happen—it hasn't yet. You know—in a fight. I always control myself. . . . Father had a temper—would tell you anything at any time. . . . If I feel I'm getting too angry I walk away. I'm the quiet type, maybe; take after my brother who was killed. I try to hold things in, more or less, although I lose my temper with the kids. The oldest boy is doing badly at school and I have to punish him once in a while. My Dad gave me spankings—he was the boss and still is."

The early reference to tiredness is recalled: "I'm always exhausted after a couple of hours in the factory . . . the idea of going into a place which you hate so much. But a job's a job. . . . Nobody there likes it. . . . I didn't prepare for anything at school and wasn't smart enough to go to college. It would have been security for the future. . . . I have no security now. Even the house I have needs a lot of work. Before that we lived at my mother-in-law's, and that wasn't pleasant, especially when we all ate together—because of her interference."

A triad involving money-worry-stomach now appears in the patient's associations, and there is concomitant, noticeable increase in irritability: "I have to handle all the bills, buying and paying where the woman should. That's happened since we moved to the new house this past year . . . before I gave her what money I earned. If my stomach trouble is over worry, nothing can be done . . . just go home, take it easy, try to forget. Here in the hospital you just do more thinking. I worry because the wife's not home . . . I can't control the kids the way a woman does . . . they need her affection. In the last few months I told her I want her to make up her own mind about her job, but she hasn't decided to stay or not. The uncertainty gets me. She has to pay my in-laws for the care of the kids, and there isn't much left. But she enjoys working, meeting people, and I don't want to take that much happiness from her . . . yet the kids are missing so much." The ambivalence, with accent on the hostility, is clearly evident.

At this point the patient again reveals his anxiety about his health—mental as well as physical: "I used to see fellows in the psycho ward—they were mental cases or maybe queer. . . . Maybe I smoke too much. I quit three or four months ago, but I'm back to it. . . . Guess I'm the black sheep of the family. When I was a kid, I wasn't sick, just active. I had a bunch of accidents: truck ran over my legs. . . . I once got cut in the eye when a lady dropped a milk bottle and I tripped . . . had a trick knee (right) playing football, which kept me from running fast—it hurt and would swell up. . . . Now I'm the sick one, but I still try to please my wife, just keep quiet and not look for arguments. I help out a lot at home while she's working: I make beds, clean house, wash dishes, and try to take care of the kids. What do I get?" The interview ends with this question, voiced in a bitter tone.

PSYCHODYNAMIC IMPRESSIONS

An analysis of the full interview material reveals that this patient has had long-standing passive-dependent traits. He had been able to cope with these and with minor environmental difficulties in a relatively successful way until a few years before hospitalization. This adjustment was accomplished with the help of a constellation of psychological defenses including overinvolvement in manly activity, denial and avoidance of emotional problems, and to some extent projective mechanisms. This defensive alignment became insufficient as external stresses continued to exert a gradually cumulative effect. It was then that the patient began to experience rather open feelings of anxiety, and physical symptoms of exhaustion and depletion. These stresses involved the patient's responsibilities as father and husband, provider for his family, effective worker, and money earner. His wife is represented as attempting to escape from her feminine role and forcing him into it—but, in turn, this is a reflection of intensifying internal conflict in the patient about his own position in this regard.

Environmental pressures appear to have reached a critical point several months before admission. A further psychophysical decompensation then occurred, with increased anxiety and instability affectively and ideationally expressed, together with symptoms now referrable to the gastrointestinal tract. The chief area of physical discomfort was localized in the stomach with the symptomatology becoming particularly aggravated after eating. These symptoms provide an associative pathway, beginning with interoceptive links, to deeply rooted oral needs connected with eating problems and stomach trouble in childhood, ambivalent but particularly hostile relationship to mother, and tendency toward feminine identification behaviorally. Somatic identifications, however, are with older brother—both were thin in childhood—and with father who injured himself while active several years before. There is also manifest superego activity that punishes any display of hostility, though anger does break through in affective discharges.

PHYSICAL HISTORY

This was the patient's first hospital admission, with chief complaint of exhaustion of one year's duration. The patient states that he was relatively well until a year ago, when he noticed the onset of easy fatigability, tiredness, and weakness. He went to a physician shortly thereafter and was told that his blood pressure and blood count were low. He was treated for a period of four weeks with liver and iron injections and perihemin capsules by mouth. The patient stated he then felt fairly well until six months ago, when weakness and easy fatigability recurred and appeared to have become increasingly progressive. His appetite had been poor for the past several months. In the past week he has noticed a sensation as if his "stomach were knotted up." There has been no nausea, vomiting, or abdominal pain. He states that he has lost approximately 10 pounds in the past year. He went to the physician at the auto assembly plant where he works and was again told his blood pressure was low and he was advised to go into a hospital for further studies. The patient denies bleeding from any body orifice, icterus, fever, or chills. There has been no change in color of urine, and no increased pigmentation of skin, but the patient states that his skin appears to be becoming looser. Past history and system review essentially noncontributory.

PHYSICAL EXAMINATION

Temperature 98.6°F. Pulse 84. Blood pressure 120/82. The patient is a well-developed, well-nourished, white male in no acute physical distress. The entire physical examination, including neurological, was negative.

LABORATORY DATA

Hemogram, sedimentation rate, urinalysis within normal limits.

ROENTGENOGRAMS

Chest, gallbladder and gastrointestinal series: all negative.

HOSPITAL COURSE

Patient was afebrile and rapidly became asymptomatic during his hospital stay. He was anxious to go home and was discharged after a week, being informed that no organic disease had been found.

DISCHARGE DIAGNOSIS

Functional nervous disturbance with gastrointestinal somatization.

COMMENT

While sensory percepts are not prominent in this patient's interview, they are basically interoceptive, with a direct link to the affects of anxiety and hostility. The physical discomfort described as tightness (probably spasm of smooth muscle) in the stomach has associative links with memory traces which refer to eating in childhood and which, in turn, reveal a disturbed relationship with mother (and currently, wife). The gastrointestinal symptoms in childhood, the dependency needs and their frustration, and the ambivalent, particularly, the hostile, ties to mother figures suggest one facet of a basic psychophysical response to stress in this patient.

Freud (1895) noted that our earliest awareness of living objects is through perception complexes which they activate, but which are also fused with memories of similar perceptions of our own body. These collective memories are in turn linked with reactive movements also once experienced in oneself. The following concept can then be formulated: "Objects are recognized perceptively through recollective mechanisms which are rooted in perceptions of one's own body." Hendrick (1951) considered the development of the special senses, particularly their discriminatory function, to be a basic and necessary precursor of any true object relation. Deutsch (1954) considered that "the psychological implications of psychosomatic processes can be fully understood only if the interaction of the sensory perceptions and their related psychic elements can be traced back to their earliest sources and shown as an entity." He also felt that early sensory stimuli are precursors of "synthetically cathected objects" to which they are connected. The ego manipulates sensory percepts for the earliest cognition of objects. Sensory constellations are formed that become specific for certain objects, e.g., the parental figures. Thus, under certain circumstances, the individual may note sensations which symbolically represent the regressive emergence into consciousness of an early form of relationship to a particular object.

CASE 1

CHIEF PRESENTING SYMPTOM	Tightness in stomach
SENSORIMOTOR CONFIGURATIONS	Sensory configurations

Interoceptive

Linked to affects of anxiety and hostility, and to deeply rooted oral needs associated with eating problems and stomach symptoms, now and in childhood, and representing a very early psychophysical expression of ambivalent relationship with mother

Motor configurations

Activity

Associated with work, stomach spasm, easy fatigability, controlling self, and past accidents which activated concern about physical inferiority

SOMATIC IDENTIFICATION	Older brother	Underweight in childhood
	Father	Back injury two years ago
SENSITIZED ORGAN SYSTEM	Gastrointestinal tract—stomach	
STRESS (*surface meaning*)	Cumulative, more acute last two months Responsibilities as father, husband, effective worker, and money earner	
STRESS (*dynamic significance*)	Increased dependency needs and castration fears	
DEFENSES	Compensatory manly activity Denial Avoidance Projection	

AFFECTS	*Intensity*	*Pathway of expression*
Anxiety	+++	multiple: affective, postural, somatic equivalents, ideational —attached to illness, hospitalization, work, money
Depression	+	ideational
Hostility	++	affective, ideational, somatic equivalents

OTHER FACTORS   Dependency feelings
                                 Strong oral needs
                                 Highly punitive conscience
                                 Father's bad temper
                                 Early development of tight controls over
                                 feelings

HOMEOSTATIC SHIFT(S)   Regression expressed in mild to moderate
                                 somatization response

DIAGNOSIS   Functional nervous disturbance with gas-
                                 trointestinal somatization

Fever and Critical Loss of Human Relationships

CHIEF PRESENTING SYMPTOM

Feverishness.

BASIC ANAMNESTIC EXCERPTS

The patient is interviewed at bedside. He speaks readily in a bland tone of voice, although his temperature has just been recorded as 103°F. No overt anxiety is noted.

The interview begins with associations involving physical symptoms and intense affect: "When I get nervous or riled up, it tends to create a fever. A week ago I gave my notice at the shop. I had asked for a raise on Friday which the old man—my employer—refused. It was on my mind over the weekend, making me very uneasy. On Monday I told him I was quitting. Then it seemed I got a high fever, 104°. I've worked for this one company during the past four years, and the only time I've been sick in my life has been during these years. I can't get along with the boss. He seems to be after me all the time."

Feverishness is further elaborated: "Before I get warm, I'm ugly at home. I have three children and can't keep them quiet. As the fever picks up momentum, I feel red-hot and just want to drink cold water because I'm so dry. The first time I had it four years ago, it came six months after I had started at this job and lasted just a week. Then, like now, I was mad at the boss. Fever occurs more often than chills. My eyes feel heavy, as if I could go to sleep; sometimes they burn. I'm restless. I have a loss of energy—it's an effort to pick up anything, and I feel unsteady. My appetite gets poor even though I enjoy food and love to eat."

Returning to the recent episode with his boss: "When I went up to ask him for the raise, I shook for a few minutes. When the old man said, 'No,' I got mad and stopped shaking and then felt better. My job is to take care of the stockroom for an electrical contractor. I've worked hard and felt I deserved the raise. To make matters worse, all the children were sick with colds; one of the youngsters was feverish and had to be kept in bed. We have three boys. We lost one about five years ago—a three-month-old boy; he died of some kind of fever. We brought it to doctors and to hospitals a couple of times. Then we took her—took him home. He seemed all right for a couple of days; then one night got very warm, but not too bad off, not coughing. We woke up the next morning and found him dead in bed."

Associated references to loss of energy lead to the theme of activity which has links well into the past: "I feel very sluggish with the fever, but I'm usually pretty active. When I was a youngster, I was more interested in play than coming home to eat. Used to get all heated up from running, playing ball, because I'd do it so hard. Mother warned me about taking it easy. But I gave it up when I started to work at 17. My mother and father separated then—so I couldn't look forward to college, and I put all my energies into work." His older brother went off on his own, and his younger brother (by nine years) and he remained with mother. "Mother had no objection to my being so active—she thought me a regular boy. My younger brother, however, was injured at birth; his right side was paralyzed. The doctors said he would never walk, but he walks and dances now. Mother paid him a lot of attention when he was a kid. ... She had an operation for a tumor in her abdomen seven years ago. I was away then in military service."

There are further references to the patient's work: "I had a dirty job at first, loading furnaces from a crane in a smelting factory; the smoke and smell were getting me down; besides, it was unbearably hot. Then I ran a crane in a neat, clean job. Then I took this job four years ago, and no more crane. But I just can't stand that old man being always after me. There'd be this tension. He'd always be checking on me. I didn't know what he wanted from me, and it got to working on my mind. I've always felt a little unsure of myself, lacking confidence, anyway. All these four years, if I had a violent argument with him, I'd be out sick three to four days; I'd feel feverish and upset. After resting for a few days, I'd go back for three to four months."

More detail about overactivity and fever follows: "I was building a house in addition to my regular work, so maybe it was too much effort. I had dug a water line in my spare time. That really knocked me out, wore me down. Shortly afterward, I had that big argument and then I ran a temperature and had no appetite for a week. It went away with aspirin and bed rest." The patient indicated that he had been overworking for years. He is bothered a great deal by warm weather but not by cold. The fever has come at different seasons.

The patient continues to emphasize how hard he has to work for his family: "I have three boys and the wife wants to be dressed nicely. They all have good appetites, so you have to keep making money in order to get along. Wife does not work, she's hard of hearing in the past year. Her mother is stone deaf. With every child my wife and her hearing get worse. She's also had trouble hemorrhaging during her deliveries. She can't have any more children because it would damage her inside, and so contraceptives have to be used. She doesn't want any more, and I don't want to injure her in any way."

PSYCHODYNAMIC IMPRESSIONS

The patient's basic feelings of insecurity and inferiority are directly linked to traumatic relationships with the boss, a father surrogate who is seen variably as powerful competitor, deserting parent, and possibly erotized figure. References to the patient's own father are meager. Reactions to mother portray her as rejecting the patient in preference for a younger brother who is physically defective. The theme of loss is impressively recurrent: older brother left the family during patient's youth; parents' separation blocked him from going to college; death of infant son; wife's loss of blood during childbirth, difficulty in hearing, as well as her inability to have more children. Then there are also the associations dealing with loss of money, job, manhood, as well as energy, activity, appetite— all referring directly to the patient.

Compulsive overactivity has been a principal defense against a breakthrough of the patient's very strong feelings of deprivation and helplessness. Within the past four years, however, episodes of psychophysical decompensation have recurred, in which, basically, crises in his relationships with his boss lead to anticipated loss of security and then, secondarily, as the organic illness progresses, physical stress factors are involved, with fever becoming a chief manifestation. Overactivity is then no longer possible. Fever is linked in the interview with the theme of inactivity–activity, which leads to recollection of early experiences and especially to his ambivalent relatonships with family figures.

While loss is represented in many different ways, and its expectation or actual occurrence appears as the principal psychological stress, neither the related depression nor anxiety are affectively expressed in the interview. Hostility and guilt are to some extent indicated ideationally in the content; they, likewise, are not represented in any affective expression.

Identification in somatic terms can be noted most directly in the references to infant son and younger brother. The link to the former is through the association to fever, and the connection with the latter is by way of the theme of activity–inactivity. A less obvious somatic identification appears in relation to women. Mother has a tumor removed from abdomen and wife hemorrhages at childbirth (pregnancy is the most common tumor).

PHYSICAL HISTORY

This was the second hospital admission of this patient with chief complaint of fever, malaise, cough, anorexia, vomiting, diarrhea. First admission to this hospital was approximately six months ago with chief complaint of fever, malaise, and diarrhea. He gave a history of recurrent febrile episodes with fever ranging up to 102° to 104°F daily, for four to six days. The first episode occurred four years ago, and the following year he had two. The next year he was hospitalized and worked up for fever of undetermined origin. Physical findings at that time were negative, except for bilateral hilar adenopathy which was treated with a 10-day course of X-ray therapy. He was asymptomatic between the febrile episodes.

On his first admission here, the physical examination and laboratory work, including sternal marrow, agglutination tests, and the rest, were essentially negative. The patient spiked a fever of 104°F for three days, and then his temperature returned to normal without specific therapy. He did not appear actually ill or toxic even at the height of his fever. Films obtained from other hospitalizations were interpreted by the X-ray department as suggestive of lymphoma.

In the interval between hospitalizations here he felt entirely well with good appetite, no weight loss, and no fever until 10 days prior to admission, when his children were sick with colds; the patient believes he also had an upper respiratory infection. He also asked his boss for a raise about this time and was refused. He then decided to quit. Apparently he was much upset during this period and became "hotter and hotter." Seven days prior to admission, he developed malaise, cough productive of two or three ounces of whitish sputum, nausea, vomiting of ingested food, and persistent diarrhea consisting of four to five loose stools daily. His temperature was noted to be 104°F. Symptoms and fever continued, and almost complete anorexia developed. He had a 12-pound weight loss since his last admission, but much of this had apparently occurred in the two weeks prior to admission.

PHYSICAL EXAMINATION

Temperature 102.8°F. Pulse 104. Blood pressure 122/74. The patient is well-developed, fairly well-nourished, and appearing moderately ill. The skin was hot and dry; lips were reddened and scaling. Tongue dry and slightly coated. Pharynx slightly injected but not remarkable. The abdomen was scaphoid, moderately tense, but there was no tenderness; the spleen tip descended two cm with inspiration. The remainder of the physical examination, including neurological, was negative.

LABORATORY DATA

On admission: Hemoglobin 12.4 g. White blood cell count 5,000 with a normal differential. Platelet count 350,000. Reticulocyte count 0.2 percent. Repeat hemograms were essentially the same, except that hemoglobin was 11.6 g and the reticulocyte count shifted to 1.3 percent. Serology negative. Urine negative. Cephalin flocculation negative. Van den Bergh direct 0.2, indirect 0.4. Four blood cultures revealed no growth. Heterophile and brucella agglutinations negative. Sputum was negative for AFB (acid-fast bacilli) on three smears. Sedimentation rate 28 to 30 mm per hr. Malaria smear was negative. Tuberculin skin test was negative to first and second strength PPD on both 48- and 96-hour readings.

ROENTGENOGRAMS

Chest: showed no change since last examination; no abnormalities visualized. Abdomen: suggestive slight enlargement of spleen since last examination six months ago; a previously noted density in the right lower quadrant was still present, had a laminated appearance, possibly an appendiceal calculus.

HOSPITAL COURSE

The patient was started on bed rest and supportive measures of cough syrup, light diet, and alcohol sponges when necessary. For the first three days of hospitalization, he ran a continual fever ranging from 103° to 105°F. Then he was started on aspirin 6 g every 24 hours. On this regimen the temperature fell to 98° to 100.2°F. However, two days after the aspirin was discontinued, he again spiked a temperature of 103°F. At this time, although a specific diagnosis had not been established, he was given 10 mg of nitrogen mustard intravenously (slightly less than 0.2 mg per kg). The patient experienced some nausea and epigastric discomfort during the procedure. He had visitors during much of this time, and sedation did not take effect. The nitrogen mustard was repeated two days later, and on this occasion, with sedation and no visitors, little epigastric difficulty was noted. Following the second course of nitrogen mustard, the patient was afebrile and felt much better for two days. On the evening prior to discharge, his temperature was noted to be 100°F. However, he attributed this to some disturbing news his wife had brought him that afternoon, and as his temperature the next morning was normal, the patient was discharged to return to the hematology clinic in two weeks for follow-up blood study.

DISCHARGE DIAGNOSIS

Fever of unknown origin, presumptive diagnosis of lymphoma, treated, improved.

COMMENT

The episodes of illness experienced by this patient have an irregular periodicity, but are preceded in each instance by recurrent crises in his interpersonal relationships. These stress situations appear on the surface to be clearly delineated, but their deeper psychological meaning for the patient is complex and not so apparent. The associative material reveals that his boss had become a key figure in his emotional life in recent years. The patient reacts to him as if he were a parental surrogate. The most intense emotional responses are evoked when the patient, who is exquisitely hypersensitive to loss situations and who has experienced many of them in the past, feels that he is about to be or is being rejected by his employer. At such times extreme hostility and an escalating sense of help-lessness are activated, and the patient becomes ill with what is finally diagnosed as Hodgkin's disease. Extensive studies done by Greene and his co-workers (1956) on the lymphomas and leukemias will be reported in the final comment on this case.

Fever appears as a principal manifestation of the illness, but this symptom is a highly complicated phenomenon, whose physical aspects are still not clearly understood. However, the role of psychological factors in the development of fever and in the individual's subsequent reactions to it has had comparatively little study and needs much investigation. A few general and specific aspects will be considered here. As Fenichel (1945) has indicated, the development of instinctual conflicts in children is considerably influenced by physical illness. For instance, when the child is sick, it may receive much parental attention. Regression may be enhanced, passive needs activated and gratified, and secondary-gain elements introduced. On the other hand, the illness may be misinterpreted to mean a punishment, at times for masturbatory or other sexual activity, and for hostile thoughts and acts. Infectious diseases are the most common form of illness which the child experiences. With the accompanying fever, the child's sensory perceptions may become confused with those associated with sexual or other instinctual drive gratification and anticipated consequences, and thus linked with both pleasurable and unpleasurable components. Emotional factors then become involved in the sickness, and the child perceives its body in new and different ways. These changes become incorporated into the totality of possible reactions to illness and then may manifest themselves later on when the individual becomes sick again.

In this patient's interview there were no references to early, infectious diseases, but there were associations linking temperature sensations, over-activity (with all its implications) and fear of the consequences, recollected from childhood. His present episodes of fever were preceded by and later linked with suggestive but repressed erotic attachment to his employer and then extensive hostility because of anticipated rejection. There was associated guilt, but it was also largely outside the patient's awareness. All these elements with their pressure for discharge entered into his "excitability." This emotionally disturbed state may have activated the dysfunction associated with the organic disease process and further disrupted heat-regulating mechanisms which appear to have been conditioned already to react sensitively to psychological stress. In addition, the patient's emotional responses to his illness, principally to the incapacitating fever, also have to be considered as playing a part in his total current response. However, they represent secondary reactions.

CASE 2

CHIEF PRESENTING SYMPTOM	Feverishness
SENSORIMOTOR CONFIGURATIONS	Sensory configurations

Temperature

Linked to affect of hostility—in connection with refused request for raise which would have been a recognition of his ability, and manifestation of continued interest in him by his employer (parent surrogate)

Motor configurations

Running, playing

Connected with temperature percepts (heated up)—with mother's warning of consequences resulting from childhood activity

SOMATIC IDENTIFICATION	Child	Died of fever five years ago (direct)
	Another child	Feverish currently (direct)
	Younger brother	Inactive due to right-sided paralysis in childhood

SOMATIC IDENTIFICATION		~~Running, playing~~
	Mother	Abdominal tumor operation seven years ago
	Wife	Hemorrhages at delivery, intermittently during past six years; is losing hearing
SENSITIZED ORGAN SYSTEM		Lymphatic system—spleen
STRESS (*surface meaning*)		Crisis in relationship with boss with threat of job loss
STRESS (*dynamic significance*)		Increased dependency needs and also a competitive, sexualized relationship with a father figure
DEFENSES		Compulsive overactivity Rationalizations Reaction formations

AFFECTS	*Intensity*	*Pathway of expression*
Anxiety	+	ideational, somatic equivalents
Depression	+++	ideational—many references to loss, some to guilt
Hostility	+++	ideational—principally toward employer, somatic equivalents

OTHER FACTORS	Mother's prohibitions and rejections Father a competitive, deserting figure, but also possibly erotized Intense feelings of deprivation and helplessness
HOMEOSTATIC SHIFT(S)	Regression to marked somatization response, premorbid defense structure becoming insufficient with continued stress
DIAGNOSIS	Fever of unknown origin, presumptive diagnosis of lymphoma, treated, improved

FOLLOW-UP DATA

INTERIM NOTE

After the patient left the hospital, he remained relatively asymptomatic for a period of several months, working at a new but temporary job as a stock clerk. However, he appeared to be constantly brooding and at times referred bitterly to his having been unappreciated and forced out of his former place of employment by his old boss. Some four months later, shortly after he was laid off his new job, he developed acute right-sided abdominal pain and underwent an appendectomy from which he made an uneventful recovery. He was unable to find another job and was on unemployment compensation for a while. His financial situation began to deteriorate and he became increasingly restless at his enforced inactivity and displayed more and more irritability at home and with his wife and children. He kept referring to "things being all over" for him. About six months after his appendectomy the patient "caught cold," developed a severe productive cough, pleuritic pain, fever, and diarrhea. He was hospitalized because of the persistence of fever. At this time there was no significant adenopathy, but splenic edge was felt one fingerbreadth below the left costal margin. The white blood cell count fluctuated between 5,600 and 2,000 with a typical differential of segmented cells 64, band cells 4, lymphocyte 28, monocytes 4. Hemoglobin ranged between 9.5 and 10 grams. Urine was negative. The patient was given 0.2 mg per kg of nitrogen mustard twice, two days apart. Several days later he was afebrile, the cough lessened, and he remained then essentially asymptomatic until his discharge.

One month later the patient was readmitted with complaints of fever, cough, and diarrhea with three to five watery bowel movements.

PHYSICAL EXAMINATION

Revealed a thin, pale, chronically ill male. Temperature 100°F. Pulse 110. Respirations 22. Blood pressure 95/65. Physical examination otherwise was noncontributory: On this occasion the spleen was not palpable; there was a right lower–quadrant abdominal scar.

LABORATORY DATA

Urinalysis: cloudy, specific gravity 1.020, 5 to 7 white blood cells per high power field on admission; subsequently showed heavy trace of albumin, 40 to 50 white blood cells per high power field and pus casts. Admission hemogram: white blood cell count 3,000 with segmented cells 75, band cells 6, lymphocytes 15, monocytes 4, and hemoglobin 9.3 g, hematocrit 31 percent; several days later white blood cell count 1,900 with lymphocytes 44, hemoglobin 9 g, hematocrit 27 percent, sedimentation rate 23 mm.

ROENTGENOGRAM

Chest: negative. Abdomen: mass, size of orange pressing on greater curvature of stomach and on proximal end of splenic flexure.

HOSPITAL COURSE

Shortly after admission the patient developed several mouth ulcers. He was started on cortisone 75 mg every six hours. A week later his condition showed little improvement and he was given ACTH intravenously. Rapid deterioration set in, however. An exfoliative dermatitis developed. The patient became disoriented, incontinent, and had increasing abdominal distention. He died one month after admission.

POSTMORTEM FINDINGS

Respiratory Tract: (1) Congestion and edema of lungs; (2) Bronchopneumonia, early.

Gastrointestinal Tract: (1) Diverticulum, descending colon.

Spleen and Hematopoietic Tissues: (1) Hodgkin's disease, sarcoma type, involving lymph nodes, spleen, liver, bone marrow; (2) Hypoplasia, bone marrow; (3) Infarct, recent, spleen.

Miscellaneous: (1) Dermatitis, exfoliative; (2) Ascites, slight; (3) Emaciation.

FINAL COMMENT

The periodic upsets with his boss over a period of four years had been followed invariably by exacerbations in the patient's physical condition. These were short in duration and responded quickly to treatment. The boss clearly represented a figure of great emotional importance for the patient. An intense father transference had been activated and maintained in this relationship. Final dismissal from work meant also a final rejection by the father-boss. The patient reacted to this critical loss with a marked intensification of hostile impulses turned inward and with a growing sense of helplessness. External circumstances did not afford any adequate substitute object relationship, possibility of defensive compensatory activity, or in fact any relief from the regressive shift in the patient's psychophysical condition. A deepening depression, blocked from sufficient affective and ideational outlet, was accompanied by increasing malfunction of the hematopoietic system.

Greene (1954) has carried out extensive studies on emotional factors and reticuloendothelial disease. His basic question has been whether psychological as well as physicochemical stress can provoke dysfunction in this system. He quotes from Piney who already in 1927 had noted that "the variety of stimuli capable of affecting the hematopoietic tissues is much greater than the number of possible modes of reaction; therefore identical reactions can result from widely different stimuli." The premise of Greene's studies is that the various manifestations of both lymphomas and leukemias result from pathological reactions of the reticuloendothelial system. Recognition of the disease by the patient does not necessarily indicate the exact onset of the illness. This recognition is probably a resultant of many factors—the patient's awareness of symptoms and signs, the doctor's clinical astuteness, and the limitations of present laboratory findings. In the 20 male patients studied, recognition of the disease was found to occur in a setting of psychological stress, despite possibilities of pure coincidence, emotional reactions to the illness itself, and variable psychophysical responses from patient to patient and from time to time in the same patient. No data were available why the reticuloendothelial system was involved or why a psychological illness was not the principal reaction. In this first study, no evidence was found that the physical response is an accompaniment of an anxiety reaction, or part of preparation for activity in relation to the demands of the external environment. Rather, "...lymphomas and leukemias may be more autoplastic and more primitive physiologically and psychologically than the psychogenic diseases operating through voluntary or vegetative control system." The reticuloendothelial manifestations may be a nonspecific response to bodily changes more directly precipitated by psychological stress. In 17 of the 20 patients, such stress included separation from an emotionally significant figure. There were also frequent coincidental life-situation problems involving work, infection, trauma, or operation. In all cases the symptoms and recognition of the illness occurred during a period of adjustment to multiple stresses.

In 1956, another study by Greene et al. on 32 women with these diseases did not point to any single personality profile. Various types of psychophysical responses were noted as in the previous group. Again, one of the conditions determining the development, remission, and exacerbation of these illnesses appeared to be separation from a key object or goal, with ensuing depression. Depression is used in the sense described by Benedek (1950) as "the psychobiological response to any disturbance of the symbolic relation which is oral or alimentary for both infant and mother." Half the separations or losses during a four-year prodromal period occurred during one year prior to apparent onset. The majority of the patients showed an affect of sadness or hopelessness for weeks or months prior to apparent onset. Separation is not characteristic for these patients alone. This factor may contribute to a number of diseases observed on a general medical ward.

Still further observations by Greene and Miller (1958) on 33 children and adolescents below age 20, with leukemia, again led to the conclusion that the same factor of separation may be one of the conditions involved in the sickness just as had been noted in previous studies with adults.

case 3

Pruritus Ani and Mouth Lesions in a Markedly Infantile Patient

CHIEF PRESENTING SYMPTOM

Bleeding, itchy, sore rectum.

BASIC ANAMNESTIC EXCERPTS

The initial references to rectal difficulty are associated with visual percepts and with eating: "One doctor looked up there with his finger, thought there might be a polyp, advised an ointment, squirted it in. They looked again this morning through a scope, and the rectum was clear. I noticed bleeding only when I wiped myself. The itching might be due to foods I eat—onions, cabbage, tonic—which cause a lot of belching of gas. Passing so much gas could cause injury which could cause the bleeding. It bitches to eat—I mean, it itches to beat anything, so that sometimes you scratch. It began eight months ago. Lately I've not been eating well. This itching bothers me so much. Today they said no polyp—no operation necessary.

"I've had enough surgery. I was shot in the left lung, and they took some lung out to get at the shrapnel. Every winter I get cold on top of cold. I'll be getting married in three weeks, and then go out to Colorado where the weather is dry. The chief surgeon at the military hospital there is a very good friend of mine. I was hospitalized there a year and a half. I had operations for empyema, resections of ribs and lung. I was very sick, had last rites three times. The shrapnel in there kept the lung bleeding, and they had to keep operating. I went down from 180 to 120 pounds, couldn't eat anything. I used to be a big smoker, but haven't smoked since, just eat candy. I was hit in a night combat attack while sleeping in the woods. I'm lucky to be alive; the shrapnel just missed my heart."

The wound ended the patient's long-standing ambitions to become a professional baseball player: "I had my mind on big things, big money. I'd play ball all day long—wouldn't eat—since I was six years old. If I get married and have kids, they'll grow up to be baseball players—even if I couldn't. They (parents) didn't like my playing, and I used to get my fanny tanned by father for missing lunch and supper or getting into mischief. They thought I was crazy, playing ball so long, getting myself run down. But I was always a big kid; when I was 18, I was six feet tall and weighed 160 pounds—bigger than father. I was the oldest child; had three younger sisters."

References to the family health follow: "Everyone in the family is well now. Fifteen years ago Mother had her gallbladder taken out; she had stones. I went fishing the day she was being operated on—tried to get my mind off it; I felt bad like anyone else would. Father was a patient here eight months ago; he told me they found an ulcer. But several years ago he had a back injury while working, got a rupture. He was operated on once, but they're supposed to do it again for a double rupture. He's got trouble behind and in front. My sisters are in great shape, better than I'll ever be. The sister just younger than me has a six-year-old boy who looks like nine; he's tall, maybe he takes after me; he's my favorite nephew. Anyway, his father's short. This boy got hit by a bus a year ago, and they barely saved his foot; they had to cut off his two middle toes. He had a lot of surgery, including a skin graft from his fanny. Luckily his leg was saved. He was in the hospital four months and still has to see a doctor every other day. The skin graft tends to develop pus." The patient now refers again to his own childhood, but this time in rather idealized terms, tending to contradict earlier references to that period in his life.

Further exhibitionistic and voyeuristic associations appear in connection with his symptoms: "When it itches, I'm finally forced to scratch. It's embarrassing, scratching my fanny. Fellows are looking and saying, 'What's he scratching there for?' I really came in for that proctoscope—that really hurt—that big thing going up—oh, did I sweat! My bowels always moved good, without trouble. I was always full of energy, but now I'm tired, short of breath."

He then shifts to his impending marriage: "I'm going to see my girl and my mother today. There's nobody like your mother. That's your best girl. Always. She does a lot of different things for me which my father wouldn't do, or somebody else wouldn't either. If I should ask her for money, she'd break her back getting it for me. Father gets mad and says, 'He'll take it to this girl and spend it.' I guess now they figure the marriage is for the best. It's funny; I'm just thinking of getting married, and this business with the rectum comes up. Everything's all set for next month (no enthusiasm), and all my girl's waiting for is my coming home (sighing). Time flies by so fast (pause). I have a nice, clean girl—no father; her mother is old and has a bad heart. My girl's the sole support of her family. We've been going together for three years, and finally we said, 'If we don't know each other by now, we never will,'—so. It was she who brought it up three months ago (laughing); she wondered if I really wanted her. I decided to—I'm not getting any younger. We'll have to live with her mother for a while before we go away. I don't like to argue, so I expect we'll get along."

The patient's associations now turn again to his military service experience: "I was homesick at first. I went into the National Guard at 18. The people overseas were unfriendly; gave me the cold shoulder. When I got wounded, I couldn't eat anything and shriveled from 180 to 120 pounds. I had terrific pain. I was aspirated all the time. They'd stick a needle a foot long into your ribs and take all that black blood out. It's a wonder they didn't hit the heart when they went inside with that big needle. They finally did an empyema job on me. The pus drained out for six months; it would stink terribly. I never had an infection before, and I was always a healthy boy until Uncle Sam grabbed me."

PSYCHODYNAMIC IMPRESSIONS

This patient has had a long-standing concern about manliness. He had defended himself against these fears by overcompensatory athletic efforts with accompanying ambitiousness, exhibitionistic (and voyeuristic) tendencies, and attempts to get close to and identify with "chiefs." He is the only boy and oldest of four siblings. There is a very close attachment to mother, both as a nurturing figure and incestuous sexual object. Competition with a strict father and associated development of marked infantile castration fears can also be noted in the interview material.

Physical characteristics and accomplishments, physical defects and consequences are highly underscored. There are indications of regressive shifts after he was wounded and during his long illness and hospitalization. Physical recovery left him with considerable doubts about his bodily integrity, and these are but thinly covered over with bragging reminiscences of his past physical prowess and recent and current associations with big-name doctors. The physical defect itself has become subject to secondary-gain influences, gaining pity and attention for the patient.

Left with this relatively unstable equilibrium, the patient has been exposed to experiences of varying stressful impact in the last two years: father's back injury, nephew's right-foot injury with skin grafting from his "fanny," father's hospitalization eight months ago—coincidental with onset of patient's rectal symptoms and impending marriage. More recently he has tended to be anorectic. The decision to get married, reluctantly and ambivalently acceded to by the patient under pressure from his girl, preceded his hospitalization by several weeks. With the wedding date three weeks away, the patient's physical symptoms noticeably worsened as his anxiety about his masculinity and his concern about leaving his mother concomitantly increased, and to a certain extent became reflected in somatic equivalents.

Anal components in his emotional conflicts are directly reflected ideationally and somatically. The anamnestic material suggests the patient's concern with recently activated infantile sexual concepts. These appear in the form of disguised fantasies symbolizing an anal penis, masochistic anal penetration, and cloacal pregnancy. This suggests a repressed anxiety about being feminine and having homosexual wishes. Oral factors appear less prominently and are associated with anticipated impending loss of the chief source of emotional supplies (mother) with insufficient replacement (fiancée). Hostility seems to be in the moderate range of intensity, and without adequate affective discharge outlets. Some curious sensory relationships may be noted: visual connected with touch-penetrating, i.e., looking with a finger. There are also many displacements with sexual symbolic meaning: from chest to anorectal area and vice versa, from genital area to chest, from extremities to genital and anorectal regions. Mixed somatic identifications with father, much more directly and specifically with a six-year-old nephew (himself at that age), and also with mother are evident in the anamnesis.

PHYSICAL HISTORY

The patient was admitted with a chief complaint of slight rectal bleeding, beginning eight months ago. At that time he noted a small amount of red blood on the toilet paper after bowel movement. This continued intermittently to the present and was associated with pruritus ani. Three months before admission, he went to a local doctor who, after a digital rectal examination, told the patient he had a "rectal polyp." Shortly thereafter, the patient noted that "he was off his feed." One month before admission, he went to another physician who found no polyp on digital examination of the rectum, advised hospitalization for proctoscopy, and gave the patient nupercaine ointment for his pruritis ani. For the past month he had been treated also with vitamin B-complex pills for nutritional deficiency manifested by a smooth, sore tongue and canker sores of the mouth.

Past history reveals that eight years ago he had a shrapnel wound of the left chest. Following bleeding and aspiration of blood, he developed empyema, and some months later his left lower lung was removed. Since then, he has had frequent colds with accompanying left-chest pain and has noticed shortness of breath on exertion.

PHYSICAL EXAMINATION

Temperature 98.6°F. Pulse 80. Blood pressure 124/80. Tongue was smooth, sore, with atrophic papillae and aphthous lesions. There were also skin lesions at the right corner of the mouth. Two scars were noted along the left sixth and tenth ribs posteriorly. The breath sounds were diminished, and there was a respiratory lag at the left base, but no rales. On digital examination of the rectum no masses or polyps were palpable, nor was there any evidence of hemorrhoids. The remainder of the physical examination was negative.

LABORATORY DATA

Admission hemogram, serology, and urinalysis were negative. Three stools were guaiac negative. Nonprotein nitrogen 28 mg.

ROENTGENOGRAMS

X-rays of the chest showed a surgical resection of the left sixth and tenth ribs with thickened pleura extending from the left apex along the axillary border to the base. The findings were those of a lobectomy and not pneumonectomy. The right lung was normal in appearance. Barium enema revealed no abnormalities.

HOSPITAL COURSE

The patient was afebrile throughout. He was sigmoidoscoped and anoscoped the day after admission. The scope passed without difficulty to 6 inches, but no further because of discomfort to the patient. The mucosa appeared normal, and there were no signs of growth, polyps, or ulcerations in the area visualized. The patient had free acid in his stomach, ruling out pernicious anemia or achlorhydria as a cause of his chronic atrophic glossitis. The latter condition was felt to be due to a vitamin B-complex deficiency, especially since he also had cheilosis. He was treated with vitamin B-complex in large quantities with diminution of the soreness of the tongue.

DISCHARGE DIAGNOSES

1. No pathology of colon, rectum, or anus found.
2. Chronic atrophic glossitis and cheilosis, secondary to vitamin B-complex deficiency, treated, improved.
3. Lobectomy following gunshot wound, old, asymptomatic.

COMMENT

In the psychiatric interview the chief presenting physical symptom is rectal, whereas the actual signs on physical examination are in the mouth and not the rectum. The associative material suggests that both body areas have considerable symbolic significance for the patient. There is more sexual symbolization of the anorectal area expressed in ideational form with displacements to and from the chest defect. In this body part (anorectal area), actual physical changes—at least detectable ones—appear to be absent, despite the presence of physical symptoms. In turn, the mouth area, associated with aggressive impulses, appears to have become the focus for development of physical changes in the presence of a vitamin B deficiency. This, in turn, appears related to a very poor diet of at least three months' duration. The insufficiency of food intake appears to be emotionally determined. The patient did not refer directly to the sore tongue and mouth lesions in the psychiatric interview. However, there were actually indirect references to these areas in the form of associative screen memories connecting failure to eat, because of overactivity, with punitive measures. He also does not like to argue (use his mouth aggressively). Thus oral components were apparent in the anamnestic material, even though the related physical symptoms themselves were not mentioned.

Wittkower and Russell (1953) have suggested a relatively simple explanation for pruritus ani: namely that it is a reflection of homosexual conflicts. Macalpine (1953) noted that pruritus ani is more severe, of longer duration, and occurs more in men than women. No distinct personality type could be established for the condition. It appears to have origins in reactivated infantile fantasies about procreation involving the anal function. It would seem that such cloacal fantasies reappear in this earliest representation as bodily sensations rather than in the form of primitive thoughts. The psychopathology of these individuals suggests a relationship to hypochondriasis.

Alexander, R. P. (1959) studied the condition in detail in a female patient who was in psychoanalytic therapy for over four years. He also reviewed other data on the subject that have appeared in the literature. He felt that pruritus ani is a psychophysical entity. Somatic symptoms include itching (most prominent), discharge, nausea, bloating of abdomen, constipation and diarrhea. Concomitantly there are defiant, stubborn, retentive personality traits, and at times marked symptoms of depression. The syndrome results from a defensive struggle against the conscious recognition of passive, oral-receptive wishes, and destructive, rivalrous impulses. Oral mechanisms are replaced by anal mechanisms. The itching (and scratching) represent symbolically both gratification of an aggressive grabbing of the desired object and punishment for the hostile, incorporative nature of the impulses.

CASE 3

CHIEF PRESENTING SYMPTOM	Bleeding, itchy, sore rectum
SENSORIMOTOR CONFIGURATIONS	Sensory configurations

Visual, tactile

Linked with spankings by parents for not eating and for involvement in childhood mischief, and with associations suggesting symbolic infantile sexual fantasies, currently activated by impending marriage, seen as test of manliness

Motor configurations

Inserting, squirting, itching

Associated with sexualized passive-feminine tendencies breaking through defensive facade of athletic prowess, ambitiousness, and boastful exhibitionism

SOMATIC IDENTIFICATION	Mother	Gallbladder operation 15 years ago
	Father	Back injury two years ago, rupture two years ago and currently requiring operative intervention, ulcer eight months ago
	Nephew	Foot operation with skin graft from buttocks one year ago (Direct?)
SENSITIZED ORGAN SYSTEM		Gastrointestinal—mouth, anus
STRESS (*surface meaning*)		Father's back injury and hospitalization, his own reluctant agreement to get married (2 weeks before)—all in a two-year period
STRESS (*dynamic significance*)		Anticipated loss of mother as chief source of emotional supplies with insufficient replacement by fiancée; increased concern over masculine adequacy
DEFENSES		Overcompensatory athletic efforts Overambition Phallic aggressiveness

AFFECTS	*Intensity*	*Pathway of expression*
Anxiety	++	ideational—infantile sexual components, somatic equivalents, and some affective
Depression	++	ideational—principally concerned with loss of mother, somatic equivalents
Hostility	++	ideational, somatic equivalents

OTHER FACTORS

Mother—nurturing figure and incestuous sexual object
Father—competitor and possible homo-sexual object
Exhibitionistic and voyeuristic tendencies
Pregenital components—anal aspects, oral less prominent
Parental punishment for childhood misbehavior—physical, "fanny tanned"

HOMEOSTATIC SHIFT(S)

Following war wounds and hospitalization, increased castration fears with increased compensatory ambitious plans but not action; bragging
Most recent—in direction of sexual symbolization of anorectal area and mild somatization response there. More marked somatization shift in mouth area

DIAGNOSES

a) No pathology of colon, rectum, or anus found;
b) Chronic atrophic glossitis and cheilosis, secondary to vitamin B-complex deficiency, treated, improved;
c) Lobectomy following gunshot wound, old, asymptomatic

case 4

Shifting Gastrointestinal and Respiratory Symptoms during Prolonged Emotional Tension

CHIEF PRESENTING SYMPTOM

Pain in stomach.

BASIC ANAMNESTIC EXCERPTS

The initial associations are in lengthy chains given without interruption by the patient: "After my duodenal operation seven years ago, I recuperated very fast. A year later I got pains again—not as hard. I took a job as auto mechanic, and the pains started getting worse. When I saw the doctor finally, he told me I shouldn't do that type of work, where I breathe dust, grease, oil, and gas. He said I ought to work in an office, but you can't make any money that way. I'm always keeping busy, haven't had a holiday or vacation since I was in high school. Over the years the pain came and went. Recently it's been getting worse, and in the last months it's been terrific. I had such pain only when I was small and my appendix ruptured. A few days ago, feeling sick myself, I brought my wife home from the hospital where she'd had a new baby two weeks before. That makes three kids. . . . I need more money, and I've lost a lot of jobs, too much time out from work. My doctor suggested I be hospitalized. I've got to get on my feet if I want to keep my job." All this is said in a calm, almost deliberate fashion.

The present pain is linked with the incident of the ruptured appendix: "It happened when I was 12 years old. They just sewed me, then they opened me, then they put a tube in. The tube acted as a drain, and was kept there quite a while. Finally I was allowed to walk—but I'd walk bent over because, mentally, I was afraid if I straightened out, I'd rip it open." There follow references to a tonsillectomy at age six: "I had a lot of sore throats. I can remember having the tonsils out. I didn't want to stay in the hospital. My mother told me she was going to call a taxi, and she just disappeared. I didn't see her till the next day. It seemed like a year—that scary night I spent alone in the hospital."

The stomach symptoms started 10 years ago while he was on board ship: "The doctor told me I was probably homesick. I just couldn't seem to get adjusted, just kept thinking about home. My stomach really kicked up on me overseas. I couldn't seem to get better and I was returned to the States and given a medical discharge. When I tried to work, I hurt myself to the extent that I passed out. I was hospitalized and with rest and diet they got me back on my feet. After that I was better for a while, then would get nauseated often and had to carry a bottle of milk to work so I could always sip on it. Sometimes, while walking with my wife, the pain would hit me so hard, I'd go down on my knees. They tried everything and finally called in a specialist. He advised an operation to take out part of my stomach, and the next morning I went in. They gave me a spinal which didn't last. I couldn't breathe, as if there was something on my chest. They put a mask on my face, and I thought I was going, but eventually I went off to sleep."

A reference to illness at age 16, involving respiratory difficulties, follows: "I was on a boat and was thrown overboard; thought I would never have strength or breath enough to make it to shore. Finally I got there, exhausted. Several days later I caught a chest cold, and my wife—I mean, my mother said I needed a doctor. He found I had pneumonia." A related screen memory is next interposed: "When I was six, I got lost. I roamed around trying to find my home. I was scared, breathing fast. Finally a cop asked me where my house was. I couldn't remember where my mother lived but knew where my grandmother lived, and she came and got me."

The patient next elaborates on his family relationships: "There's just my sister and myself. Mother was a sickly woman. When I was little, she had a woman's operation where they removed part of the ovaries or something. She was in the hospital again when I was 10; she had a blood clot on the brain and didn't recognize me when I visited her. She got over that but used to have dizzy spells. Then, eight years ago she died of cancer. She suffered for a year and toward the end she had terrible, awful pains. From big-size she went down to nothing at all. The doctors treated her for dropsy and drew water from her legs, but the autopsy showed cancer of the stomach. I missed her a lot. In the following year I had my own operation."

The patient wonders if the interviewer is a nerve doctor: "I once went to a psychiatrist for a while. She told me my biggest trouble was too many bills. I guess I am a little nervous; I worry about the family. On the date I was originally supposed to take my wife home, they discovered a couple of pieces of afterbirth were left, and she had to be operated on. Then the baby had to be isolated for a while—something wrong with his chest; it was like a woman's breasts, bigger than normal. A piece of cord was also left over in him. . . . I can't do much sitting around here. I have a job waiting—a machinist's helper with lots of weight-lifting. It hurts me, but I still get that kind of job, I don't know why."

Eating is next briefly referred to: "I'm not much for breakfast—so that's against me. It's in front of me, and I get nauseous. But after I work for a couple of hours in the morning, I may get hungry enough to eat. I never ate regularly as a kid, mother being sick so much. My father-in-law had eating troubles, too. He had a gastric ulcer. My own father died when I was born, and mother remarried when I was five years old. My step-father was a good man and tried to take care of us the best he could." As the interview ends, the patient then mentions that he has been put in a room by himself, but doesn't know why.

PSYCHODYNAMIC IMPRESSIONS

Extreme sensitivity to deprivation and loss is a basic characteristic of this patient's psychological problems. Both emotional and physical experiences of an especially traumatic nature occurred early and frequently in his childhood. From birth on till five, there was no father figure in the family background. Mother is remembered as having many illnesses, being often incapacitated or away in hospitals, leaving the patient in the care of his grandmother. There are recollections of childhood eating problems. The gastrointestinal system appears to have been particularly involved during emotional upsets at that time. Tonsillectomy and appendectomy before puberty are each associated with a double sense of loss, both of his mother and a part of himself. The latter operation left him with a residual fear that any but limited activity might cause severe bodily damage. Stomach symptoms became especially marked when he was approximately 20 years old and were associated with intense homesickness, inability to adjust to military service overseas, and in turn, with considerable, but for the most part, repressed hostility related to inadequate gratification of activated, basically oral needs. Attempts at defense by denial and a largely verbal insistence on wanting to be active, became insufficient, following exposure to this major stress. There followed a regression to the somatic pathways of discharge, with subsequent remissions and exacerbations.

A severe emotional relapse followed the mother's death, and the subsequent gastric resection favored fixation of symptoms and enhanced the sensitivity of the gastrointestinal tract as a target organ. A chronic condition resulted, in which a conditioned somatic discharge pattern would be activated by stresses, particularly related to his responsibilities as a family man—husband and parent—and most recently activated by the wife's complicated delivery and the birth of a son who appeared physically defective. Somatic identification, with a recurrently ill mother who died of stomach cancer, is quite marked. In addition, there is a less well-developed identification with a father-in-law who also had an ulcer. Castration fears and, to a lesser extent, pregnancy fantasies are symbolically represented in the symptom of pain, but masked depression is the basic affect which the patient struggles against.

PHYSICAL HISTORY

This patient experienced persistent stomach pain 10 years ago while in military service. He was then hospitalized, and an ulcer was found by X-ray. For several years he had recurrent episodes of pain for which he was hospitalized. Seven years later he had another such episode which did not respond to a medical regimen, and he was then operated on and a part of his stomach was removed, but with partial and only temporary relief. There were subsequent intermittent bouts of the usual epigastric pain and nausea after eating, and more recently, a sharp, gnawing left lower-quadrant abdominal pain. Four months before admission, a chest film taken by a survey unit revealed a "scar" on the left lung. There had been no cough, sputum, or night sweats. The patient experiences some vertigo on getting up from a reclining position. He is an unusually tense person, married, has three children, has been in debt, and has always had to struggle. He has repeatedly lost jobs because of time away from work due to his ulcer.

PHYSICAL EXAMINATION

Temperature 98.6°F. Pulse 88. Blood pressure 130/80 in the recumbent position and 100/70 in the standing position. The patient is a thin, hyperkinetic male, professing to be in severe pain, yet not showing it objectively. Abdomen showed two laparotomy scars (gastrectomy and appendectomy). There was tenderness on deep palpation in the epigastrium and in the left lower quadrant. No masses were palpable. The remainder of the examination including neurological was negative.

LABORATORY DATA

Admission hemograms, urinalysis, and serology were negative. Stool guaiacs were repeatedly negative. Serum amylase and nonprotein nitrogen were within normal limits. Tuberculin skin test was positive in the first strength PPD.

ROENTGENOGRAMS

Chest plate showed patchy consolidation at the apex of the left upper lobe, suggesting an acid-fast infection. Gastrointestinal series showed only partial resection of the stomach with a gastroenterostomy; a considerable portion of the stomach remained. No abnormalities of the stoma were noticed, and the function through this area appeared normal on fluoroscopy. Barium enema showed no abnormalities.

HOSPITAL COURSE

The patient was afebrile throughout. On admission he was placed on an ulcer regimen including Gastric I diet which was gradually raised to a Gastric IV, sedation, antacids, and antispasmodics. On this regimen plus assurance that the X-rays showed no ulcer, his "severe" epigastric distress all but disappeared. Since his chest film showed nodular lesions in the left apex, strongly suggestive of acid-fast disease, he was put on tuberculosis precautions. Because he was not raising any sputum or coughing, three gastric aspirations were done, and sent to the laboratory for guinea-pig inoculation and culture. Meanwhile, a chest film taken five months earlier was obtained, and comparison of the films of the present admission with that X-ray revealed no significant change. The patient was seen in consultation by the chest service, and discharge was advised with monthly follow-ups.

DISCHARGE DIAGNOSES

1. Pulmonary tuberculosis, left upper lobe, minimal, inactive, unchanged.
2. Partial gastric resection with gastroenterostomy, functioning normally, no ulcers found.
3. Orthostatic hypotension, unchanged.
4. Anxiety reaction, moderate, treated, improved.

COMMENT

Respiratory symptoms are not elicited in the physical history, and the physical examination of the chest is negative. References to the respiratory system, however, do appear in the psychiatric interview. These also are not in the form of physical symptoms. Rather they come up indirectly as associations about breathing difficulties and lung disease, all of which occurred in the patient's past. There are other but even less direct references to chest trouble in the associations about his newborn son. Interestingly, shortly after the patient's discharge it was confirmed that there was indeed an active area of lung pathology which was ongoing at the time of hospitalization but which was not then known.

Vertigo was not mentioned by the patient as one of his symptoms in the anamnestic interview, though it appears in the physical history taken by the internist who also elicited blood pressure changes in the patient from recumbent to standing position. However, *indirect* references to dizziness and trouble in getting up from the recumbent position can be noted in the anamnestic material, in the context of past experiences and concerns with mother's symptom of vertigo, and later with the patient's difficulties in standing straight after his appendectomy. These data suggest the possibility that a physical illness (such as lung disease in this case) may go through a "silent phase" when a physical symptom is not evident as such.

Though this patient had had a gastric resection for his ulcer, he subsequently experienced only partial and temporary relief. Browning and Houseworth (1953) undertook an investigation designed to test the hypotheses that removal of ulcer symptoms by medical or surgical means, without concomitant removal of emotional conflicts giving rise to them, might be followed by the appearance of other, new symptoms. Thirty patients treated for ulcer by gastrectomy (57 percent then had no symptoms) made up the experimental group. A control group was made up of 30 ulcer patients treated by conservative medical regimen without complete remission of symptoms. The group treated surgically showed significant decrease in ulcer symptoms after gastrectomy, but had a significant parallel increase in other psychosomatic and psychoneurotic symptoms. The medically treated group in whom ulcer symptoms were not particularly reduced, did not show similar redistribution of symptoms. The hypothesis appeared to be supported. A follow-up of the gastrectomy group, 12 to 18 months later, revealed that 4 more patients or a total of 17/30 were having some ulcer symptoms, though only 4/17 were moderately severe. Two more or a total of 4 had moderately severe, sustained hypertension. Two additional, now a total of 5, developed asthma; 2 additional, total 17, developed troublesome physiologic manifestations of anxiety; 1 developed tuberculosis. The gastrectomy, although lifesaving in most cases, did not decrease the incidence or relative severity of total symptoms, presumably because it did not resolve the basic psychopathology.

CASE 4

CHIEF PRESENTING SYMPTOM Pain in stomach

SENSORIMOTOR CONFIGURATIONS Sensory configurations

Pain

Associated with highly traumatic childhood, especially loss of mother, operations involving gastrointestinal tract, homesickness in military service, and current unpleasant work, with chronic activation of sensitivity to deprivation and hostility turned inward

Motor configurations

Walking

Connected with loss of breath, chest colds, and anxiety about assuming the erect position, symbolizing manliness

SOMATIC IDENTIFICATION

Mother		Ovaries removed many years ago, blood clot on brain—vertigo many years ago (Direct), cancer of stomach death eight years ago (Direct, organ constitutional)
Father-in-law		Gastric ulcer (Direct)
Wife		Operated on for afterbirth recently
Child		Operated on for cord remnant recently

SENSITIZED ORGAN SYSTEM Gastrointestinal
Respiratory
Circulatory

STRESS (*surface meaning*) During war—inability to adjust to military service; mother's death, responsibilities as husband and parent: most recently —birth of seemingly defective son. Chronic with acute exacerbations

STRESS (*dynamic significance*) Chiefly—Increase in dependency needs; less—increase in castration fears

DEFENSES	Denial	
	Verbal insistence on activity	

AFFECTS	*Intensity*	*Pathway of expression*
Anxiety	+++	moderate ideational, minimal affective, and some masked somatic equivalents
Depression	+++	some ideational, mostly masked somatic equivalents
Hostility	+++	masked somatization with little ideational or affective outlet

OTHER FACTORS	Extreme sensitivity to loss Childhood traumata Secondary gain
HOMEOSTATIC SHIFT(S)	Regression: moderate–marked somatization when secondary process defenses insufficient
DIAGNOSES	a) Pulmonary tuberculosis, left upper lobe, minimal, inactive, unchanged; b) Partial gastric resection with gastro-enterostomy, functioning normally, no ulcer found; c) Orthostatic hypotension, unchanged; d) Anxiety reaction, moderate, treated, improved

FOLLOW-UP DATA

The patient, whose lung pathology had been thought to be inactive, remained out of work and in difficult financial circumstances. Approximately three months later, positive gastric contents (for acid-fast bacilli) were reported. The patient was again hospitalized, this time in a tuberculosis sanatorium, after he was found to have active pulmonary disease. The chief areas of involvement were in the left lung: fibromottled infiltration extending into the apex above the second interspace with small areas of rarefaction in the first interspace. The right lung had adhesions in the outer third of the diaphragm and there was thickened pleura below the fourth rib and apex. Patient remained in the sanatorium for six months on a rigorous chemical treatment regimen, but toward the end of that time began to complain again of his old stomach symptoms: epigastric pain and nausea after eating. He was transferred to a general hospital for a specialized gastro-intestinal workup, particularly with regard to the possibility of vagotomy being done. A gastroscopy revealed no marginal ulcer and it was decided that surgery was not indicated. The patient was not eating well and was returned to the tuberculosis sanatorium on a strict regime in order to avoid nutritional deficiency with probable detrimental results to his pulmonary condition. The patient became very restless, insisted he could not stand being "cooped up," and after several months left the hospital without permission.

He remained at home, jobless, and after a short time went to a clinic for a checkup. He was advised to reenter the sanatorium to complete his treatment, although he insisted that he had no complaints. Approximately one and a half years after the original hospitalization described above, he was again admitted to the sanatorium. He was asymptomatic and afebrile. However, sputum was reported positive for acid-fast bacilli. Chest films compared with previous ones showed no essential changes, but tomograms revealed thin-walled rarefactions in left upper lobe, probably localized emphysema, and there was also a definite irregular rarefaction noticed directly under the first rib and presumed cavitary.

A segmental excision of the left upper lobe was recommended and done, followed by a post-resection thoracoplasty, approximately two years after the originally reported hospitalization. The patient was then treated vigorously with chemotherapy. Sputa continued negative. Physical activities slowly increased and the patient began to gain weight. He received an ulcer diet and remained fairly comfortable except for occasional episodes of anorexia. However, he again showed signs of great restlessness, and kept referring to his personal and family troubles. He told hospital personnel repeatedly how difficult his financial situation was and what a hard time his wife was having, trying to take care of the three children and to manage somehow on very little money. He felt guilty, bitter, and insisted on being discharged. He emphasized that he would feel less tense if he could return home, pointing out that he had his own room and was fully aware of precautions he needed to take in being near his children. His request to leave was refused because of his fairly recent surgery, but he left, despite medical advice, over two years after his original hospitalization. The discharge diagnosis: tuberculosis, pulmonary, chronic, moderately advanced (segmental resection, left upper lung, 4½ months; postresection thoracoplasty, left, 3 months) active (1 year), IV, treated, improved.

The patient subsequently did not return to the hospital, but instead began to attend a tuberculosis clinic fairly regularly. His condition continued to improve. His case was assigned to a social worker who took a particular interest in him. She helped in making arrangements to bring his financial affairs into better order and also assisted him in getting a part-time job. He then joined a group which met at the clinic to discuss problems common to the tuberculous patient. These moves appeared to have a considerable influence in the patient's continuing improvement both physically and psychologically. His psychophysical condition became stabilized after a year of these experiences and continued to remain so. He appeared less restless, more cheerful, and his relationships with his wife and children became considerably better than they had been for a long time.

FINAL COMMENT

Two factors formed the basis on which favorable psychophysical changes finally developed for this patient. One was the relief of critical environmental stress—largely financial. The second and more important was the positive transference relationship with the social worker; she represented a kindly, giving mother figure who, he came to feel, would not leave him, and to whom he could reveal his anger without fear of reprisal. Added to this relationship was the group experience which relieved to some extent the feelings of inferiority—especially of a physical nature. While the patient did not receive any formal psychotherapy, his experiences at the tuberculosis clinic were more than routine physical checkups and adjustment of medication; they were actually psychotherapeutic, providing outlets for accumulated hostility, lessening tensions, supplying emotional needs, relieving guilt, and shifting psychophysical homeostatic alignments to a more favorable level.

Wittkower (1949) suggests that prognosis in tubercular patients may at times be more reliably estimated on the basis of personality and emotional conflicts rather than on the basis of the shadow in the chest X-ray.

Calden et al. (1960) point out that only recently has there developed experimental evidence that the course of illness in pulmonary tuberculosis may be associated with the patient's emotional makeup. More rapid recoveries are seen in the more outgoing, nonconformist, overtly aggressive patients who are less preoccupied with themselves, while slow recoveries can be noted in patients who are more depressed, hypochondriacal, self-preoccupied, and generally withdrawn. These observations appear to be in line with previous clinical reports associating faster recovery among both tubercular and cancer patients who can overtly express their hostility. Slower recovery occurs more in those whose anger is pent up. That despair or depression prolong disease and hold up recovery cannot be summarily dismissed as folklore.

case 5

Painful Joints and Disguised Psychological Stress

CHIEF PRESENTING SYMPTOM

Pain in joints.

BASIC ANAMNESTIC EXCERPTS

The patient is in a wheelchair. In the beginning he speaks in a loud tone of voice, and there is a rapid flow of speech.

"I'm a man who has worked from six in the morning till eight at night for the last seven years. When I started having pain in my back, I first thought it was from my bad hip, causing a strain. Two weeks ago I fell down carrying a refrigerator and landed on my left knee. I developed a terrific pain in the leg and couldn't seem to walk and had to stay in bed. Then my jaw got sore when I tried to eat. Then the fingers of my right hand, and after that my left ankle got swollen. I think it's from working so hard and getting overtired, lifting furniture and appliances, and driving a delivery truck. The pain comes and goes. When it's in my left leg, I limp. That's my bum leg, where I was hit in the hip by a shell. I was operated on, and they told me I would never do any heavy work again. I loafed for a year and rested. Then I had to do something—I had a family to support —so I went into the trucking business, got some helpers. But I've probably been overdoing it."

A further elaboration follows of associations to pain: "It's sharp—like a needle sticking into you. The hip trouble is different—like nerves tightening up on you, making it impossible to sleep on that side. The sharp pain starts from the back and goes up and down to different joints; it's a traveling pain. I think my body needs rest, and I need to get away from work and go out and enjoy myself, instead of being always on the go. I never took pain pills before; I just lay in bed when the leg hurt, and it got better. But these new pains I couldn't stand and had to take pills. It was a shock to hear the doctor say it was arthritis. Maybe it's something worse."

The patient next refers to his parents' health: "I lost my parents when I was about 19. We had a big family of nine boys; I'm the fourth oldest, but I was one of the smallest. Father died of cancer of the spine. He was a hard-working railroad man. One day he fell down near the tracks. He was rushed to the hospital, where they discovered he had cancer. I was in military service then. He suffered such terrific pain for a year that mother prayed, when her turn came, she wanted to go quickly. She had heart trouble, was a heavy-set woman. Her fatness would pull on her—and she found it hard to breathe. One night, a year after father's death, I visited her at home, and everything seemed fine. An hour after I left, she suddenly passed away. She had been complaining of chest pains for years....The rest of the family has never been sick. Eight of us were in service, and I was the only one that got wounded.

"My father was a man who could never stay still. As a kid, I, too, was always on the go, running around, raising hell, though mother wanted me to help her out a lot at home. I didn't go for that sissy stuff; I always liked the outdoors best. I didn't care to be tightened up by too many clothes, wanted my body to feel free. Now I'm bound down, can't seem to get away from the business because it might go to hell; I really ought to break a man in to run it until I recuperate."

The patient returns to his present joint symptoms: "It's mostly in my right hand, and there's still some pain in my ankles. I've been exercising my hand because I don't want to stay here in the hospital. It all came on so suddenly. I'm not nervous—so could it be from nerves? I'm not usually sensitive to pain. I'm built for it, and I'm strong enough to be able to take lots of pain (loudly).... The leg seems good, the knees are fine, but not the hands (displays hands, moves and exercises them). If it's arthritis, it should be all over me. It's hard for me to move now, and I've always been so active. I would line everything up each day and know how much time was needed for each job."

The patient next reveals his phobic tendencies, his rigidity, and his narcissism: "When I'm not working, I spend my time at home. I'm no drinker, so I don't go to bars. Sometimes it pays to drink because the more alcohol in your system, the better you feel. I don't go much for visiting even if they force me. But they wouldn't get anywhere because I wouldn't go anyway. I never went out, even before marriage. I can be mean. My wife asks me to go visiting, and I wouldn't go visiting for the Pope. I've done some traveling, but if I go anywhere, I go alone; I don't say anything to anybody, not even my wife. I'm a funny guy. If I see any trouble, I ignore, it, leave it alone. What I don't see won't hurt me and vice versa.

"I was taught how to do moving by a big Swede when I was a youngster. The rigging never let go on him or me. I can't understand how

I had this accident. My men watch me to see how to do things, and carry out my orders just as I tell them. They call me if there are any problems."

There is a continuing self-description: "I rarely blow off steam. I just walk away and it's over. I don't take it out on the men. They'd say I'm a bastard. I keep it to myself, and when night comes, it's all over. I'm not the type of guy that gets very angry. There's plenty of aggravation with customers, but you've got to keep it in your chest. You've got to keep quiet because they're your bread and butter. Your hands are tied."

In the last few minutes of the interview the patient reveals a stressful situation that took place several weeks before his joint symptoms began: "There's lots of money that's handled in the business, and men today, you can't trust them. Three weeks ago someone broke into my office and stole $450 dollars out of my money box. It was an inside job. Somebody knew, because they went right to a particular drawer. It's the papers that were important—my insurance, bankbook—I was shocked, losing those papers. How did the crooks get in unless one of my men told them?" The patient sits stiffly in his wheelchair, his hands clenched, his face set in a grimace.

PSYCHODYNAMIC IMPRESSIONS

This patient has attempted for many years to ward off feelings of physical inferiority and insecurity by compulsive "he-man" type work. Even childhood is referred to in terms of activity and need to be free. Both parents, particularly the father, appear as rather distant figures except in physical terms, and there seems to be no close relationship with any of the eight brothers. He was then a "loner" and now too, though he is the boss of a fair-sized business. The patient's current somatic identification involves both parents, but the identification with father—his falling down and developing a serious illness—appears more marked. Following the patient's hip injury, which required a fusion operation and left him with a shortened left leg, there was activation of both his passive trends and his concern about his manliness. These were defended against by his entering the rough and tough moving business and making a success of it.

Thus for some seven years he was able to maintain a kind of psychophysical equilibrium, though at a cost. His work was not only all-consuming, but gave rise to secondary tensions about security, about satisfying others, about controlling frequently activated hostile impulses, and about representing an adequate leader (father figure) to his employees. Social situations tending to arouse anxiety about being exposed as defective (a castrate) were avoided and explained away by stubbornly adhered-to, narcissistic rationalizations and suspiciousness (projection). Three weeks before his symptoms began, the patient's office was robbed. He was shocked by the crime. The deeper (unconscious) significance of the event was that one of his employees had challenged and sought to strip him of his power, and this stirred up uncertainty about his adequacy, and guilt over his own hostile impulses toward father figures. A week later another incident occurred which had a dual—physical as well as emotional—impact. He fell (like his father at work) while carrying a refrigerator—a most unusual occurrence since he was considered the expert in his company and often demonstrated correct moving techniques to his employees. Once again (unconsciously), his role as powerful leader was endangered, and in addition, fantasies of terrible consequences (father's death) were activated. Two events representing significant losses had occurred in rapid succession, upsetting the psychophysical equilibrium. Anxiety deepened and hostility became intense but found insufficient ideational and affective pathways of discharge. A regressive psychophysical shift occurred in the direction of a somatic response with the sensitized musculoskeletal system as target. This sensitization is indicated by sensory clusters, mostly tactile and proprioceptive, but more so by the presence of many varieties of motor referents which appear in associative connection with the presenting symptoms, and also provide a pathway into the past. They reveal the psychological importance and significance of motor activity for the patient, long before his present illness, as a means of warding off feelings of passivity and inferiority. It should be noted that there is multiple identification with the father: the patient could never remain still, was always "on the go" (like father); he had been engaged in heavy labor—involving the musculoskeletal system —for many years (like father); he fell down and suffered from severe pain in the back (like father).

PHYSICAL HISTORY

Patient was admitted with chief complaint of sore, swollen joints for six days. He was well until six days before admission, when his right jaw became very sore when chewing. The following day he noted marked pain and swelling of the left wrist. An LMD put him on oral penicillin without improvement. Since their onset, joint pains have been continually present, although the marked pain subsides and then recurs. Right wrist and fingers have also become involved. No symptoms in legs or back. He has had no upper respiratory infections or sore throat in the past two months. Eight years ago he received a gunshot wound in the left hip which resulted in hip fusion and shortening of the left leg. System review negative.

PHYSICAL EXAMINATION

Temperature 97.4°F. Pulse 100. Blood pressure 126/80. A well-developed, well-nourished, white male with acute pain in the left wrist. Pain over the right temperomandibular joint was noted on pressure and on movement of the jaw. Extremities: Fused left hip due to old gunshot wound—well-healed scars; tender, swollen, hot left wrist; slightly tender right wrist. Axillary and inguinal nodes were slightly enlarged but non-tender. Otherwise the physical examination was negative.

LABORATORY DATA

Blood: white blood cell count 7,850 with 70 segmented cells, 10 band cells, 18 lymphocytes, 1 monocyte, 1 eosinophile. Hemoglobin 13.4 g. Hematocrit 43 percent. Sedimentation rate 34 mm. Uric acid 4.2. Serology negative. Repeat hemoglobin 12.8 g and hematocrit 41 percent. Urinalysis showed a slight trace of albumin and 25 to 35 white blood cells without clumps. Throat culture showed alpha streptococcus and Staphylococcus aureus, coagulase negative. Antistreptolysin 0 titer was 166 units.

ROENTGENOGRAMS

Chest and left wrist normal.

ELECTROCARDIOGRAM

Interpreted as within normal limits. Serial cardiograms showed slight elevation of some of the ST segments in the limb and precordial leads, suggesting the possibility of pericarditis. However, these changes were not significantly altered over the next 10 days, and it was finally considered that they were of no significance.

HOSPITAL COURSE

The patient was put on penicillin initially and salicylates for joint pain with marked improvement symptomatically. After five days of penicillin, this was discontinued, but he was maintained on bed rest and salicylates, requiring occasional doses of codeine in addition for pain. Aspirin caused him to sweat profusely, and he was changed to sodium salicylates. The pain moved from wrists to right foot and ankle, and sometimes involved the shoulders. An orthopedic consultant felt that the patient had had excellent results from his hip fusion. After one month in the hospital, he developed generalized aches and pains, fever rose to 103.2°, and then fell to normal, after being elevated about three days, responding to penicillin which was given because of the possibility of rheumatic infection. The patient was finally discharged after five and a half weeks in the hospital.

DISCHARGE DIAGNOSES

1. Acute rheumatoid arthritis, treated, markedly improved.
2. Grippe, cured.
3. Old fusion of the left hip.

COMMENT

Two events occurred shortly before the patient's physical symptoms manifested themselves. The first, a robbery, several weeks before, was an obviously stressful situation. However, the second, the patient's fall, one week later, seems on the surface to be of less importance as a stress. Actually, the emotional impact of both events on the patient was far greater than a superficial appraisal would indicate. Its extent could be determined only by exploring the hidden and disguised (unconscious) meaning of the incidents for the patient. This revealed that the two events had grossly upset a psychophysical alignment, which for some time had been successful in containing powerful emotional conflicts, coping with environmental pressures, and maintaining health. Now this was no longer possible because the patient's physical and emotional well-being had sustained a severe insult.

A very recent review of the literature on psychological aspects of rheumatoid arthritis (Moos, 1964) indicates that personality data on over 5,000 patients have been reported. Characteristics particularly stressed have been overreaction to illness, self-sacrifice, masochistic tendencies, shyness, perfectionism, rigidity, and interest in physical activity. Although different personality constellations have been proposed, there has been general agreement that emotional factors play an important role in the onset and course of the disease. Moos and Solomon (1965a), comparing 16 rheumatoid arthritis patients and their closest-aged, same-sexed, healthy siblings, found that the arthritics showed more compliance, restlessness, and depression and were more masochistic, compulsive, introverted, and security-seeking than their siblings. However, no significant difference in dependency traits was noted in contrast to the findings of Ludwig (1952, 1954) who had felt that arthritics were overly dependent. Moos and Solomon also concluded that the extreme physical-muscular activity and use of this to discharge hostility, which other observers had commented on, was not borne out in the comparative study which showed little actual difference in physical activity between the arthritics and their siblings, though the former spoke of their childhood experiences in this respect with more emphasis and longing. There were also some conflicting results about the duty orientation and conscientiousness of arthritics compared with their siblings, also in contrast to Ludwig's earlier findings. In the second part of their investigation, Moos and Solomon (1965b) noted that the patients showed a great deal more masochism, self-sacrifice, and denial of hostility. In still another article, Solomon and Moos (1965) suggest that "... given a genetic or constitutional predisposition to rheumatoid disease, expressed in some individuals by the presence of rheumatoid factor (in the serum), only those individuals with significant emotional conflict and psychologic distress go on to the development of disease, the rate of progression of which may be related to the degree of psychic turmoil." Furthermore, "... a propensity to formation of rheumatoid factor might be linked to psychological mechanisms but still needs to be coupled with some degree of emotional decompensation to lead to disease."

CASE 5

CHIEF PRESENTING SYMPTOM
Pain in joints

SENSORIMOTOR CONFIGURATIONS
Sensory configurations

Pain
Tactile-proprioceptive
Associated with father's work, illness, and death

Motor configurations

Constant activity
Connected with rebellious tendencies against mother's attempts to put him in a passive position in childhood and also linked in an identifying way with father

SOMATIC IDENTIFICATION

Father   Back accident, pain, cancer of spine death 11 years ago (Direct, organ constitutional)

Mother   Chest pain, cardiac death 10 years ago

SENSITIZED ORGAN SYSTEM
Musculoskeletal system

STRESS (*surface meaning*)
Office robbed; accident at work

STRESS (*dynamic significance*)
Role as powerful leader endangered, with activation of fantasies of terrible consequences. Robbery and accident signified critical losses, activating dependency needs

DEFENSES
Compulsive "he-man" type of work
Narcissistic rationalizations
Projection

AFFECTS

Anxiety

Intensity	*Pathway of expression*
++	ideational, and phobic behavior response

Depression	+++	ideational—particularly concerned with loss and helplessness
Hostility	+++	somatization

OTHER FACTORS

Parental figures distant in childhood
No close relationships to siblings
Mother's attempts to restrain his impulsivity; his rebellious reactions to her

HOMEOSTATIC SHIFT(S)

Marked somatization as previous behavioral and ideational pathways became insufficient, and already inadequate affective outlets became less so

DIAGNOSES

a) Acute rheumatoid arthritis, treated, markedly improved;
b) Grippe, cured;
c) Old fusion of left hip

case 6

Hematemesis, Abnormal Electroencephalogram, and Psychotic Episode

PRELIMINARY NOTE

The patient was first interviewed the day following admission (designated Part One). At that time he was on the verge of an acute psychotic break which developed more fully 12 hours later, when he was transferred to a closed psychiatric ward. Acute psychotic manifestations lasted 24 hours, then there was gradual subsidence of his panic state, and a week later he was transferred back to the medical service. The subsequent interview was held four days later or two weeks after his admission to the hospital (designated Part Two).

PART ONE

CHIEF PRESENTING SYMPTOM

A little nervousness.

BASIC ANAMNESTIC EXCERPTS

The patient is in bed. There are prominent ecchymoses around both eyes. He sips milk occasionally, is euphoric, frequently laughs loudly, and is variably disoriented for time.

The first associations are about the tensions connected with his work: "My job is an awful responsibility. I work for a critical woman and her husband. I got short-tempered, smoked a lot, drank some. Today, is it January twelfth (actually February twelfth)? Tomorrow is mother's birthday. Hell of a note, was so busy I didn't think of it. Makes me sad. I'm feeling sorry for myself . . . I got so I'd black out. Yesterday I fell into an open bottom drawer where there's nothing but women's pocketbooks and sharp edges. (Hawks up big blobs of phlegm.) A friend said he would get

85

me into the hospital for three days' rest, where I'd get out of everybody's sight and wouldn't have to worry about working. I'd ship my wife off for those three days. I have three kids boarding out. It's too much of a strain on everybody."

References to medical procedures follow: "I've been here since yesterday. They pumped my lungs and stomach and kept me up all night with blood transfusions. There are marks where different needles have been shoved into me. I must have had 20 (laughter). They were giving me the old business—here into the nose and then into the stomach. They pumped it out this morning—nothing but yellow bile. Maybe there was a gallbladder infection. I feel good now. I slept the sleep of the dead before you came in."

Prior to admission into the hospital: "I felt lousy, bitter, cynical towards my boss. She is miserable to work for. She'll antagonize. I'll be in the basement working, and she's in the attic calling me up to hang up a coat hanger. She'll criticize my wife's cooking. She also says the car is dirty, and I told her one day, 'Why in hell don't you clean it yourself!' I'd get so damn mad, I'd want to throw things and had to curb myself. I'm so tired—as though I've taken all I could. They haven't found anything wrong with me so far, although my stomach needed pumping out. They can't hold me here then.

"My stomach trouble is probably from just nerves. Been two years with this rich family. My health's been good on days off, but on the job I get so irritated and disgusted at some of the asinine things the old girl does. They're both pushing 60. He gave me a couple of nice suits, shoes, and a 100 dollar check for Christmas, but he says I don't use initiative. I told him to kiss my ass. (The patient exhibits feminine mannerisms as he vents his rage.) Last Saturday there was a dinner party, and those drunks didn't leave until one o'clock. She has these big dinner parties; the women come in minks and furs and crap like that; the men come in topcoats, gloves. She says, 'You can take the ladies to the blue room and the gentlemen to the pink room'—I mean the opposite. Why don't they do it; their bellies are full, and they have nothing to do, except criticize me all the time."

Here the patient switches to the theme of marriage and laughs frequently as he talks: "When I said I got married January eleventh I meant we renewed our vows for the fifth time. I was originally married while still in the service in a military funeral—I mean, military uniform. I want my wife to get me out in a couple of days. I don't like being away from her —like Mary's little lamb tale—wherever Mary went. . . . She's my second wife. Her kid and my two from previous marriage live with our relations. My first wife's married again. . . . We never got along. . . ."

The interview is terminated at this point because certain treatment procedures have to be carried out.

Note: *Several hours after the first interview, reality testing became grossly disrupted, and a further marked regressive shift in the direction of psychosis took place. The patient's elation began to subside and evidence of increasing apprehensiveness again appeared. Some 36 hours after admission and 12 hours after the interview, he was in a full-blown state of panic with complete disorientation and auditory hallucinations of female voices calling him evil and dirty, and threatening him with death. Sedation brought this panic under control and the acute terror and motor activity gradually diminished, but a loosely organized delusional system then appeared: His employer had him imprisoned, she was out to see that he received punishment for wrongdoings; he was in a jail, not a hospital, awaiting execution. He also had inconstant visual hallucinations that she was peering at him through the window.*

In the meantime, he had improved physically. The internal bleeding had completely subsided, and the hemoglobin had begun to rise. On the fifth hospital day the patient was oriented but still deluded and hallucinated. A kindly ward nurse had undertaken to feed him and give him the medications prescribed. At first he called her his employer, refused her ministrations, and made threatening gestures to her. Later a dramatic change in his attitude toward her had occurred when, as he looked at her and had the impulse to kill her, he had the hallucinatory experience that her body was becoming blank and empty. Suddenly his rage was gone, and he took the milk she was offering him. This substitutive hallucinatory wish fulfillment had relieved the extreme anxiety associated with the attempt to contain his murderous impulse. Through the hallucinatory experience it was possible to discharge the intense hostility, avoiding a highly dangerous conflict with reality. Here a restitutional phenomenon had also served a defensive function. From then on he began to question his delusional ideas. On the tenth hospital day the psychotic episode had subsided, and he was transferred back to the medical service. He was again sarcastically hostile about his employer, laughed frequently, but there was no return to euphoria. On the twelfth hospital day he had a slight hematemesis which was easily controlled, and then none thereafter.

PART TWO

CHIEF PRESENTING SYMPTOM

Pain in the back.

BASIC ANAMNESTIC EXCERPTS

It is two weeks later, and the patient is ambulatory and very talkative. He vaguely recollects having seen the interviewer once before. His opening remarks are laughingly put: "I feel pretty good—outside of that pain in my back. The doctor says it's a muscle strain. I don't know how I could have strained it. Actually he—I thought it might have been from throwing up so much—so much blood."

The patient soon returns to the episode of bleeding which resulted in his hospitalization: "The doctor said my stomach had gone up into my esophagus. When I awoke that morning, I felt nauseated and kept coughing. My heart was thumping. I seemed to have an awful, dull, throbbing headache. I thought it might be sinus trouble, and when I lay down, I'd drain and hawk it up. So I moved the wastebasket over to the bed. All of a sudden there was a shooting pain; everything started going around. I let out one scream for help, and my wife came flying up the stairs. Before she got to me, my mouth wasn't big enough, and just like that a solid stream of blood went into the wastebasket. The doctor sent me here. I was delirious then. I don't remember much afterward. I had a faint recollection of being in somebody's house, a nice house, where I was being beaten with chains. Everybody wanted to kill me. I was screaming. So they brought me to the psycho ward. I tried to dive through the bars. I butted my head against the door. They had me locked up for a week before they moved me back. I would have been crazy if I had stayed there. . . ."

Further associations to the back pain: "The doctor looked me over last night, stethoscoped me, poked me, said it might be a strain. When I go to bed, my back right here feels hollow, all bloated up, swollen. It's sore to the touch, maybe because I've prodded it so much myself. It's sharp, flowing, not deep. It comes if I'm tired or upset. I get upset easily, and sometimes I'll throw up. Like when I have a run-in with the boss. . . ."

The patient refers again to another bleeding episode that occurred five years ago: "I had mushroom warts on the end of my penis and in my rectum. Some I had to remove myself, and others were taken out by a specialist with an electrical needle. He was merciless. The pain was terrible. He never gave any novocaine. I had to wear Kotex on my tail for quite a while. A colonel took off the wart I had on my penis, but he injected novocaine and it didn't hurt." Other associations about bleeding lead to recollections from adolescent years when the patient had aspiration to be a boxer, and was badly pummeled in fights and once knocked down by a punch in the nose which then bled profusely.

Further associations about the patient's past health are next elicited: "I had pneumonia when I was six months old and again when I was seven. I'm told I had to go to the hospital. I remember when I was seven, I was very feverish. Mother packed my chest with hot fried onions and forced yellow sulphur down my throat (laughing). I must have had a pretty good constitution to take that! But I was pretty active as a kid, played a lot of sports and worked, too. I also had pneumonia before I got married, and I was delirious for three days then.

"We lived on a farm where I was brought up by my grandparents. They were too old and crotchety. Father died when I was six, so mother had to go to work to support me. He died from the same thing I had—bleeding through the mouth. He was out hunting, got lost, and didn't come back. They found him the next day, his shirt torn at the throat, hunting jacket ripped, and blood all around. He bled to death from the mouth. An autopsy didn't tell why. I remember being in school, and the teacher sent me outside to mother, and she was crying. It dawned on me after a while that I wasn't getting any more candy or tricycles, even though I was an only child. I thought father was away on a long trip. A stupid, cruel aunt told me to stop making up stories, that my father was dead. I felt sad for a long time, afraid of being alone, especially after mother left to work as a cook fifteen years for the same family. She has a business of her own now—a tea room—and caters to nothing but the highest class of clientele. She's very particular, fussy, so clean—in fact, to an extreme. Always has been that way and with me, too."

PSYCHODYNAMIC IMPRESSIONS

The patient's conflicts are reflected in his references to work and the married couple who are his employers. The woman is seen, for the most part, as a hypercritical, demanding, nongiving, and even sadistically injuring mother figure. She arouses in him a concomitant mixture of intense hostility, rebelliousness, and anxious anticipation of dangerous retaliation and consequences. A more benign aspect of his relationship to women is represented in the nurturing figure of his wife. There is also evidence of many mannerisms suggestive of feminine identification. Relationships with men are also, though somewhat less, disturbed. Some are seen as powerful and penetrating, some are devaluated. Others are pictured as more giving, and less critical and authoritarian than the women.

The patient's being an only child is briefly mentioned, but there are suggestions that the patient had very early in life experienced a kind of spoiling. Then the traumatic loss of his own father at age six, recalled as being due to a fatal exsanguination and what is remembered as abandonment by his mother, who had to go to work, appear to have activated an early depression. The grandparents appear only in passing reference and as apparently inadequate replacements. Since childhood, loss situations have been closely associated with fears about bodily integrity, at times verging on the extreme of expected dissolution. While many oral elements are present in the associations, there are also frequent anal (and sadistic) indicators. They can be noted in highly sexualized versions of medical procedures, for example, and suggest not only castration anxiety but also feminine rape fantasies. Identifications are mixed: somatically with the father as the one aggressed against; in mannerisms and occupation, with the mother seen as aggressor. Defensive structures, particularly utilized in the past, appear in connection with boasting about his interest in sports and his scholastic achievements. Another, at times prominent, defense is that of projection.

This patient's hematemesis occurred then against the background of increasing internal and external conflict in his work situation and relationships with his employers. He was threatened with loss of his job if he could not control his intense anger. Dependent needs were being strongly activated but could not be contained by his increasing alcoholism. Powerful guilt feelings were increasing. All the makings of an emotional turmoil were present.

PHYSICAL HISTORY

Patient was admitted to the medical service with a history of a few hours of vomiting bright red blood, passing a dark liquid stool, and then losing consciousness. It was not until later in the patient's hospitalization, after he had been transferred to the closed psychiatric ward for an acute paranoid psychotic reaction, and later to the neurological service for work-up in regard to an abnormal electroencephalogram, that additional past history particularly relative to seizures was obtained. The patient denied any history of convulsions, except for two periods as a child when he was told he twitched all over because of high fever and constipation.

The pertinent information was obtained from his wife. She stated that the patient's first seizure occurred five years ago and was characterized by sudden loss of consciousness, falling to the floor, with generalized rigidity for about 10 minutes. On regaining consciousness, the patient was somewhat confused and amnesic for the episode. A second episode occurred several months later. The patient was then symptom-free for about three and a half years. He then again had two seizures within a week. He was placed on dilantin, three capsules daily, which he took sporadically for two or three weeks. He then had a fifth seizure eight months later, and dilantin was reinstituted. On the day of admission the wife stated that he had a seizure at 6 A.M. while still in bed. Later that morning he had vomited blood, had lost consciousness, and had struck his left forehead on a dresser while falling. Patient revealed that at age 12 he was kicked by a horse, sustained fractured ribs and extremities, and was unconscious for 20 minutes.

Patient had always been interested in interior decorating, but shifted work to associates and subsequently lost his own small business. While in military service, his first enlistment was marked by numerous disciplinary difficulties and ended in a general discharge. During the past several years, the patient had been drinking a considerable amount of alcohol, but managed, together with his wife, to remain employed as a domestic couple.

PHYSICAL EXAMINATION

On admission to the medical service, temperature was 99°F, pulse 128, blood pressure 120/84. The patient appeared well-developed and well-nourished. He seemed to be on the verge of a panic reaction and kept repeating he did not want to die. He had gross tremors, but the general physical examination was within normal limits.

The neurological examination performed later during his hospitalization revealed that the patient then was alert, cooperative, somewhat guarded about his early history and family relationships, but rather verbose in his description of his heavy alcohol intake and numerous difficulties with authority figures. There was some suspiciousness but no overt psychotic behavior. The examination was essentially negative.

LABORATORY DATA

On admission, the hemoglobin was 11.4 g with an hematocrit of 36 percent. The white blood cell count was 11,100 with a moderate shift to the left. Urinalysis showed a trace of albumin and a trace of sugar. Serology was negative. Subsequent blood studies showed a fall of the hemoglobin to 9.4 g with a rise later in hospitalization to approximately 12 g. A lumbar juncture revealed an initial pressure of 180 mm, with the patient moderately tense. The dynamics were free. Final pressure was 150 mm. The tap was somewhat traumatic, and the fluid contained 150 red blood cells, 1 polymorphonuclear leukocyte, and 3 lymphocytes. The complement-fixation test was negative, and the gold curve flat. The globulin was negative, and the total protein 27 mg percent.

ROENTGENOGRAMS

Chest and skull negative. Film of left knee showed some soft tissue swelling without evidence of fracture. A gastrointestinal series revealed a small diaphragmatic hernia, which was reducible in the upright position. No ulcer or esophageal varices were noted.

ELECTROENCEPHALOGRAM

A routine EEG was reported as being markedly abnormal and showed almost continuous seizure discharges without focal features.

HOSPITAL COURSE

On admission the patient was treated for an acute gastric hemorrhage and received sedation and whole blood transfusions. His bleeding subsided, but 36 hours following admission the patient was described as being restless, suspicious, and partially out of contact, expressing paranoid ideas. He was transferred to a closed psychiatric ward, and there, initially, was described as being in a state of acute terror. The patient was extremely anxious about bodily harm being done to him by persons outside of the hospital. He was also confused and disoriented. The panic state subsided quite rapidly within 24 hours. About nine days later he was no longer psychotic and was transferred back to the medical service, where further work-up suggested that the source of bleeding was from a small diaphragmatic herniation of the stomach. Surgical treatment was not indicated.

With a history and EEG findings consistent with epilepsy, the patient was transferred to the neurological service and remained there until his discharge from the hospital. Despite the markedly abnormal brain waves on two different EEG's, the patient had no seizures. He refused an air encephalogram. He felt that he could not remain in the hospital for other investigative procedures because of financial difficulties. He was placed on dilantin, 0.4 gr daily, prior to his discharge, and was instructed in the necessity for using this medication with follow-ups by his own physician.

DISCHARGE DIAGNOSES

1. Diaphragmatic hernia. Untreated, unchanged.
2. Gastrointestinal bleeding, believed secondary to diagnosis No. 1. Treated, improved.
3. Psychotic reaction, paranoid type, with marked panic and delusions of persecution. Treated, improved.
4. Epilepsy, grand mal type, symptomatic; etiology undetermined.

COMMENT

The patient's escalating psychological turmoil was manifest indirectly through marked dysfunction of somatic systems at the time of his admission to the hospital. He arrived there in a state of physical emergency. As the physical systems were being stabilized by appropriate treatment, the still insufficiently discharged aggressive excitations from the continuing high level of emotional conflict had to find another pathway of discharge. This occurred in the patient's psychological systems in the form of an acute withdrawal from overwhelming reality. The severe mental symptoms of a psychotic break began to overshadow the physical manifestations more and more as the latter responded to the vigorous medical therapy that had been instituted. However, the psychotic state itself was quite labile. Restitutional processes appeared very quickly in the form of frightening hallucinations, which represented in particular the patient's projected aggressive drives and expected retaliation (superego pathology). Shortly thereafter, delusions with similar content appeared. The dynamic observations of the patient's conflicts that had been made in the immediate prepsychotic period were strikingly reflected and confirmed in the psychotic symptoms. As the psychotic illness subsided, a further adaptive, but now, progressive shift took place in the direction of realignment of former neurotic psychological defenses and appearance of previously unreferred-to somatic pathways—pain in the back. It was at this point that a relative stabilization of the patient's condition finally began to be apparent. Both physical and psychological systems may be drawn either concurrently or interchangeably into the service of the organism's adaptive responses to stress. When psychological systems serving this purpose prove inadequate, then somatic pathways may be utilized. If the latter are successfully dealt with medically or surgically but stress continues, a further and more regressive psychological shift may be evoked to handle the continuing excitations, as occurred in this case. An economic factor may then have limited the duration of the deep psychological regression—the conflictual energies may have spent themselves in a short period of time, making possible restoration of a more favorable psychophysical equilibrium.

Liddell (1953) has noted that, when epileptic seizures were brought under control by medication, psychological difficulties increased. Decrease in medication and greater number of seizures were accompanied by a diminution in psychological difficulties.

Epstein and Ervin (1956) studied two patients with psychomotor epilepsy to investigate the psychodynamic significance of the highly organized seizures and the accompanying psychic phenomena. They found that the seizure can be understood as motivated behavior, has meaning as a wish fulfillment and symbolic riddance, and follows the psychodynamic patterns exhibited by the patient. Studies were also made of seizures and psychotic episodes in each of the patients. Seizure behavior and psychotic behavior were similar and at times identical, both in terms of the conflict being expressed and in the method of resolution. Seizures diminished when psychosis appeared. The adaptive significance of the seizure seemed to be a miscarried attempt at coping with rising psychological tension.

In 20 cases studied by Chafetz and Schwab (1959) serious emotional problems were present before onset of epileptic seizures. Feelings of neglect and parental disinterest were noted in many of the histories. Seizures were infrequent, irregular, with occurrence in clusters. The clinical character of the convulsions tended to be atypical. EEG findings were equivocal and confusing. There was no family history of epilepsy. Most seizures began in early adult life. Response to anticonvulsant medication was unpredictable. In general, the patients did not seem to present either pure neurological or psychiatric problems but rather a curious interrelationship. The authors advanced the possibility that "severe emotional conflict in susceptible individuals lowers the seizure threshold beyond a certain critical level, directly or indirectly, by altered physiological states resulting in a seizure or seizures." The factor of heredity heightens susceptibility. Increased seizure incidence is associated, among other conditions, with alcohol withdrawal.

CASE 6

CHIEF PRESENTING SYMPTOM	Part One: A little nervousness Part Two: Pain in back
SENSORIMOTOR CONFIGURATIONS	Sensory configurations

Interoceptive, pain

Associated with early loss of father through fatal exsanguination, with childhood sickness and negative maternal behavior, with unfulfilled, chronic, intense oral needs, and current hostility toward employers

Motor configurations

Falling, fainting, being operated on

Connected with physical activity, hemorrhage, rising tensions, and with highly sexualized versions of medical procedures

SOMATIC IDENTIFICATION	*Father*	Hemorrhage from mouth many years ago (Direct, organ constitutional)
SENSITIZED ORGAN SYSTEM		Gastrointestinal Brain, central nervous system
STRESS (*surface meaning*)		Conflict with employers
STRESS (*dynamic significance*)		Threat to body integrity if intense anger could not be controlled Strongly activated dependent needs
DEFENSES		Boasting about sports and scholastic achievements Projection Rationalization Denial

AFFECTS	*Intensity*	*Pathway of expression*
Anxiety	+++	Somatic
Depression	+++	Ideational relating mostly to loss
Hostility	+++	(1) Somatic, minimal ideational with (2) shift to maximal ideational and behavioral and diminution of somatic, and (3) then reversal

OTHER FACTORS

Hypercritical, sadistic, nongiving versus nurturing mother figures
Father figure seen as powerful, penetrating—or devaluated—or more giving than mother
Only child
At age five, traumatic loss of father and "abandonment" by mother
Oral–anal elements marked

HOMEOSTATIC SHIFT(S)

Marked somatization which was vigorously treated, but a further and intense regression to psychoses then followed. This latter equilibrium was maintained for a few days and then followed by restitutional phenomena, diminution of severity of regression, and a shift to a less severe somatization response with reinstitution of previous neurotic defenses

DIAGNOSES

a) Diaphragmatic hernia. Untreated, unchanged;
b) Gastrointestinal bleeding, believed secondary to diagnosis, treated, improved;
c) Psychotic reaction, paranoid type, acute, treated, improved;
d) Epilepsy, grand mal type, symptomatic; etiology undetermined

case 7

Lower Extremity Pain Related to Multiple Psychological Factors

CHIEF PRESENTING SYMPTOM

Pain in right leg.

BASIC ANAMNESTIC EXCERPTS

"My leg pains me terrifically right inside, practically the whole leg. It bothers me more when I sit or lie down. It doesn't bother me as much when I'm walking or standing up. It's been getting worse for the past six months. It started five years ago when I had meningitis. X-rays show nothing and heat treatments don't help. At times the pain is sharp, then it's like an electrical shock, and other times it's just a dull, steady draw. Sometimes it gets so bad, I can't even stand up straight . . . When it's sharp, it's as if somebody poked me with a stick or something. When it's dull, it's like a toothache, but I don't have them any more. My teeth were taken out last year because they were all bad with pyorrhea. The dentist said that might be one of the causes of the leg condition, so we removed the teeth. But the pain is worse.

"It might be muscles or nerves, but it's not the bone. One doctor told me it might be sciatica, but I can't see his point because distribution of the sciatic nerve doesn't cover that area . . . I know some anatomy because I went to school and studied for embalming. I'm still a student, but in sanitation and public health now, that is, I was until last week when I had to drop out on account of the pain. I decided to find out what was wrong now because I can always pick up my studies later. In one semester the pain kept me out at least 20 days."

References to other causes of pain appear next: "About nine years ago my left thumb had to be stitched up. It was done without anesthesia. Before that I had a pilonidal cyst taken out. They sewed it up without anesthesia, too. Well, actually the spinal had worn off. I've had six operations for a pilonidal since I was 17 years old. When I was 13, I lost the sight of my right eye. I was hit by a stone thrown by two brothers fighting. I was just an innocent bystander. It was really the fault of my parents because they didn't take me to the doctor right away, even though money was scarce then. I still remember what the specialist said—that I'd never see again in that eye." At this point the patient appears perturbed and gets up. "I have to stand up now because the pain in my right leg has just gotten worse. I can't sit. That's why it bothers me in school where you have to sit at the lectures and take notes. If you get up and walk around, everybody looks and asks, 'What's the matter with that guy?—Is he foolish or something?'"

The patient now brings in further recollections from his early life: "I quit school when I was 14 to go to work. I was the oldest of seven children. Father didn't make enough, and he was sick for quite a while, too. He's had a bad skin condition on his right leg—must be all of 30 years that he's got it. There's a big red spot on the skin. I suppose it's as much his fault as anybody's. He puts some kind of medicine on it, but it itches, and he probably scratches it, and it bleeds, and then it starts all over again. When we were kids, he was always changing the bandage or putting medicine on it. But even when he was sick he was kind. I used to take kids to the store and splurge on candy and ice cream, and my father would somehow find the money to pay for it."

There follows, in a depressed tone: "I come from a big family (four boys, two girls). When I was four I had double pneumonia and was very sick. I had to be in bed a long time, and it left me weak on my feet for quite a while. I couldn't keep up with the others until I got older. My father—I mean, my mother died almost five years ago. They called it a subdural—a shock. I was out working but was called home; my wife was with her at the time. We couldn't get a doctor until just before she died. She wasn't breathing right and had a rattle in her throat. She was paralyzed all over. She died in my arms while I was trying to move her up in the bed. We were all there except my father. I'll never forget those moments."

The patient now refers directly to the interview: "Maybe I'm seeing you because they believe my condition might be psychosomatic. Some people feel sick for no reason at all. But there's nothing on my mind that's bothering me too much. Of course, most people have things on their mind —family, job, or school." Asked about these: "I wasn't doing too well in school—I failed exams last month. The questions were unfair. My little boy's been sick a couple of weeks. There are all those household and doctor bills, too. But there's nothing greatly worrying me."

Growing anger becomes openly manifest: "Why is it they won't tell you anything in this hospital? Your condition, diagnosis. What the hell kind of business is that? I wish I could speak up in public. It's like a glass wall that comes up before me; as if I'm paralyzed. If I could speak up, I would ask for my diagnosis. I've always had trouble that way. That's why I can't be a leader, even though I have the other qualifications and ability."

The patient returns to the theme of illness; this time in connection with his wife, a nurse: "She hasn't worked since her sickness with T.B. four years ago. Her doctors says she's well enough now to go back to work. She's been working too hard at home, doing most of my chores in the house, but since she's been sick, I don't make her do so much, and we aren't together often as man and wife. We've been married eight years. She was deserted by her first husband when their girl baby was nine months old."

The patient continues with his grievances against the doctors; "I'm going for X-rays, but it's a waste of time and money. The picture I want them to take, they won't take—of my right knee—that bothers me most. It feels like there's something in there—a swelling. You can get injured and not feel it until years later. It happened to my uncle. I saw my previous X-rays; they showed nothing. Maybe I should have a myelogram. It's the nerves—pressure, like a shock. When I have to pick the leg up, I have no feeling for that moment. When I try to stand on it, I can't bear the weight."

The patient scratches his head vigorously and is asked about this: "I always have skin trouble, always itch." Up to this point no mention whatsoever has been made of these symptoms. "Years ago all I had was a mild acne. I first noticed it when I went overseas. I had a hard time getting adjusted. It was shortly after my marriage—you know what I mean. Now I have an itch all over my body. Sometimes I have to put stockings on my hands when I go to bed, so I won't scratch. It's strange—the pleasure you can get from it, as well as the hurting. I don't itch in the legs. Only from the crotch up . . . Mother taught us to be clean. She was very fussy, strict, couldn't stand dirt, was always hitting and yelling at the kids, washing them and changing their clothes, even two—three times a day."

PSYCHODYNAMIC IMPRESSIONS

This patient's long-standing concern about himself is fixated on his physical adequacy. This appears in connection with references to early illness, many surgical procedures, and loss of body parts or tissues. In childhood he felt physically inferior to his siblings, though he was the oldest. There is a general physical identification with father who is pictured in a devaluated way, either in terms of his health or as wage earner. While mother appears as the dominant, active, strict, compulsive parent, she is the one who dies suddenly, probably of a cerebrovascular accident. Specific somatic identifications, connected with the patient's leg symptoms, are derived both from father—who also had a right leg difficulty, involving skin—and from mother—with her paralysis from brain disease. In addition to chronic anxiety over his physical strength and health, there are also persistent, troublesome phobic reactions, especially in school and social situations. Sexual frustration and probable repressed masturbatory tendencies are indicated in some of the associative links to his skin symptoms. The latter first became manifest while the patient was experiencing considerable tension in adjusting to overseas military duty.

The interview material reveals that bragging references to his (over-rated) medical knowledge and intellectual capacities have combined with avoidance, projection, and hostile rationalization as a relatively unsuccessful constellation of defensive mechanisms against the predominant affect of anxiety. A major breach in this defensive alignment occurred together with a marked psychophysical shift after the traumatic impact of his mother's death in his arms. At that time a benign meningitic involvement and masked depression were followed by the persisting leg symptoms which are undoubtedly on a conversion basis. The latter manifestations have many associative connections. There are tactile, visual, and proprioceptive percept clusters, postural configurations, and motor referents which, in turn, are further elaborated on, some in highly symbolized fashion. They represent not only associative links with his parents' somatic difficulties but also with his own frequent illnesses, beginning at age four with a serious pneumonia.

Subsequently, his wife's illness and incapacity acted as a stress which reinforced the patient's regression. She was unable to fulfill his infantile expectations (to be a dominant mother) because of her invalidism. The patient's responsibilities as husband, father, and student have also been stresses, particularly in the months prior to admission.

Strong secondary-gain elements have become associated with both skin and leg symptoms over the years. The former are now closely linked with receipt of a pension. The leg pain is a major, convenient excuse for explaining away his failure to pursue consistently a course of study or further his career in general. The effect is to fixate the symptomatology still more.

PHYSICAL HISTORY

The patient entered the hospital for the first time, complaining of right leg pain of four years' duration. Four years ago he developed severe headaches and dizziness, and was hospitalized for three months. A diagnosis of "lymphocytic meningitis" was made at that time, and studies to rule out tuberculosis were said to be negative. Actually, prior to that admission, the patient had aching, pressing pain localized along the medial aspect of his right thigh, but didn't report it.

During the subsequent four years, the pain allegedly increased in intensity, and during the past month has spread to involve the right hip and knee, and to a lesser extent, the medial aspect of the right leg. Sitting brings the pain on, while lying down aggravates it temporarily, then relieves it. Aspirin has no effect on the pain.

Two weeks prior to admission, X-rays of lower spine, pelvis, and right hip were normal. Several heat treatments gave no relief. Past history reveals that there has been a chronic recurrent skin condition, developed while in military service, and characterized by itching, excoriated lesions of the face, arms, and chest. Patient has had six operations for pilonidal sinus. He has been blind in the right eye following trauma to that eye at age 13.

PHYSICAL EXAMINATION

Vital signs were all within normal limits. Eyes: old injury with scarring of right lens, resulting in complete blindness. Back and extremities: tenderness on percussion over the midlumbar spine, but inconstant. Neurological: knee and ankle jerks diminished, but equal bilaterally; inconstant anesthesia to pinprick over the right anterior thigh, but the localization of this area could not be sharply defined. Skin: sacral spine, scarred and pigmented from old operative procedures; face, pitted; over the shoulders and trunk were crusted, linear, and punctate lesions, with numerous excoriations and other follicular, pustular lesions.

LABORATORY DATA

Negative, including spinal fluid examination.

ROENTGENOGRAMS

Chest, lumbosacral spine, and right hip: normal.

HOSPITAL COURSE

Psychiatric consultation was requested when all physical findings referable to the leg were negative. A psychiatric consultant considered the skin condition and pain to be conversion reactions. The patient was then referred for outpatient psychiatric care.

DISCHARGE DIAGNOSES

1. Psychoneurosis, severe, with anxiety and conversion symptoms.
2 Chronic recurrent folliculitis, with an element of factitia.

COMMENT

Pain in the absence of organic disease is the chief presenting symptom in this patient. Rangell (1953), writing about pain as a specific somatic sensory modality, notes that its experience depends not only on the intactness of neural mediating pathways but also on the individual's emotional state. The threshold for its perception and for reaction to it are particularly influenced by psychological factors. Wide differences in these thresholds are related to the particular past life experiences, personality makeup, and associative responses to precipitating events that are to be found in any given person. Pain is often a conversion-like response resulting from exposure to stress, varying in intensity and duration. When tension builds up in an individual, then slight stimuli may cause overreaction, with lowering of thresholds for perception and reaction, and this applies to pain. Under these circumstances pain may not necessarily have a specific dynamic meaning of its own. Muscle spasm of many kinds related to this dammed-up state may be the pathway by which pain is expressed. It should be noted that anxious people overreact to pain as they also do to other sensations. More anxiety results. Pain in anxiety hysteria becomes a more specific reflection of the pressure of forbidden impulses or of defense against and punishment for it. Pain may be so greatly feared that any and all situations, in which it might occur or is anticipated, are avoided. An opposite or counterphobic response will result in exceptionally high tolerance for pain and marked stoical attitude toward it. Pain as a full-fledged manifestation of conversion is a specific symbolic expression of a repressed emotional conflict. In hysteria there may be an opposite phenomenon, diminution of pain ranging from hypalgesia to analgesia, or sensation in general—producing anesthesia. In obsessional states and depressions where guilt is associated with hostile, sadistic, and anal impulses, pain is often related to symbolic atonement and punishment. Patients who are often involved in painful or pain-producing situations may be masochistically seeking out suffering. In addiction, pain may be simulated or may be due to unconscious factors, but basically pain is for the purpose of obtaining drugs, or other "supplies" which represent attempts at satisfying intense persistent, deeply dependent needs. Clinically, overdetermination and multiple etiological factors go into the formation of the symptom of pain. In any event, pain has generally a protective function and serves as a warning signal, but many departures from its normal function occur.

CASE 7

CHIEF PRESENTING SYMPTOM	Pain in right leg
SENSORIMOTOR CONFIGURATIONS	Sensory configurations

Pain, visual, tactile

Associated with frequent illness, beginning in childhood, injuries (blindness in one eye), and operative interventions, and connected with symptoms manifested by parents, all resulting in marked preoccupation with physical adequacy

Motor configurations

Walking, postural changes

Linked to anxiety about becoming immobilized, and hostility at not having his dependent needs satisfied by wife who herself is sickly

SOMATIC IDENTIFICATION	Father	Right-leg skin condition, chronic, many years (Direct, organ constitutional)
	Mother	Subdural hemorrhage, shock, death five years ago

SENSITIZED ORGAN SYSTEM	Skin and lower extremities
STRESS (*surface meaning*)	Wife's illness and incapacity, most recent Responsibilities as husband, father, student—chronic
STRESS (*dynamic significance*)	Infantile expectations for wife to be a dominant mother figure frustrated Inferiority feelings activated
DEFENSES	Bragging Avoidance Projection Hostile rationalization

AFFECTS	*Intensity*	*Pathway of expression*
Anxiety	+++	ideational, conversion symptoms
Depression	++	affective and ideational
Hostility	++	affective, ideational, somatization

OTHER FACTORS

Early illness
Many surgical procedures and loss of body parts
Mother dominant, strict, compulsive
Exhibitionism
Repressed masturbatory tendencies
Secondary gain

HOMEOSTATIC SHIFT(S)

In direction of mild somatization with development of conversion symptoms and skin disturbance

DIAGNOSES

a) Psychoneurosis, severe, with anxiety and conversion symptoms;
b) Chronic recurrent folliculitis, with an element of factitia

case 8

Cough and Depression

CHIEF PRESENTING SYMPTOM

Cough.

BASIC ANAMNESTIC EXCERPTS

The patient is in bed during the interview. He refers repeatedly to his cough as he describes a symptom cluster which also includes chills, weakness, "plugged-up head," and hoarseness. Cough is associated with having a "bad cold—maybe a touch of pneumonia." A variety of further associations is elicited, and these in part suggest that coughing has come to represent symbolically a psychological need, namely, to rid himself of offending thoughts in general or dissociate himself from a personal relationship in particular: "I've been coughing for nothing—no phlegm—can't bring her up though I have the desire to cough all the time—can't dislodge whatever's there—it's an irritating cough, can't free myself of it."

Further references in this connection are to the sensation of weakness and helplessness which emerges only briefly at this time, revealing a deep and ordinarily concealed feeling of insecurity and inadequacy—almost like a child's. Later there is another, less direct reference to concern about physical defect when he talks about his child's cough. At this point, however, defensive associations emphasizing the patient's activity become quickly manifest: "I'm always on the go—don't want to lie down. I work hard—never stop—held two jobs for a while, day and night. Maybe overwork is why I'm run down." The theme of activity–inactivity becomes still further interconnected with references to his past physical condition and threats to its integrity. He has not been in a hospital since an appendectomy at age eight: "I hurt myself in the crotch riding a bike, and the appendix ruptured—I was almost a goner—the surgeon was a butcher who left me with a deep, ugly hole (castrated)."

In the associations that follow about his family, the patient describes himself as the "middle one" in age among four sisters and two brothers. The connotation is that he may see himself as a "neuter." Somatic identification with the father is suggested in rather vivid recollections of that parent's death when the patient was five years old: "Father was sick just a few days—coughing all the time—lung trouble, pneumonia they called it. Mother cried so much, never remarried." Somatic identification with mother is indicated by references to her illnesses: "She had quite a few things cut out—a tumor due to woman's trouble, gallbladder, and appendix. She was in hospitals a lot while I was growing up, and things at home were run somehow by my older sisters. I've often wondered how mother could raise such a big family." These doubts are further elaborated and followed by a less direct reference to the child-mother relationship in associations about his own wife and 20-month-old boy: "One is quite a handful for her. She's busy with him all the time and I feel neglected, but I don't say anything to her. That's the way I am—I keep it in. When he cuts his teeth, he gets a fever, running nose, bronchitis—coughs all night and keeps us up. It goes away as soon as the tooth comes up, but I worry about him."

The symptom of cough is further elaborated, and again there are associated oral components: "Coughing a lot—can't get rid of whatever's in there—can get only a little phlegm up, like spit without color and taste-less." There follow percepts referring to dryness–moistness, and these lead to a description of a "habit"—drinking several quarts of water daily in addition to coffee and "cokes," whether thirsty or not. This compulsion is especially noticeable at work, which in certain respects has been chronically stressful. The patient has a special assignment in an auto assembly line where in the past he has had to work ahead or get a relief man in order to have time to get his needed drinks or be able to go to the toilet. However, recently he has devised a "system" designed to fool the authorities so he can get away from his work and indulge in the aforementioned activities without interference or punishment, but in turn he has become increasingly concerned that he might be found out.

Returning to his present illness, the patient underscores how different it has been from all other colds he's had. He's had colds often before: "Used to have three to four a winter and at other times. But I'd shake them off and they'd never cause me any worry. As a kid had bad ones that kept me out of school. Getting wet and being out in the cold used to do it. Mother would worry and look after me then." Now he can't "shake it off," can't get rid of whatever it is that's bothering him. Everyone around him has had a cold: his sister-in-law, wife, and the baby—but they all recovered except for him. He had been urged to take "shots" to prevent his getting so many colds, but he never completed the series. He now feels that he is paying for his negligence.

As the interview ends, another emotionally disturbing experience is brought up by the patient. His baby accidentally cut his lip in a recent fall and bled badly, choking on the blood. He had to rush him to a surgeon to have the laceration stitched, and several days before he "came down" with the cold, he brought the child back to have the stitches out. This was an upsetting scene, with the baby "terribly scared" and crying.

PSYCHODYNAMIC IMPRESSIONS

The associative connections suggest that there is an underlying concern about being as helpless as a baby. The infantile roots of the anxiety are linked with references to being exposed to the discomforts of coldness and wetness. The basic feeling of insecurity appears to be defended against by overactivity, which, in turn, might lead to a chronic fatigue state. Other associative chains connected with memories of a ruptured appéndix are highly suggestive of the reactivation of old fears about physical adequacy. They contain disguised symbolic references to masturbation which leads to consequences of being mutilated and castrated. In the family constellation the patient refers to himself not only as the middle one, but at times as a "neuter"—sexless.

Somatic identification is multiple: with the father—suggestively in terms of respiratory disease—during the oedipal period, and with the mother in the various instances of her abdominal operations later on.

The water-coffee-coke addiction appears to be an attempt to satisfy rather strong oral needs and to ward off chronic low-grade depressive tendencies, intermingled with episodic upsurges of anxiety. Hostility is considerable but has had little recent affective outlet. There is a recurrent theme in the associative material which refers to getting rid of the offending object—his wife, who doesn't give enough. The patient's work situation appears for some time now to have become neurotically distorted into one of fooling the authorities (parents, superego) so that his narcissistic needs might be indulged in without interference or punishment. There is accompanying guilt and tension about possibly being "found out." In the last month before hospitalization a rather sharp disturbance in psychophysical equilibrium occurred because of increasing concern about money and also about maintaining his now "self-protected" position at work; at the same time he was being exposed to many colds. Finally an emotionally traumatic experience in which his child cut his lip, which had to be sutured, obviously added to the stresses from other sources.

PHYSICAL HISTORY

Patient entered the hospital with a chief complaint of chills, fever, and malaise of three weeks' duration. He was well until three weeks before admission, when he awoke one morning with a feeling of malaise accompanied by a shaking chill and a feverish feeling. There then developed a persistent cough, essentially nonproductive, except for a small amount of morning sputum which was brown. Two and a half weeks before admission, he saw his local doctor who gave him one injection of penicillin and prescribed cough medicine and bed rest. The patient, however, returned to work and continued to complain of persistent cough and malaise. His doctor gave him another injection of penicillin. One week before admission, he developed a "tender spot" over the left posterior rib margin, not related to respiration or coughing. He was told by his doctor that he had a "touch of pneumonia," but no x-ray was taken. He then received for seven days before admission daily injections of penicillin and took a total of 6,000,000 units additionally by mouth. One day before admission, he developed a fine maculopapular rash on the forehead which his doctor told him was a "penicillin rash."

PHYSICAL EXAMINATION

Revealed normal temperature, pulse, and respiration. There was slight pharyngeal injection. He had a maculopapular rash over the forehead and cheeks. The lungs were clear except for some coarse rales in the left axilla near the rib margin. A Grade I systolic murmur was heard both at the apex and base of the heart. There was a soft, noninflammatory swelling below the left elbow (old hematoma).

LABORATORY DATA

Admission white blood count was 10,300 with 68 percent polymorphonuclear leukocytes. A repeat white blood cell count was normal. Sedimentation rate was 35 mm per hr on admission and 18 mm per hr at the time of discharge. Sputum culture showed alpha streptococcus and Neisseria catarrhalis. Sputum smear negative for acid-fast bacilli. Cold agglutinin test and heterophile agglutination test both negative.

ROENTGENOGRAM

Chest film revealed blunting of left costophrenic sulcus, either by pleural thickening or small amount of fluid.

HOSPITAL COURSE

The patient remained afebrile and received no antibiotics. Within a few days after admission, the rales in the left axilla were no longer audible. The patient became entirely asymptomatic, and it was felt that he had entered the hospital with a resolving bacterial pneumonia which had been treated by large doses of penicillin. On discharge the patient was instructed to rest at home for one week longer before returning to work.

DISCHARGE DIAGNOSES

1. Bronchopneumonia, left lung, resolving, treated, improved.
2. Penicillin reaction, improved.

COMMENT

The psychological tensions in this case have at least two possible conditioned somatic pathways of discharge: the respiratory and the gastro-intestinal. The former has been the site of frequent minor infections in the past. These illnesses are associated with recollections of getting attention from mother. The mother was also involved in the past, and associated with castration fears. The patient's addictive tendencies appear to have become insufficient to ward off increasing depressive tendencies. During the period of mounting emotional tensions the patient was exposed rather heavily to infectious agents—viral and/or bacterial. He then developed a respiratory illness. Presumably he was in a state of so-called "lowered resistance" at this time. This expression generally has been used to refer to an individual's physical condition. It would be more meaningful if it included his psychological state also, as described above.

Seitz (1953), reporting on the results of hypnotic experiments in symptom substitution for investigative purposes, described the reactions in a 39-year-old, very obese woman. On one occasion, after being hypnotized, she was told that during the following week she would not overeat. During that period she developed chills, fever, and a painful cough, a condition diagnosed as bronchopneumonia, her third bout of this disease in 10 years. Recovery was rapid. In a subsequent interview she focused on how depressed she had been, rather than on the somatic illness. This was followed by associated material centering around anger toward an older woman neighbor. In a previous experiment the subject had developed pleuritis when bulimia was removed hypnotically. Both the pneumonia and pleuritis appeared to have been actual substitute reactions, perhaps because of alterations in the patient's immunologic response. In any event, depression, linked with unconscious hostility toward a mother figure, appeared as the main affective response, preceding the somatic illness.

CASE 8

CHIEF PRESENTING SYMPTOM	Cough
SENSORIMOTOR CONFIGURATIONS	Sensory configurations

Auditory, temperature, tactile

Associated with concern about weakness, threat to physical integrity, and linked to father's illness and death

Motor configurations

Hyperactivity, getting rid of

Connected with hostility toward mother and wife, seen as neglecting him

SOMATIC IDENTIFICATION	*Father*	Cough, pneumonia death when patient aged five (Direct, organ constitutional)
	Mother	Operations for tumor (pelvic), gallbladder, and appendix during patient's growing up period
	Child	Bronchitis, chronic, recently (Direct, organ constitutional, reverse)
	Wife, sister-in-law	Recent upper respiratory infections

SENSITIZED ORGAN SYSTEM	Gastrointestinal Respiratory
STRESS (*surface meaning*)	In last month, increasing concern about money and maintaining "cushy" job, and most recently, his child's accident
STRESS (*dynamic significance*)	Activation of an underlying feeling of insecurity and castration fears
DEFENSES	Overactivity

AFFECTS	*Intensity*	*Pathway of expression*
Anxiety	++	Ideational, some affective
Depression	++	Ideational
Hostility	+++	Somatization, relatively little affective

OTHER FACTORS   Oral components considerably developed
                                 Fooling authorities (parents, superego)

HOMEOSTATIC SHIFT(S)   Addictive tendencies plus gastrointestinal
                                 somatic pathway insufficient, followed by
                                 activation of respiratory system

DIAGNOSIS   Bronchopneumonia, left lung, resolving,
                                 treated, improved

case 9

Vertigo in Gastrointestinal Disease: Somatic Equivalents of the Affects

CHIEF PRESENTING SYMPTOM

Dizzy spells.

BASIC ANAMNESTIC EXCERPTS

"Two weeks ago I got these dizzy spells. Things looked wavy like they do when the sun is hot and the heat comes off the road. . . . I had to lie down. When I finally got up, there was some throbbing in my head. You know when a dentist pulls a tooth, he puts in the needle and freezes your jaw. Well, my whole mouth was like that—frozen. It then went down into my right arm, getting worse all the time."

The earliest episode of dizziness occurred nine years before: "I was in the Coast Guard on shore patrol. . . . They thought it was my eyes. When I got the spell, I had only half vision, although previously my eyes hadn't bothered me. It's happened about 15 times since then. The dizziness is like waves that rock a boat. . . . After such a spell I got bound up. I usually don't dare to take physics because my ulcers could bleed. Last summer while working at the Navy Yard, I lost 25 pounds when I bled for three days. When I was in the Coast Guard, on the base and on shore patrol, I felt as if I were trapped. I've had that same feeling while working at the Navy Yard. Everything is at high speed. They're always watching you: the Navy Commander, the foreman, the big eagle. The least little thing that goes wrong and they're on to you. If you get black marks in your record, you can't get a raise in pay. Got to keep the record clean. It all gets you keyed up."

Previous health is described as good, except for an injury at age 6, when he was bitten over the left eye by a dog. There follow references to the change in family fortunes: "Father used to be rich—but he lost everything but the house during the depression years. They made it into a rooming house, and for a while father worked as a janitor. He also used

111

to take fishing parties in his boat. Every once in a while I'd go with him. I began to work when I was 14; left high school in my second year."

There are further associations about being trapped, regimented, and controlled while in military service: "Finally I was assigned to a boat, and then my stomach acted up. This boat was riding 60-foot waves, and I, who had been on water for years, felt unnerved. That's when they found the ulcers. Couldn't understand it. I always had a boat when I was a kid. When I first started, my father was mad because he was afraid I'd go too far down the river. He said I'd drown. But I was always careful, because one summer when I was 16, some friends and I were sunk in a speedboat. We swam about a mile to shore, clothes and all, then walked for miles back home without shoes. It was quite an experience with those waves coming at you. I could have drowned."

Some references to his family come next: an older brother is mentally ill, in and out of hospitals; a younger brother is married and a good scholar. His mother is very active, shovels snow, and would just as soon walk as take a taxi.

The patient now focuses on his stomach pain: "When I don't eat, the ulcer starts chewing on me. No food this morning; I had to go for X-rays. So it's been a gnawing pain. But I can't let the pain stop me. I've got to be out of here in a few days. I have to work because there's no money in the house, and I have a wife and two kids. They depend on me. I have a girl five and a boy three years old . . . we have debts for TV and washing machine. If we don't pay, they come and take it away. You pay the next installment, and they bring it back. We've managed to hold on to the stuff for almost a year (laughter). I'm the only sick one . . . father's dead. He used to have these angina attacks, pain in his chest and right arm. He died at age 74, suddenly. He was out fishing in his boat one day, and the next day he was dead from a heart attack. That was six years ago. That's what started my older brother off. As for myself, my nerves get upset. It's from being in some place I can't get out of, and when I have too many things to do. I feel trapped here in the hospital, and if I ever went to jail, I would be sad. Being in military service was like being in jail. At one time I was going to go AWOL. The constant telling you what to do. . . . I remember once being confined when I was five years old. Mother and father went downtown to get the Christmas tree, and I woke up before they got home. I was in a crib with iron bars (laughing); I screamed and hollered, until finally they came back."

The theme of being confined and punished is developed further: "All kids get punished. Father was once driving down to the beach in his car. I tried to go with him, and he pushed me away. I got mad. He drove the car out, and I heaved a rock at it, denting a door. It was a new car. He caught me and threw me into the garage and closed the doors. He had me trapped in there. He gave me a good licking. Mother never hit me; she tried to shield and help us when father got mad. . . . I still owe money for father's tombstone."

The patient goes on to characterize himself as a child of the great depression: "We fellows born in the twenties really went through a bad time when things were scarce and we weren't fed the right stuff. Sometimes there wasn't too much food in the house. One of our roomers would buy jars of food; my mother would cook it for him, but she'd take a little off for us (laughing). Things aren't too easy now, either. Everything's so high and you run behind; then they're always after you. All kinds of headaches. I try to make some money by going out in a boat to catch tuna. But we haven't got the capital to stock our boat right. Still, when you're out there on the water, nobody bothers you. You're on your own; your own boss. But when it's time to go home and no fish, you can't buy any groceries. Then the ulcer starts to act up. There's some danger being out there on the water. Suppose your ulcer ruptured. It would take hours to get in. I've seen other fellows with ulcers that ripped open. Even if they operate, they don't fix it for good."

The associations now turn to hostility: "When I have nothing to bring home, I feel pretty bad, but I don't ever get mad. Never. It's my nature. Once in a great while I may get really mad; when something crosses me up. Like once a selectman wouldn't give me a license for a junk yard. My wife stopped me from going after him (laughing). One other time a fellow and I went partners to buy and sell old cars. Somebody telephoned the police and told them I was selling cars without a license. If I caught that informer, I would have really worked him over. But groceries is the whole thing (loud laughter). If I had an account at a supermarket, and they said I could have all the groceries I need, I'd be all set. The kids have got to eat. My eyes are watery (eyes are reddening). I hate to admit I feel like crying, but it's been a tough deal."

PSYCHODYNAMIC IMPRESSIONS

Father is seen as a once-powerful figure, who subsequently "lost everything" and assumed a devaluated role. An older brother follows this pattern —once strong, later a weak figure, mentally ill. The patient fears his future will be like father's and brother's—that he will become helpless and need to be taken care of, or else that like father he will meet death while out on the water. There is an identification somatically with father's anginal pain, and a further identification in terms of work—trying various jobs and finally winding up a poor fisherman. Mother appears as a vigorous, active person and is pictured in a relatively less negative light.

Strong claustrophobic tendencies, sensitivity to loss situations, and powerful hostile and rebellious impulses are all present and can be traced back to the patient's childhood, involving both parents and particularly father. The concern about manliness is overshadowed by powerful oral needs—to be provided for and looked after. The patient struggles against both by overcompensatory activity, but this becomes insufficient as persistent, though minor, stresses relating to work and finances continue to activate anxiety and dependent needs. Other defenses of denial and a smiling cover-up of hostility also prove unable to maintain an adequate psychophysical equilibrium. It was during the stresses of military service that physical symptoms first began to appear prominently as anxiety equivalents, and somatic pathways as discharge routes for frustrated oral needs and related aggression. This has become a chronic reaction.

PHYSICAL HISTORY

This patient was admitted with a chief complaint of dizzy spells of two weeks' duration. Nine years ago the patient had recurrent episodes of gastric pain, intermittent vomiting, and several dizzy spells with temporary dim vision. He was hospitalized at that time, but apparently no organic basis for his symptoms was established. Thereafter, he continued to have epigastric pain and vomiting, was again hospitalized, and this time the diagnosis of peptic ulcer was made. Five years ago the patient had a dizzy spell with temporary paralysis of the left arm and right leg, associated with severe back pain. He was hospitalized and given injections with sudden marked improvement of symptoms. Three years ago hospitalization was again necessary because of nausea, vomiting of green material, and passing of tarry stools. One year ago he had a similar episode. Three months before his present admission, he again noted epigastric pain and intermittently black bowel movements. Two weeks ago the patient developed frontal headache, dizziness, an inability to express what he wanted to say, and a sensation of tingling at the mouth spreading to the entire outside of the face and thence to the right arm and right leg. However, he could move his extremities and was able to feel touch and pain. The whole episode lasted several hours, and the symptoms disappeared by the time a doctor arrived. Nine days before admission, he again developed headache and dizziness, and hospitalization was advised.

PHYSICAL EXAMINATION

Essentially negative, except that the right pupil was larger than the left, but both reacted well to light and accommodation. There was slight nystagmus on right lateral gaze.

LABORATORY DATA

Urinalysis negative. Serology negative. Hemogram negative except that first differential white blood cell smear showed 10 percent eosinophiles, but in a repeat differential the eosinophiles had dropped to 3 percent. Several stool examinations guaiac negative.

ROENTGENOGRAMS

Chest and skull: negative. Gastrointestinal series: duodenal cap showed a deformity characteristic of duodenal ulcer, but there was no crater and no evidence of pyloric obstruction.

EEG

The record was interpreted as borderline because of a moderate buildup on hyperventilation.

HOSPITAL COURSE

The patient remained very tense, continued to complain of dizziness, headaches, and heat waves. It was planned to do a thorough neurological work-up, but the patient refused a lumbar puncture. He was consequently discharged at his own request.

DISCHARGE DIAGNOSES

1. Duodenal ulcer, improved.
2. ? Conversion reaction.

COMMENT

This patient has had acute and chronic low-grade depressions with interspersed episodes of moderate anxiety. The depression is generally manifested in somatic equivalents derived from a long sensitized pathway—the stomach. Anxiety, when it builds up, is also somatized and then is manifested in the form of probable conversion symptoms related to visual, tactile, and temperature-sensory percepts, and, to the conditioned skin, musculoskeletal and equilibratory systems. Depression and anxiety both are linked with still another basic affect, hostility, but each in a rather different way. Depression is associated with quantitatively great, relatively unneutralized aggressive drive energies. The effect of these, if not adequately discharged through ideational, behavioral, or affective pathways, but deflected onto organ systems, may be to critically activate organ dysfunction so that a potential for the development of physical disease is reached. In this case, a duodenal ulcer formed. The recurrent depressive tendencies appear to be related to the maintenance of chronic stomach dysfunction. In addition, the stomach symptoms have come under the influence of secondary-gain elements. The latter are evident when the patient's organic illness is used as a frequent rationalization for his not being able to devote himself consistently to productive and remunerative work.

Anxiety, when present, appears to be accompanied by an effect on the body which tends to be less disruptive of physicochemical processes, and the subsequent dysfunction is of a lower order of intensity. Under these conditions, organic changes are much less apt to occur. More specifically, physical symptoms representing symbolic types of "body or organ language" may then be noted to be transient and reversible. In this case the chief physical complaints referable to vertigo and presented to the interviewer were considered by him to be conversion symptoms, which subsided shortly after the patient left the hospital.

CASE 9

CHIEF PRESENTING SYMPTOM	Dizzy spells
SENSORIMOTOR CONFIGURATIONS	Sensory configurations

Visual, tactile, temperature, proprioceptive percepts

Associated with passivity, being trapped and controlled, symbolically castrated by male authority figures

Pain

Related to deprivation of food and love, mostly by paternal figures

Motor configurations

Chewing, gnawing

Connected with hostility toward depriving male figures

SOMATIC IDENTIFICATION	Father Pain, cardiac death six years ago ago
SENSITIZED ORGAN SYSTEM	Gastrointestinal—stomach Equilibratory and musculoskeletal apparatuses
STRESS (*surface meaning*)	Concern about money and work recently Difficulty in adjustment in military service
STRESS (*dynamic significance*)	Activation of dependent needs, concern about helplessness

DEFENSES	Overcompensating activity		
	Denial		
	Smiling cover-up of hostility		
AFFECTS		*Intensity*	*Pathway of expression*
Anxiety		++	Ideational, some affective, some somatic equivalents
Depression		+++	Ideational, minimal affective
Hostility		+++	Somatized, rarely affective, some ideational
OTHER FACTORS	Punitive father; containment of anger by patient		
	Father and brother once powerful, later devaluated		
	Mother vigorous, active		
	Claustrophobia		
	Sensitivity to loss		
	Strong oral needs		
	Secondary gains		
HOMEOSTATIC SHIFT(S)	First-line defenses inadequate, shifting to marked somatization response and intermittent conversion reactions		
DIAGNOSES	a) Duodenal ulcer, improved;		
	b) ? Conversion reaction		

FOLLOW-UP DATA

INTERIM NOTE

Following this hospitalization, a period of about four years elapsed before any major stresses occurred in the patient's life. By dint of hard work, considerable activity, and taking some chances, the patient was able to build up a small contracting business and achieve a measure of financial stability. In all other respects a relatively steady equilibrium was maintained. However, toward the end of this period, the patient began to experience increasing difficulties in obtaining business contracts and maintaining personnel. This was followed by an episode of acute physical illness. The patient had a sudden massive hematemesis, requiring (private) hospitalization and transfusion of 16 units of blood. An emergency laparotomy was performed on the second hospital day, but "nothing specific" was found; however, the duodenal vessels were ligated.

After discharge, the patient returned to his business which continued to deteriorate. Nevertheless, the patient seemingly felt well until one month prior to the next hospitalization, approximately two years later. His business had failed and he was in bankruptcy. At this time he had vague abdominal discomfort relieved by alkali, and some episodes of weakness; however, stools appeared normal. Several weeks prior to admission he noted that stools had become loose and black. He was readmitted to the private hospital where he had been previously. He was again given multiple transfusions, and on the third hospital day an exploratory laparotomy was performed, again with negative findings; no specific surgical procedure was carried out. Postoperatively he continued to bleed, again had 16 units of blood, developing urticaria after one transfusion. His stools were no longer tarry shortly before transfer to the hospital where he had originally been admitted six years ago.

PHYSICAL EXAMINATION

Revealed a well-developed, mildly obese man. Blood pressure 120/70. Pulse 80. Temperature 100°F. The patient was hyperkinetic, spoke rapidly. Anisocoria was noted, right pupil being larger than left. There was a healing right rectus incision, somewhat indurated. The physical examination was otherwise negative.

LABORATORY DATA

Hematocrit 36 percent, hemoglobin 10.4 g; white blood cell and differential count: normal. Urinalysis and serology negative. Total protein 5.1 g; albumin 3.4 g. Liver function studies: negative. Bleeding and coagulation time: normal.

ROENTGENOGRAMS

Chest: negative. Gastrointestinal series: deformed duodenal bulb without definite evidence of ulceration; two loops of proximal jejunum fixed, probably due to old adhesions; slow transit time. Barium enema negative.

HOSPITAL COURSE

The patient became rapidly afebrile and asymptomatic. He was put on a six-meal, bland diet, hourly feedings of antacids, and given a course of imferon intramuscularly. His hematocrit remained relatively stable at 33 to 36 percent. Stool examinations became guaiac negative. The massive gastrointestinal hemorrhage was related to the ulcer. A subtotal gastrectomy was felt to be necessary in the future. Surgery at this time was deferred because the patient was not bleeding and was convalescing from recent surgery. He was discharged in 10 days and advised to continue on a medical regime of bland diet, probanthine, and antacids for six months.

DIAGNOSIS

Duodenal ulcer, with recent upper gastrointestinal hemorrhage, treated, improved.

FURTHER COMMENT

This is a patient who, as noted years before, reacts with marked sensitivity to loss, while powerfully reactive hostile and rebellious impulses are not afforded affective outlet. He has struggled for a long time with the fear that he will be like his father, once active and able to carry on effectively—only to become ill and helpless, needing then to be taken care of. A principal defense has been overactivity, especially directed toward business ventures. It seems that as long as the patient was able to utilize this defense effectively he was able to ward off unfavorable homeostatic shifts in his psychophysical equilibrium. His success in business served as a reassurance to him about his adequacy as a man. However, when his business began to fail, his involvement in it was no longer able to be used in the service of defense against simultaneously reactivated powerful dependent needs and feelings of inferiority. In turn, strong hostile impulses were generated. The changes in external environment caused a regressive shift in the patient's psychophysical state. The gastrointestinal tract, which had responded to stress in the past with increase in already existing dysfunction, once again reacted similarly. This time the escalated dysfunction led to erosion of a blood vessel.

A serious hemorrhage ensued, but the hospitalization, lifesaving measures (transfusions), and surgical intervention restored the patient to a favorable psychophysical state in which he remained for two years. Then he was confronted with the bankruptcy of his business. At that time another regressive shift occurred in his psychophysical condition and there was a repetition of the previous hemorrhagic episode, followed by similar medical and surgical interventions. This time, as far as is known, the patient has gone for over five more years without hospitalization.

Weisman (1956) in his study of six male patients with exacerbations of chronic duodenal ulcer found a nuclear emotional conflict centered around passivity–activity with struggle over dependence–independence as a special aspect of the former. He noted that recurrence of ulcer always took place in a setting where the patient was vacillating between active seeking and passive yielding. The accompanying basic affects were "restrained resentment, angry guilt, and guilty fear." The patient fearfully anticipated a state of helplessness through narcissistic hurt, demands that might be depleting, or loss of object that supplied strength and support.

Weisman found that while phobic and obsessional symptoms were frequent, depression was conspicuously absent during the exacerbations of ulcer. Weisman concluded that "ulcer symptoms recurred most often when the threat of depletion exceeded the promise of replenishment and the resulting angry protest was restrained." Ulcer exacerbation required the presence of multiple factors including nuclear conflict, basic fear, special ego defenses such as compliance, defiance, inhibition, denial, fantasy formation, bisexual identification, inaccessibly high ego ideal, and also ambivalent interpersonal relationships.

CLINICAL EXCERPTS FROM ANOTHER CASE

In the case just presented, various somatic pathways were involved simultaneously in the original hospitalization, though the gastrointestinal system had been and continued to be the predominant one. There are instances when two or more organ systems are utilized only briefly, though interchangeably, as discharge outlets for emotional tensions. Thus a rapidly shifting spectrum of symptoms may be observed within a short period of time. However, these may present a pattern which is repeated, though the order of appearance of the symptoms is not always the same. For example, in one patient who had no organic disease but "somatized" frequently when under tension, the following symptoms occurred within a three-hour period after an acutely stressful situation in which he had been involved in a violent quarrel with his wife: There first appeared infrequent extrasystoles, which after a few minutes were replaced by abdominal discomfort turning into fairly persistent cramps for over an hour. These subsided and the extrasystoles returned and were shortly replaced, this time, by nausea. The patient took a sleeping pill, fell asleep, and when he awoke had no recurrence of any of the physical symptoms. One could consider these symptoms to be reflections of autonomic nervous system disturbances, involving interchangeably two specific organ systems—gastrointestinal and cardiac. These were already sensitized or target organs which had responded in generally similar symptomatic fashion to many previous stress situations.

case 10

Itching Ears: Adaptive Processes in Chronic Illness

Itching, throbbing ears.

BASIC ANAMNESTIC EXCERPTS

The patient refers many times to *it:* "I've had it for almost nine years. It began while I was in the military service. For the last two years I've been bothered the most. In the last two weeks it got so I couldn't stand it. My ear gets dry and scaly; the salve takes the scales off for the time being, but not for long. It itches then, and there's a throbbing sensation—like a heartbeat, like you cut your finger. During the day when I'm more active and walk around, and my mind is occupied with other things, I don't mind it as much. But when I try to relax at night, that's when I can hear it going, just like a little pump in my ear, all the time. It feels just like my fingers used to, when I was in high school playing ball. I would get blood blisters from swinging the bat, and the doctor had to cut them out. They would throb so badly at night I couldn't sleep.

"Now I'll nonchalantly start feeling the ear, then twist it, and finally scratch it. Once I start, it's hard for me to stop; it seems to build up. Then a little leaking will come out. I don't know if it's some kind of matter, or what it is—maybe pus. It looks whitish. The itching gets so bad I feel like grabbing the ear, and I have to use a lot of willpower to bring my hand away. The right ear has always been worse than the left. In fact, it's beginning to look like a cauliflower ear such as the wrestlers have.

"I used to be fit as a kid, never had any trouble. I began in sports as a kid. My father used to be a ballplayer. He worked in a shop, but after hours he would go out with me at night. The first time I played first base I was seven years old. I was a fair ballplayer, but father was good. When some people see us together, they might call us brothers. He's small, not a big man like me. I take after my mother. She's been gone since I was

121

eight years old. She died when she was 29. I guess it was cancer. I remember father telling us she was operated on for a tumor in her stomach. She was very sick for a long time. My older sister and I had to go live with my grandmother who was strict. I can remember seeing mother right in the casket. She'd been a big person, about 200 pounds, and when she passed away, she was down to 80. It was hard for me to cry; it always has been. . . . After three years father remarried."

Returning to his own health: "I had child diseases but never had an earache. In fact, my hearing was always very sharp. At night I would hear the slightest noises, and this would often keep me awake when I was a kid; afraid something bad was going to happen. Now it's the appearance of the ear that bothers me. It doesn't look neat by any means. I remember using a salve and other people must have seen that white stuff on me and wondered what it was. I'm very fussy about neatness; my wife will tell you that. I was brought up to be good and neat. Our house is immaculate; it's all white, every room. My three kids don't bang it up or make marks. The playroom isn't dented. We don't allow bicycles or planes in the house. My stepmother was awfully fussy and irritable—everything had to be just right. My wife is the same way. Well, I tried to be cooperative; that's my nature. I used to take a shower every night after work. You see, I work on cast iron, and it leaves a lot of rust. Lately, I couldn't do it because I'm afraid to touch the ear. It looks bad, and I wouldn't want to go around and have everybody talking about my appearance.

"I don't know if it's eczema or a fungus. I had a brother-in-law who came down with fungus on his feet. It was an awful case. I saw one case of athlete's foot in the Army, but he wasn't a very clean boy. When I entered military service, I had a nice assignment close to home. Then they shipped me to a staging area, after breaking my outfit up. I felt kind of low. Three days after I got there, my ears began to bother me. We were slated to go overseas as replacements and didn't know where or when, or what was ahead of us. It was enough to get anyone on edge. Besides, my new platoon leader was an impossible guy."

Further associations: "The pressure has been going down a little. The saline soaks seem to draw out what's in the ear. I've seen it in others: A buddy of mine had a fistula, something in the spine. I understand they were draining him down to his rectum." Other troubles developed in recent years: "I was operated on for a hernia five years ago. It accumulated overnight. I did it on my job, while working on a cotton loom. It's a two-man job, and this fellow let the other end go, and I was hanging on to this one—quite a strain. I was in the hospital for hemorrhoids two years before the hernia. I don't fool around if there's something wrong; I want to have it done. It used to be an uncomfortable sensation, felt like everything was hanging right down there. It hurt quite a bit there after the operation. Now I'm in the hospital for the third time. Well, one more time—you have three strikes against you, and when you have three strikes, you're out (laughing). I'm the unlucky one. Maybe I'll shrivel up and blow away."

The patient's closing references are to his wife and children: "She was in the hospital three times herself. We had three babies—they were all big, weighing over eight pounds. My wife had to have stitches down there— she's a small woman. We don't want any more, four would be a headache. So it's a problem, how to be together without her getting pregnant."

PSYCHODYNAMIC IMPRESSIONS

This patient, who has an obsessive–compulsive personality, experiences sensitivity to loss as a basic emotional problem. Separation from home and mother's death are early traumata, later reactivated during military service in separation from wife, buddies, and familiar surroundings.

His identifications are mixed; body size and image being more closely related to mother when she was well, and certain masculine activity (sports) more to father. The patient has considerable anxiety about his own physical fate; what happened to mother could happen to him—he could shrink in size and die.

Prominent psychological defenses are reaction formations of neatness and cleanliness directed against opposite impulses of dirtiness. These appear insufficient under stress, especially since marriage and wartime experience, so that physical pathways of discharge have become involved. When the patient's military assignment was changed, he experienced a definitely regressive emotional reaction. He became anxious about his future, insecure and depressed because of the separation from familiar objects, and considerably annoyed, because of his frustrations and then dislike of his new commander. He had never been able to express truly his feelings of anger and guilt. The ears do not seem to have been the site of illness during childhood. However, there are associations between hearing and fears of unpleasant consequences. Symbolically, itching could well represent irritation somatically expressed; scratching then might indicate hostile impulses turned from outside objects upon the self. Transudation of fluid could lead to the development of "weeping lesions" suggestive of "a crying into the skin."

The patient has experienced recurrent stresses after return to civilian life, especially in his marital and work relationships. Anger, guilt, and anxiety seem to have found a somatic outlet in the persisting dermatitis. A complicating factor has been a repressed and inhibited sexual drive which to some extent may have led to an erotization of the sensitized skin of the ears. The itching and scratching may thus have also a sexual significance, and the sensations experienced may be grossly similar to those in stimulated genitalia, that is, represent masturbatory equivalents associated with castration anxiety and guilt.

References to swellings he has had (hernia and hemorrhoids) appear in close associative temporal sequence to his wife's last two pregnancies, both of which were stress situations for him. This suggests a somatic identification with her.

PHYSICAL HISTORY

The patient began to have trouble with his ears nine years ago when itching, scaling, and weeping lesions appeared on the pinna and in the canal. There was no associated hearing difficulty. Since that time, the dermatitis has been present constantly with flare-ups and remissions. It has been treated with various antibiotics and every kind of salve without any real success. Eight weeks before admission, the patient experienced dull occasional, intermittent pain in the left lower quadrant. This pain lasted a week. A local doctor did a barium enema and found a "spasm of the bowel." There were no further related symptoms except moderate constipation for many years. Seven years ago the patient had a hemorrhoidectomy; five years ago he underwent a left herriorrhaphy.

PHYSICAL EXAMINATION

Weight 240 pounds. Vital signs: normal. Skin: ears showed a scaling, red, weeping type of lesion with vesiculation extending somewhat into the ear canal, but the tympanic membrane was free of disease. An external hemorrhoidal tag was noted during rectal examination.

LABORATORY DATA

Only positive hemogram findings were: white blood cell count 14,555 with 62 segmented cells, 7 band cells, 22 lymphocytes, 5 monocytes, and 4 eosinophiles. Sedimentation rate was 15 mm per hr. A throat culture showed alpha streptococcus and Neisseria catarrhalis. Ear cultures for bacteria and fungi negative.

ROENTGENOGRAM

Chest film: normal.

HOSPITAL COURSE

The patient was put on a regular diet which was later reduced to 1,000 calories. Saline soaks to the ears were prescribed, and after a week, the patient was switched from soaks to aquaphor ointment. There was gradual improvement in the symptomatology referable to the ears. During the second week of hospitalization, he developed malaise, sore throat, and low-grade fever; during this time a number of patients on the ward developed similar symptoms. The patient's fever lasted about three days, then fell to normal, after he was started on penicillin, although it was felt this probably was not the decisive factor in the subsidence of the fever. After three weeks in the hospital, he was discharged, having lost 16 pounds.

DISCHARGE DIAGNOSES

1. Dermatitis therapeutica, probably superimposed on infectious eczematoid dermatitis. Markedly improved.
2. Upper respiratory infection. Cured.
3. Obesity, treated, improved.

COMMENT

This patient's sickness began nine years before this hospitalization. It has become chronic in every sense of the word. Like other long, drawn-out illness it has had exacerbations and remissions. However, because of its particular nature—it has never really incapacitated the patient in the sense that he has been unable to work or carry on with his usual daily routines. Consequently, while there will be secondary psychological reactions to such a prolonged sickness, these will be of a different order than those noted in more serious and more disabling chronic disease. In any event, chronicity makes for the intrusion of unpleasant or even painful physical symptoms and sensations of all kinds into the awareness of the individual. There is a tendency then to become body-centered to a much greater degree than before the illness. Many perceptions and apperceptions especially concerned with body image, including body size, and possible alterations or shifts in it, are activated. Adaptive processes in response to all these changes are evoked and, of course, vary from individual to individual. It must be emphasized that all too often the physical aspects of adaptation to chronic illness are the main object of the physician's attention, with complete or relatively considerable neglect of the psychological components of adaptation. The latter cover a broad spectrum from intense denial to relatively complete preoccupation with the illness. The premorbid psychological makeup of the individual and the further influences of environment both are basic determinants in how the adaptation will go. Changes from activity to passivity in the patient with chronic illness are more frequently seen than the opposite. The symptoms and sensations may become fixed and acquire secondarily determined symbolic significance for the patient, or they may alternate with one or another, briefly retaining prominence, and again this may not altogether be due to corresponding physical changes.

Kepecs et al. (1951) induced emotional states in subjects under hypnosis and simultaneously measured changes within the skin. Blisters were raised by applying cantharides cerate, and quantitative fluid measurements were taken from the base of these blisters. They found that fluctuations at the blister site, both in patients with exudative disease and subjects with undiseased skins, were related to weeping. They came to the conclusion that "the emotional state of which weeping is the highly visible expression is not limited in its effects to the lacrimal glands, but finds expression in other parts of the body, including the skin." They also felt that dermatoses previously dry and involuting may become suddenly edematous as a result of increased passage of fluid into the skin, associated with changes in the individual's emotional state, if this is sufficiently disturbed and if constitutional and other elements are present. There appeared to be a close correlation between mobility to express feelings and rises in gastric secretion, blood pressure, and rate of exudation of fluid at blister sites. They inferred that such changes take place in skin untraumatized by cantharides. Saul and Bernstein (1941) have written on emotional settings characterized by inability to cry and their relationship to attacks of urticaria.

CASE 10

CHIEF PRESENTING SYMPTOM	Itching, throbbing ears
SENSORIMOTOR CONFIGURATIONS	Sensory configurations

Tactile, visual, auditory

Linked with fearful and guilty reactions to screen memories of primal scenes, to cleanliness enforced by maternal figures, and to losses of significant objects

Motor configurations

Cutting, scratching

Connected to hostile competition with parental figures and suggestive of symbolic masturbatory activity and castration

SOMATIC IDENTIFICATION	Mother	Physical size, cancer of stomach, death 22 years ago
	Brother-in-law	Fungus infection of feet
	Wife	Pregnancy, swellings during recent years
SENSITIZED ORGAN SYSTEM	Skin, ears	

STRESS (*surface meaning*)	Separation stress while in military service Work tensions Anxiety over birth control, wife's pregnancies
STRESS (*dynamic significance*)	In military service, concerned about future, increased insecurity and depression because of separation from familiar objects, and heightened hostility especially toward new commander, seen negatively In civilian life, chronic inadequacy feelings, activated infantile sexual impulses..
DEFENSES	Reaction formations Overcompensatory masculine activity

AFFECTS	Intensity	Pathway of expression
Anxiety	++	Some ideational, somatic equivalents
Depression	++	Some ideational, somatic equivalents
Hostility	++	Some ideational, somatization

OTHER FACTORS	Primal scene experience Masturbatory equivalents Sensitivity to loss Superego tensions
HOMEOSTATIC SHIFT(S)	Anger, depression, anxiety, and sexual drives insufficiently discharged through affective, ideational, behavioral character, resulting in utilization of somatic pathways
DIAGNOSES	a) Dermatitis therapeutica, probably superimposed on infectious eczematoid dermatitis. Markedly improved; b) Upper respiratory infection. Cured; c) Obesity, treated, improved

case 11

Sore Legs, Alcoholism, and Secondary Gain

CHIEF PRESENTING SYMPTOM

Sore legs.

BASIC ANAMNESTIC EXCERPTS

"My symptoms all started when I was doing so much drinking that I didn't feel like eating. Six months ago I noticed the muscles of my legs started aching and then they started prickling like. Then I felt it all the way down to my toes. Now that's being eliminated in the hospital here. My legs can move pretty well, but when they were sore, I was real shaky. The soreness was like a toothache. The legs felt numb, as though there seemed to be no support there. Every time I moved a joint, it seemed to cramp up on me. When I went to pick up my leg, I couldn't do it. . . .Too much drinking gets you nervous. I'd just have a cup of coffee for breakfast, wouldn't have lunch, and just a little bit to eat at dinner time. Besides, I had lots of worries. My house had to be repaired, and I was trying to establish a business. I was always on the go."

Overactivity, diminution of food intake, and increased drinking are further elaborated on: "After working 12 hours, I'd come home at night, and my wife would have dinner warming over on the stove. It's not like when it's freshly cooked (loud burping). I'd take a few bites, watch television, and drink and drink until I was feeling good, and then go to bed. I would do that day in and day out, starting at seven in the morning. I'm a wholesale food dealer. I also have a store of my own and couldn't afford much help. I just worked too hard and didn't have the appetite to eat. Here my appetite's returning. I've been drinking three quarts of milk a day (laughing). At home I'd drink liquor until it made me fall asleep. About six years ago, I drove a cab for a while, but then I started this business of my own. Before that time I wasn't a drinking man. I didn't have a house, nothing to worry about. Too many responsibilities get me down.

My wife is no comfort to me. I feel alone in all this. I keep my feelings and thoughts to myself like I did when I was a youngster.

"I kept putting off seeing a doctor. Finally my legs hurt so much I had to go see one. The pain made me terribly nervous. Three months ago I had all my teeth pulled out—I thought that would help. I got sick of going back and forth to the dentist, and I said, 'Pull them all.' I always had bad teeth, like my father. When I was seven or eight years old, I remember being forced to go to the school dentist. He was a butcher, and I didn't want to go. While you waited, you could hear the kids hollering blue murder. You'd be scared even before you'd go in. Well, I didn't go to a dentist again until I was 15. I used to pull the teeth out myself. After I began to earn some money, I'd go on my own to see a dentist, paid him myself and kept my mouth shut (laughing). If my parents had known about the condition of my teeth, I would have gotten holy hell from them. Now my legs feel just like those aching teeth."

Next follow references to injuries: "When I was 16, I dropped a big steel drum on the edge of my left foot. My toes were broken. A half hour after the accident I was in a cast with X-rays and everything taken. I know what crutches are. I got married on them. This injury happened two weeks before my wedding. I had all my plans made and reservations for the honeymoon. Well, my wife went to work, and I stayed at home. We got by—you know how it is when you're in love. My wife was 17 and I was 16. (Looks at watch and appears impatient.) There were lots of arguments about the marriage; the folks didn't approve of the step I was taking, but they finally gave in. Then the accident happened. For a good month I couldn't use that foot; it was very sensitive. Then it started throbbing and got very sore and stayed that way a long time."

The patient returns to the subject of the care and condition of his teeth in childhood: "I never brushed them, always eating candy and things that were not good for you. Often when I couldn't have the things I wanted, I would try to get hold of some candy—something sweet. Today I'm paying for what I shouldn't have done. My two kids—they don't want to eat much either, but I'm right there to see that they do, and that they brush their teeth. When they saw how all my teeth were pulled out, they asked why, and I told them because I didn't brush. I scare them that way. False teeth are no fun. Your food doesn't taste good to you. I'm paying for being a bad boy. Everything my mother told me to do, I'd do the opposite. She'd tell my father, and he'd give me more hell, but she was the real boss. I never got a licking for it. They would just talk to me; that's why I was getting away with it all the time. I wouldn't eat, just take a bite and take off, play football, baseball, whatever it happened to be. I used to be very active in sports, even after I was married. I never weighed too much—you have to have the vitamins. Mother is bigger than father; I'm like him. I have a younger brother who's big, too. He's 10 years younger —must have been an accident."

Current troubles are again emphasized: "I have to pay up on my taxes or be in a jam with the government. It's a big worry. If I go home, I can work on my books and get the thing settled. I think that's 100 percent of my sickness. But the doctor wants me to stay another week. What he's afraid of is that I'm going to start hitting the bottle. But I'm not. In my business I walk from one barroom to the other, selling seafood. You've got to buy from them if they buy from you. Now I'm not going to bother with the wholesale end of it. I'll stay right in my own store where there's no liquor around and where I won't be tempted. It'll take a couple of weeks to get my books straightened out so I can send out my tax return." At this point anger is marked. "I don't want to get holy hell from Uncle Sam."

PSYCHODYNAMIC IMPRESSIONS

The interview material indicates the pressure of underlying passive-dependent traits. These have been kept in check with variable success by a facade of activity. The patient's oral problems are reflected in the references to childhood eating problems, craving for candy when feeling deprived, the association of such indulgence with deleterious effect on his teeth, and the warnings and verbal punishment from parents. The adult equivalent of such oral tendencies has been the patient's alcoholism. The musculoskeletal system has been heavily involved in the defensive over-activity. In childhood, play and flight, particularly running, have also been associated with parental admonition and threats of consequences. In adolescence, the left foot was the site of "accidental" trauma—occurring against a background of considerable emotional stress, connected with marriage and the warning disapproval of parents. The sensitization of the lower extremities was thus reinforced. Currently, the patient has been overinvolved in business and tax problems, likewise associated with an unpleasant outcome.

The piling up of responsibilities activates the patient's feelings of insecurity and dependency. He then feels little, in size and capability, like father with whom there is a further somatic identification in terms of poor teeth. He indicates that he gets no support from his wife and feels all the more alone. Frustration of dependency needs or overreaction to authority figures stirs up considerable hostility which finds inadequate affective discharge. For many years the patient has not shared his feelings or thoughts with others—whether parents or wife or friends. His attempts to avoid or escape from his reality problems by increasing alcoholism are not only unsuccessful, but a complicating pharmacotoxic factor is present which finally exerts its effect on the sensitized lower extremities at the time of his most recent business crisis.

PHYSICAL HISTORY

The patient was admitted with a chief complaint of weakness and tingling in his legs of two months' duration. For the past 10 to 12 years he has had a fairly heavy alcoholic intake in order to combat insomnia and nervousness. Alcoholic beverages were restricted mostly to wine and beer. Six months before admission, the patient apparently began to drink quite heavily, averaging two quarts of wine and four or five shots of whiskey a day. The patient very frequently began his day with a drink in order to deal with his increasing "shakes." He consulted a physician and was given several weekly injections over a period of two months. The injections were discontinued because of an acneform eruption which developed on the patient's forehead. Three months before entry, the patient had full-mouth extraction, and since then his dietary intake has been inadequate. Two months before entry, he first began to notice a sensation of pins and needles in his toes which was at first felt only occasionally, but gradually became constant and extended to his knees. He has had some dull, aching pain across his lower abdomen for the last month. Patient denies dizziness and syncope, but has noted some increasing difficulty in walking. When his alcoholic intake is especially heavy, he has been troubled with bouts of diarrhea.

PHYSICAL EXAMINATION

An apprehensive, tremulous young man who was oriented and co-operative. Temperature 98.6°F. Pulse 84. Blood pressure 148/112. Tongue: reddened smooth edges. Lungs: hyperresonant with somewhat diminished breath sounds and a slight expiratory wheeze. Abdomen: tense with voluntary rigidity; dullness and slight resistance in right upper quadrant; liver edge not felt. Extremities: gross tremor, hyperesthesia of feet (over soles) and lower legs. Reflexes: hyperactive but equal.

LABORATORY DATA

Hemoglobin 13 g, hematocrit 43 percent; white blood cell count 6,700 with normal differential. Urine on admission revealed 2+ albumin and 0 to 4 white blood cells per high power field. Repeat urine revealed a trace of albumin. Total protein 7.3 with negative formal gel. Alkaline phosphates 2.1. Cephalin flocculation 1+. Van den Bergh 0.1 direct, 0.6 indirect. Two hour urobilinogen excretion was 0.4 Ehrlich units.

ROENTGENOGRAM

Chest film: negative.

HOSPITAL COURSE

Patient was given a high protein, high carbohydrate diet and daytime sedation. The dietary regimen was supplemented with multivitamins, brewer's yeast, injections of thiamin hydrochloride and Beroca C daily. Antitensives were also prescribed. During the first four hospital days, the patient continued to complain of shakiness, sweating, difficulty in sleeping, burning pains over the soles and in his legs. His speech was rapid and remained slurred, and he expressed much anxiety about his condition. However, approximately one week after entry, the patient felt considerably improved with marked diminution in his tremor, and he slept well. He was seen by the social worker, and arrangements were made to have him join Alcoholics Anonymous. A clear-cut diagnosis of delirium tremens could not be made as the patient had no visual hallucinations during his present illness or during his hospital course.

DISCHARGE DIAGNOSES

1. Alcoholism, chronic and acute.
2. Peripheral neuropathy due to vitamin deficiency, treated, improved.
3. Nutritional deficiency, treated, improved.
4. Hypertension, treated, improved.

COMMENT

This patient tries to avoid depression and anxiety, particularly the former, by constant hyperactivity, and when this is inadequate, he supplements it by alcoholism. An escalating deprivation syndrome developed as his dental caries and abscessed teeth led him to agree to have a full-mouth extraction, so that subsequently the already reduced food intake became even more insufficient. As the peripheral neuritis localized in his lower extremities, and the clinical manifestations of soreness and pain and inability to walk became increasingly more severe, these symptoms also became associated with permanent secondary-gain factors.

Such an association had occurred at least once before when the patient was 16. At that time, just before his marriage, which he approached with great ambivalence, he "became careless" and injured his foot. The symptoms and incapacity that developed became reality reasons for his avoiding his family responsibilities, which he was obviously not prepared to undertake, for what he described as a "good month." Good meant not so much a whole month as one in which he stayed at home, "took things easy," while his wife went out to work as well as looked after him. In the present difficulties which surround him, the neuritic symptoms are realities which he can point to as reasons for not being able to get his finances and taxes in order, despite his protests that he wants to go home to do this. As it turned out, he actually spent another "good" month, this time in the hospital. The improvement in his current physical symptoms did not really begin until he learned that his wife had been able to get a skilled accountant to straighten out his books for him. His cardiovascular system showed evidence of dysfunction, but symptoms referable to it were not elicited.

CASE 11

CHIEF PRESENTING SYMPTOM	Sore legs
SENSORIMOTOR CONFIGURATIONS	Sensory configurations

Pain

Closely associated with toothache and defective teeth, forbidden oral activity and defiance of dominant mother, resulting in subsequent punishment by father and, symbolically, by butcher dentist

Motor configurations

Overactivity

Linked to sports and work as compensatory defense to prove manliness, with passive retreat made possible by injuries in the past

SOMATIC IDENTIFICATION	*Father* Bad teeth for many years, physical size (Direct, organ constitutional)
SENSITIZED ORGAN SYSTEM	Skin, ears
STRESS (*surface meaning*)	Business and tax problems
STRESS (*dynamic significance*)	Activation of inferiority feelings, frustration of dependency needs, and overreaction to authority figures, activating much hostility and guilt
DEFENSES	Overactivity Rationalizations

AFFECTS	*Intensity*	*Pathway of expression*
Anxiety	++	Ideational

Depression	+++	Minimal ideational plus affective, some behavioral plus much addictive
Hostility	+++	Minimal ideational plus affective, mostly somatization
OTHER FACTORS		Oral problems Warnings and verbal punishment from parents
HOMEOSTATIC SHIFT(S)		Increasing alcoholism with introduction of complicating pharmacotoxic factor, insufficient to cope with activated aggressive drives, resulting in reinforced somatization
DIAGNOSES		a) Alcoholism, chronic and acute; b) Peripheral neuropathy due to vitamin deficiency, treated, improved; c) Nutritional deficiency, treated, improved; d) Hypertension, treated, improved

FOLLOW-UP DATA

Following discharge the patient continued to drink, despite his resolution to give up liquor. For the next eight years, however, he did not require hospitalization for illness. Then a series of major environmental changes occurred. He lost his business. His mother developed high blood pressure and his father began to suffer from a stomach ulcer. During the next four years the patient's alcoholic intake became increasingly greater and a series of decompensations in his physical and mental state began. He was hospitalized several times because of delirium tremens complicated by "seizures." On other occasions he had to be hospitalized for "drying out." His employment was erratic and his financial condition worsened. Six months before his most recent hospitalization (12 years after the one originally reported, the patient now being 42 years old) he had lost a menial job. He was drinking wine, whiskey, and especially beer, and usually eating breakfast and supper. He again began to feel very jittery and sweaty, but there was no dizziness. Although he had noted some dark urine several weeks before admission, there was no abdominal pain, nausea, vomiting, melena, or hematemesis. No history of jaundice, chills, or fever could be elicited. The patient did complain of pruritus over both lower extremities, especially after a hot shower.

PHYSICAL EXAMINATION

A well-developed, well-nourished, hirsute male in no acute distress. Weight 156 pounds. Temperature 100°F (rectal). Pulse 98. Blood pressure 160/110 in left arm and 170/110 in right arm. Not icteric. Liver down three fingerbreadths below right costal margin and one finger breadth beyond midclavicular line; not tender. Neurological examination revealed very brisk but equal reflexes and slightly decreased vibratory sensation bilaterally in lower extremities.

LABORATORY DATA

Hemoglobin 16 g, hematocrit 43 percent, white blood cell count 11,500 with a normal differential. Urinalysis negative. VDRL negative. Bromsulphalein showed zero retention in 45 minutes. Blood urea nitrogen 8. Glucose 90. Bilirubin 0.2. Thymol turbidity 3.5. Total protein 7.7 g with albumin 4.6. Alkaline phosphatase 1.7. Transaminase 20.

ROENTGENOGRAMS

Chest: within normal limits. Upper gastrointestinal series revealed no evidence of varices.

ELECTROCARDIOGRAM

Probable old posterior myocardial infarction, based on the presence of small Q waves in 2, 3, and AVF leads.

HOSPITAL COURSE

The patient became rapidly asymptomatic. He was given antitensives and Librium 5 mg four times a day. Since there was no evidence at this time of any liver damage, it was felt the patient could be quickly discharged.

DISCHARGE DIAGNOSES

1. Chronic alcoholism, unchanged.
2. Hypertension, treated, improved.
3. No evidence of cirrhosis of the liver at this time.

FINAL COMMENT

For approximately eight years and through a number of minor situational crises, the patient maintained an uneasy, uncomfortable modus vivendi by a combination of attempted overactivity in his business and periodic bouts of alcoholism. As time went on, there was gradual lessening of activity and parallel increase in drinking. It was obvious that any more marked changes in the patient's life situation could have a shattering impact on his increasingly vulnerable psychophysical equilibrium. This indeed did happen in the form of a series of events that signified both outright and impending loss, involving his business and both parents. A steadily downhill course began with periodic psychophysical regressions following hard upon each other. Years before, after severe environmental stress he had become ill, and the nervous system had been the target organ. In particular he had had a peripheral neuropathy of the (sensitized) lower extremities, and there had been a question of whether delirium tremens had not also occurred. Now full-blown bouts of delirium tremens and persisting residual symptoms referable to the lower extremities became the chief clinical manifestations. In addition, a persistent hypertension indicated that the cardiovascular system continued to be another vulnerable somatic pathway. A long, now escalating, self-destructive trend is evident. The patient has been resistive to all suggestions of psychotherapeutic intervention or any kind of related, adjunct approach to his emotional problems. He is entering an age period which in itself will present additional possible sources of tension. At this point the outlook for this patient is indeed a grim one unless an environmental change of a favorable nature should occur. An example of this would be the substitution of a less deleterious source of emotional supplies than that provided by the alcoholism and might be in the form of a new or favorably modified preexisting relationship with a person emotionally significant for the patient.

Reiser et al. (1951a), observing over two hundred patients with varying types and severity of hypertensive disease, found that their data demonstrated the high frequency with which stressful life situations adversely affected the course of the illness. They also found that emotionally relaxing conditions may frequently help to improve the patient's clinical condition. Among these is a favorable doctor-patient relationship.

CLINICAL MATERIAL FROM ANOTHER CASE

In the case already described, the first hospitalization had been for illness in which certain unfavorable environmental events had played a stressful role, contributing to a regressive psychophysical shift. Then, subsequent alterations in these reality situations which significantly lessened their stressful character appeared to be important factors in shifting the psychophysical homeosasis in a direction which resulted in quick improvement in the sickness. Later, environmental stress again exerted an unfavorable effect. The influence of the changes in the environment cannot be ignored either in the development and exacerbation of illness or in its remission, because the impact on the psychophysical equilibrium can cause shifts in either direction.

In another case, a patient with a diminished but lingering sense of insecurity following psychotherapy developed rapidly increasing anxiety when confronted by the need to make a decision about an impending business transaction. This involved the buying of a building where he could expand his business, but which involved some element of risk financially. He became mired in indecision, could not speak up at negotiating conferences, and as his tension mounted, he found himself unable to shake off a rather severe cold with sore throat and slightly elevated temperature. He ate and slept poorly. A course of antibiotics was given once without influencing his symptoms particularly. As the illness dragged on, he kept telling himself and others that he was in no condition to make any decisions, though his actual physical incapacity was rather slight. He was again started on a course of another broad-spectrum antibiotic and was on the fourth day of this treatment when he heard that the building had been sold to someone else. Two hours later, when he took his temperature, it was normal and remained so thereafter. The throat symptoms disappeared that day. A reality event had taken the decision out of his hands and resolved the situation in a way he had secretly wished for, but had been unable to verbalize for fear he would be called a "weak sister." He was the only boy and the youngest of six siblings. He had always been concerned about his manliness.

case 12

Epigastric Pain and Indigestion: Symbolic Aspects

CHIEF PRESENTING SYMPTOM

Pain associated with indigestion.

BASIC ANAMNESTIC EXCERPTS

"I've had constant indigestion and heartburn and several severe attacks. When the doctor examined me this morning, he poked me under the ribs (right side); I felt a sharp pain as if he had stuck a knife there. After each meal everything I eat comes back up on me. I got the first attack at home. I thought it was appendicitis. I called the doctor who gave me some pills to take, but I still had indigestion, heartburn, and had to burp. Finally I couldn't even hold cornflakes and milk down. I wouldn't actually throw up, but it would come back up on me. I've had only two attacks on the right side, but I always get pain in the center; the pain is like a gnawing feeling. I get headaches from it. It goes up the back of my neck, making it stiff so I can't lay down or get comfortable. I have to stand up.

"The gnawing pain is there all the time. I press on it, and it feels as if I got something there. It's raw all the time. When I get a belch or a burp off, that's when it relieves me a lot. It kicked up three or four months ago, and the doctor told me it was gallbladder trouble due to greasy foods, so I stayed away from greasy foods. About three weeks after that, I had another attack on the right side. This time the doctor said it might be gallstones or peptic ulcer, though I thought it might be appendix."

A comparison is made between the pain in the side and pain from a cut finger: "When I was 18, I was making a screen, and a piece of copper screening stuck me in the left thumb. I paid no attention to it. The first thing I knew it swelled up. So I went to a doctor who said it was blood poisoning, and he cut it open. That pained me a lot, and I suffered for months. It used to throb away like anything. Other times I hit it with the head of a hammer while doing carpentry. That was while I was learning the trade."

138

Further references to pain and eating are brought up: "My appetite is good at work unless I've had an argument with the boss. It's when I come home that I get these headaches; then I don't feel like eating. It's pounding, throbbing, just like something banging on your head. It comes around the side of the head. It feels as if someone is trying to take my scalp and pull it off. At other times it feels as though it's all filled up, and my head is just going to break. It's worse if I move. I use an ice pack or Vicks rubbed over my neck—all over. It has a cooling effect. I've had headaches in front—my forehead—for several years. I went to an eye specialist. He said I had sinus trouble, so he unplugged my nose and gave me some stuff to put there, and then my eyes never bothered me again. I was also getting the headaches while working in the shop. The nose doctor fixed that—he ran a stick up my nose around the side, both sides."

The reference to "both sides" leads the patient to the subject of appendicitis: "I don't know where or on what side you could get it. I had a buddy who was always going to the drugstore, getting stuff for heartburn and indigestion in the middle of his stomach, and the doctor told him he had appendicitis. My older brother had it also. I was then about 10 or 11. He had a sudden attack of terrible pain. It was scary. They rushed him to the hospital and operated on him. I have three brothers and five sisters. I was in the middle. My youngest brother died when he was a baby; he had breathing trouble. They say it was a combination of pneumonia and diphtheria."

Eating habits are next referred to: "I do most of my eating at home; that is, I try to. Wife prepares the food. It doesn't bother her or the children, but it bothers me. I bring my lunch from home. It's still the same food. It's still lou ... it still acts up on me. I'm a boss carpenter on the inside finish. When the boys don't know what to do, they come to ask me the best way to do it. If anything's done wrong, the big boss comes back, and I'm supposed to correct it. I suppose I could tell the big boss I want to go on the outside, but I guess he would rather keep me inside. I don't say noth ... I mean I guess I'm satisfied to be inside, even though I like fresh air. That's why I could never work in a mill—it was too stuffy. I've always liked to work outside, because it's healthier. I was born in the country (cough), and I'm used to country air (laughing). Father used to work very hard, daytime in the mill, nights in his barber shop, which was part of the house. He's crippled. One leg—the left—is shorter than the other. His mother says he was born that way, and he says no—she must have dropped him when he was a baby. The two of them would have big arguments about it. Once when he was sick, he fell asleep for 24 hours. The doctor said he'd been working too hard."

The patient talks about his attempts to get into military service: "I tried to get into the Navy when I was 17, but they told me I was color-blind. Anyway, my folks were against it. When the war broke out, I signed up with a Seabee construction outfit and worked as a carpenter. I got along pretty well except for one accident. Once I felt drowsy going from home to the Seabee camp; I opened the side window in the car and turned on the radio, but I dozed off. I crashed into a tree and woke up with a bang. They took 13 stitches in the right side of my face. I've got a hole between my eyes, a scar from what they call impetigo which I caught from my youngest brother when I was 13.

"I'm a good, sound sleeper. Last week there was a thunderstorm, lots of noise, but I didn't know anything about it till I woke up the next morning. My wife told me about it. She had gone to look out the window to see if her father and mother had returned home. I'm living with my in-laws. We have no other place to live—the rents are too high. We've been there a year. We had originally lived with them, then moved out, but we didn't find that any better, so they invited us to come back and live with them. I agreed to go back to help out the wife, so she could be on the first floor. But I didn't like the idea. Living with in-laws is not like living alone. You've always got somebody around and can't do just as you please. I avoid arguments by just going to the bedroom and staying there until I get over my anger. Mother-in-law is getting old, and the kids bother her, so I take them into another room to get them out of the way. Father-in-law is away a lot. He's an easygoing chap who never says much. Mother-in-law does the talking. She'll not speak directly to me but to my wife, and my wife will tell me. They both nag a lot."

PSYCHODYNAMIC IMPRESSIONS

In this patient, conflicts about masculinity appear to be more prominent than those involving deeper needs to be taken care of and nurtured. Competitiveness with father or sibling figures alternates with their devaluation and finding of defects in them. There are references to a crippled father who, somehow, has managed his responsibilities for years, and the patient sees himself in such a role. Identification with a brother and a buddy can be noted in terms of gastrointestinal symptoms. The patient's own mother does not appear in the associations; instead surrogates appear—grandmother and mother-in-law and wife. There are, however, negative references to all these. Grandmother is perceived as a crippler; his hostility to her is modified by attempts at humor. Mother-in-law is an interfering, to him cold, domineering figure, and he handles his anger by avoidance and by not being able to "stomach" her. Wife does not give him the right kind of attention and support; she, too, is seen as a domineering, castrating kind of woman. His tension is reflected somatically again in recurrent headaches.

Activation of the patient's symptoms is associated with a number of chronic and at times acute stress factors: At work he has many responsibilities; there he is cast in the role of an older sibling who is accountable to the big boss—father figure—for any mistakes. There are feelings of frustration and both suppressed and repressed anger at this parental surrogate for keeping him inside, limiting his freedom. Psychophysical sensitization of the respiratory tract is manifest less often than that of the gastrointestinal system. Conversion reactions in the form of physical symptoms are more prominent when the defense structures of avoidance and dilution of anger by humor become insufficient.

PHYSICAL HISTORY

The patient entered the hospital with a chief complaint of epigastric pain of three months' duration. He had felt well until three months ago, when he developed a stabbing pain in the right upper quadrant, relieved by an unknown type of pill given by his physician. He then again experienced gnawing epigastric pain which was present without relief for two weeks. This time the pain was relieved by an unknown type of antacid powder given by a pharmacist, but was not relieved by food. He noticed frequent post prandial eructations with flatus. There was no specific food intolerance. The epigastric pain was associated with constant headaches, radiating from the back of the neck to the back of the head, and lasting four to six hours. These, however, disappeared in the week previous to his admission. The patient claimed to have lost 20 pounds in the three months prior to his admission, though appetite and intake remained normal. The past history, systems review, and family history were essentially noncontributory.

PHYSICAL EXAMINATION

Essentially negative, except for tenderness in the right upper quadrant and epigastrium on deep palpation.

LABORATORY DATA

Essentially negative.

ROENTGENOGRAMS

Chest, gastrointestinal series, and gallbladder studies revealed no abnormalities.

HOSPITAL COURSE

The patient was placed on a Gastric III, and later on a bland diet, with moderate relief of symptoms. He remained afebrile, and the hospital course was uneventful. The patient was discharged with moderate symptomatic improvement.

DISCHARGE DIAGNOSIS

Anxiety reaction, improved.

COMMENT

The physical symptoms are frequently linked with associations involving references to attack, castration, penetration, intake and expulsion, and engorgement. There is thus a considerable degree of sexual symbolism in the interview material. There also appears to be a dilution or reduction of intensity of the aggressive drives so that they do not exert any marked effect through somatic or other pathways. In addition, no single organ or organ system is involved. No physical disease has developed thus far in this patient, though somatic complaints have been long-standing and numerous. The remarks made under *Comment* in Case 7, concerning pain in neurotic individuals in whom anxiety and conversion manifestations are prominent, apply in this case also.

CASE 12

CHIEF PRESENTING SYMPTOM	Pain associated with indigestion
SENSORIMOTOR CONFIGURATIONS	Sensory configurations

Pain, interoceptive

Linked with associations suggesting pregnancy fantasies and symbolically sexualized passive-feminine relationships to male authority figures

Motor configurations

Activity, being attacked

Connected with hostile, competitive references to parental figures and concern about symbolic retaliatory castration by them, especially the women

SOMATIC IDENTIFICATION	*Older brother*	Appendicitis pain in childhood
	Younger brother	Impetigo in childhood
SENSITIZED ORGAN SYSTEM	Gastrointestinal Respiratory Head	

STRESS (*surface meaning*)	Work problems Mother-in-law and wife nagging
STRESS (*dynamic significance*)	Cast in role of older sibling accountable to big-boss father with recurrent frustration, competition in connection with this figure. Exposed to castrating behavior of wife and her mother
DEFENSES	Humor Avoidance Introjective—projective combinations

AFFECTS	*Intensity*	*Pathway of expression*
Anxiety	+++	Ideational, somatic equivalent
Depression	+	Ideational
Hostility	++	Numerous somatic outlets, ideational

OTHER FACTORS	Pregenital components—especially oral, but of secondary influence Conflicts about masculinity more prominent Strong libidinal drives Preoccupation with body
HOMEOSTATIC SHIFT(S)	Dispersal of somatization against numerous rather than one somatic target area Regressive shifts under modifying influence of libidinal drives
DIAGNOSIS	Anxiety reaction, improved

case 13

Dyspnea Related to Anniversary Stress

CHIEF PRESENTING SYMPTOM

Shortness of breath.

BASIC ANAMNESTIC EXCERPTS

"It's gotten to a point where I can't do any kind of work. I'd work for 10 or 15 minutes and then have to sit down. I get short of breath, especially when I get a pain. And of course I know I have a murmur. My own doctor told me. When I'm working, I'm out two, three, or four days a week sometimes. I'm lucky that I work for my father, and he gives me a little soft job. If I was working for somebody else, he'd drop me. You see, I can come in just when I want to."

The next associative references are to the heart: "Often I can feel it pumping hard. I don't know whether I hurt myself or what I've done. I remember one time I fell overboard while I was working on a crane on the waterfront. My co-worker who controlled the hawser let go, and I went down between the pier and the crane. I was in the water 20 minutes before I came up. I kept thinking he wanted to get rid of me. Right after that, I was getting some awful pains in my chest, and for a week I was coughing up a little blood. But I was paying no attention to it. Then later it started bothering me—my heart—so I had an electrocardiogram taken. What bothers me is how bad is it. It seems to be getting worse. Often at work, I'll take my pulse, it'll move one, then three, then skip, then one, then skip. That's when I start losing my breath."

Further elaboration of dyspnea follows: "I can't seem to take a deep breath and get enough air in. When I'm working and that happens, I can feel my heart pounding like a son of a bitch. If I stay home a few days, it curbs it. The heart still skips, but I don't get shortness of breath after two–three days' rest. But the first day I go back to work, there's the short-ness of breath, and a couple of hours later, I get a pain in the back of the

144

head. I get a lot of sharp headaches, but they don't last long, just a couple of seconds. I also get sharp pains in the wrists and ankles. If I were working for somebody else besides my father, I'd be starving. For the past four years it's cost me between 15 and 20 dollars a week for medicines. I first noticed the shortness of breath six years ago, but it didn't bother me. Then when I did go to the doctor, it was on account of the pain in my chest. He noticed my heart was skipping, and he gave me digitalis pills. I was taking them for more than a year. Then I swung over to something else. When I first noticed my symptoms, I figured it was an irritation and let it go at that."

The shortness of breath is brought into further causal relation to work: "I drive trucks, load and unload them. If I drive a truck too long, I'll get that shortness of breath. I can feel a pounding, then all of a sudden I'll get a little catch in the throat. Sometimes it feels like a chill going through your body. It seems to travel right down from my head to my feet. If I work three days in a row, I'll then be so tired I'll be half dead the next morning and won't be able to get up. My wind used to be good when I first began to work for father at the age of 17. Before that I worked summers in a fish-packing plant, and also played a lot of football and baseball as a youngster. No trouble with my heart or wind then."

References to his home situation follow: "When I take time off, I stay in the house, lying around, watching TV. Sometimes my wife makes me go visiting. My mother-in-law lives on the third floor of another house. I go up there, and when I do, I'm dead. I have to get my wind. My own place is on the first floor. That's why I bought a house. Even when I rest, my heart skips, too, but it doesn't bother me. The only time I take my own pulse is when I would feel it throw a couple, go on, throw another couple. After I've eaten too much, there's a lot of skipping. I have to check my pulse to see how irregular it is. Now instead of eating three big meals, I eat five small ones. My wife will give me just so much. She knows I've got a heart condition, and that I have to rest at home."

There is next an elaboration of associations about his family: "Besides my wife, I have one child—a boy of three and a half. I had two, but the other one died. He had a congenital heart condition when he was born. He was the first. He died just about a year ago—March 17. (Patient admitted March 13.) The specialist told me he didn't expect the boy to live a year anyway. The condition could be helped by an operation when he was three years old, but they couldn't cure him. If the baby cried he would turn blue, change color. When he died, he went right before our eyes. Of course, I knew he'd be going from the day he was born. It never bothered me, but it bothered my wife. She didn't know from the beginning like I did; only after six months. She took it hard."

There is a return to concern over the meaning of the symptoms: "The doctor on the outside heard a murmur and found the heart skipping. That's why he sent me in here. They haven't found any murmur here. You know, this condition has never bothered me as much as it's done in this past year. I've just noticed it more, can feel every move of my heart. While I've never passed out, I get an awful tired feeling. I just can't seem to get enough breath into me. It feels clogged up. I never had that as a youngster. I was just underweight. I worked to help out at home; there were 10 children, and I was one of the oldest. All the others were alright. My parents, too, though my mother used to complain of fluttering in her heart because she had so much to do. Now I'm the sick one."

PSYCHODYNAMIC IMPRESSIONS

Narcissism and preoccupation with body are prominent throughout the interview. As a youngster, the patient felt lost and inferior among the large number of siblings in his family. He began early to try to stand out by his activities, at first in sports and later at work while he was still in high school. The physical trauma that he sustained seven years before hospitalization apparently was minimal, but triggered off psychological responses, in which the actual experience was distorted as an attack (castration) by a hostile competitor. The heart then became the organ of great preoccupation and concern, with symbolic representations, particularly of a displaced phallus with its sexual and aggressive connotations. It also came to represent a defect somatically identified with his mother and also with his own dead child. The interview material further indicates that he, when he was younger, was much concerned about his body, and that this was linked with considerable hostile feelings directed toward the mother who had so many others to pay attention to besides him. The father appears as a protective and solicitous parent, almost maternal, but vaguely defined in the associations.

Anxiety has become established currently as a predominant affect and is intermingled with hostile reactions which are, however, of a lesser degree of intensity. These affective responses are manifested frequently in the form of somatic equivalents. In addition to symptoms in the cardiovascular system there is a concomitant disturbance in the respiratory tract with concern about losing his breath, related particularly to activity which has anxious and hostile implications.

It should be noted that there is an anniversary factor involved here. One year before admission, his firstborn child (whom he seems to reject as not being his because he was defective) died of a congenital heart condition. The patient deals with his emotional response to this by denial, masking what appears to be an underlying depression.

PHYSICAL HISTORY

This patient enters with the chief complaint of having a heart murmur, known to be present for about five years. Following an accident in which he fell overboard while in the Navy seven years before, he began to notice the irregular recurrence of sharp pains over the right anterior chest. A few months later these seemed to become more frequent and were felt as sharp, knife-like pains in the right second and third anterior interspace, which would last two to three minutes, not radiate, and be accompanied by a gasping for breath, but no sweating. They would occur seven or eight times per day, not related to meals, position, activity, excitement, or type of food. They never occurred at night. Simultaneously, he began to notice mild exertional dyspnea after long walks or after three or four flights of stairs.

He then visited his local physician, who told the patient he had a heart murmur and that his heart was skipping. He treated the patient with digitalis, two pills a day for eight months, then one per day for about five months. At that time there was no ankle edema, orthopnea, nor nocturnal dyspnea. However, there have been palpitations noted for about five years, usually at night after lying down. There have also been times when his heartbeat was rapid, associated with shortness of breath, but these always subside spontaneously. Digitalis seemed to make his dyspnea worse. The chest pains have persisted, although less frequently, and now may occur at work but not when resting or quiet at home. In the past year, dyspnea and fatigue have become marked, and he has missed an average of several days per week from work. There is no history of previous rheumatic fever, hypertension, and no chronic cough, previous pleurisy, or pneumonia.

PHYSICAL EXAMINATION

Within normal limits except for an occasional extrasystole.

LABORATORY DATA

Entirely negative.

ROENTGENOGRAMS

Chest: There is deformity of the left third rib in the posterior axillary line which may be due to old fracture.

ELECTROCARDIOGRAM

Left axis deviation, normal sinus rhythm with a rate of 100, frequent auricular and ventricular premature beats, the latter from varying foci.

PR interval .16, QRS interval .09. The tracing was interpreted as being within normal limits.

HOSPITAL COURSE

The patient had no disturbing symptoms during his period of hospitalization and remained afebrile. It was explained to him that it was perfectly normal for a young adult of his age to have extrasystoles, and that this did not mean heart disease was present. A cardiac consultant concurred. The patient was advised that there was no organic basis for his dyspnea and discharged on no medication.

DISCHARGE DIAGNOSIS

Neurocirculatory asthenia. Untreated, unchanged.

COMMENT

In this case, an anniversary turned out to be a contributory stress. Anniversaries such as birthdays, deaths, dates of traumatic events, may well be within the awareness of the individual, but their unconscious or symbolic significance is usually not. In other instances, the event itself is "overlooked" or repressed and consequently not mentioned directly, so that it may be difficult to even begin to connect the individual's current reactions to it. These reactions may be chiefly in the form of psychological manifestations or may appear as physical symptoms. Both kinds may be brief or prolonged, depending on many variables, one in particular being the immediate and related (though not obvious) environmental stresses which might act in varying degree to potentiate a response. The anniversary may precipitate, at times, the onset of a severe mental decompensation. It may exacerbate an ongoing neurosis (or psychosis). It may also signal the beginning of developing organic disease or be closely associated with exacerbations of already present physical illness.

In this patient, the anniversary was temporarily related to the culmination of an escalating anxiety about what was wrong with him and about his ability to meet his everyday responsibilities. The particular locus of the physiological dysfunction, namely, the conduction mechanisms of the heart, appears to be determined by both a psychophysical constitutional predisposition and developmental–environmental factors. The persistence of the symptoms may, of course, be due not only to major stress with its possible long-lasting effect, but it may also be and often is related to everyday lesser stresses which, though using various pathways for discharge of tension, may then settle into a particular or prevailing somatic one.

Duncan et al. (1950) in their study of 25 unselected cases of cardiac arrhythmias noted that 50 percent did not have organic heart disease.

Certain psychological traits occurred significantly often in the group. These included hostility inadequately or not at all expressed, compulsive tendencies, particularly rigidity, perfectionism and orderliness, unusual ambition, and chronic anxiety of long duration. The patient's ability to adjust to stress was interfered with by his rigidity, and it was during such periods that the arrhythmia was apt to develop. This was especially true if there were concomitant physical factors such as activity, sudden postural change, sneezing, or coughing. It would seem that the work of the heart may be increased by exertion, and in these patients the arrhythmia could be brought on by exercise. More prolonged, even chronic demands on the heart may be due to persistent, unresolved, repressed emotional conflicts.

CASE 13

CHIEF PRESENTING SYMPTOM	Shortness of breath
SENSORIMOTOR CONFIGURATIONS	Sensory configurations

Pain

Linked especially with heart, focus of pre-occupation and concern, and with symbolic sexual and aggressive impulses, the latter particularly directed at mother

Motor configurations

Working

Connected with pumping, skipping, pounding, throbbing, and anxious associations about physical integrity and death, which serve as basis for passive retreat from responsibilities

SOMATIC IDENTIFICATION	*Child*	Congenital heart disease resulting in death one year ago (Direct associative connections; constitutional factors)
	Mother	Heart flutter (Direct associative connections; constitutional factors)
SENSITIZED ORGAN SYSTEM		Cardiovascular—heart
		Respiratory tract
STRESS (*surface meaning*)		Anniversary of death of firstborn child

STRESS (*dynamic significance*)	Escalating anxiety about adequacy and ability to meet everyday responsibilities reinforced by recollections of the cardiac death of child
DEFENSES	Overactivity—school, sports, work Denial

AFFECTS	Intensity	Pathway of expression
Anxiety	+++	Affective, ideational, and in form of somatic equivalents
Depression	++	Ideational—but masked
Hostility	++	Somatization

OTHER FACTORS	Body narcissism prominent, but secondary
HOMEOSTATIC SHIFT(S)	Affective and ideational systems unable to contain mounting anxiety, resulting in a greater shift toward somatization responses
DIAGNOSIS	Neurocirculatory asthenia, untreated, unchanged

case 14

Stomach Pain: Psychological Aspects
of Clinical and Laboratory Procedures

CHIEF PRESENTING SYMPTOM

Pain in stomach.

BASIC ANAMNESTIC EXCERPTS

"The pain in my stomach is a constant one. I feel cold—freezing. I'm on edge. I'm resigning my job. The pain is vicious—so vicious I want to tear it out. It gets so bad that I feel like hitting my head against the table. I get very little relief from milk, no matter how often I drink it. Besides I've got a new baby; it was born about six weeks ago, and the regular routine of the house has been upset. It has to be fed, it cries so much, keeps me awake at night. Well, that doesn't lead to any healing of what's causing my pain.

"I've been on constant suction since coming in. That relieves the pressure, and controls the pain better. That's something I couldn't have at home, even though my wife is a nurse."

The next references are to the onset of the symptom 10 years before: "I was overseas in England when I noticed these pains coming on, and getting more and more severe. I didn't like being so far away from home. The food didn't taste right, and anyway, I was under a lot of tension with a hard-driving set of fellows around me. When I was in high school and beginning college, I had what you'd call a nervous stomach, butterflies, you know. That would happen especially before exams, and also if I had to do any public speaking. When I went to midshipman school, there was terrific pressure and competition, and I'd feel it in my stomach the whole four months I spent there. The whole thing blew up when I got this severe abdominal pain. They rushed me to a hospital and told me I had a ruptured appendix. That was a tricky appendix, deeply imbedded they called it, and it was quite a business getting it out. I thought afterward that was the end of my troubles, but when I went overseas, I began to get these stomach pains like I have now. It seemed as if the only thing that would help would be rest and being away from my assignment.

"When the pain is at its worst, it's like gnawing, something chewing away inside. I was never a big eater but always on the go. Mother paid special attention to what I ate. My two younger sisters who had no trouble eating would get frankfurts, but mother made sure what I ate was good, like steak. When I was six years old, father died. They told me he had cancer of the stomach. He lost a lot of weight, couldn't eat; in fact, mother had to feed him, and all he could take was small amounts—and just a few different things. He suffered a lot toward the end from terrible pain. Mother would take me to visit him in the city hospital. I was there in the room with father when he died. (At this point in the interview, the patient put a forefinger into each nostril, but a trickle nevertheless came out, and his eyes appeared suffused.) I remember the day of the funeral—it was in a pouring rain. Afterwards, mother had to go to work, and I had to get my own food until she came back in the evening. There were plenty of lonely, hungry days for me and my sisters then."

The patient's associations turn once again to the present and current tensions: "I'm a law school graduate. Now I'm trying to get my practice going, but things have been slow. I'm a married man—got married four years ago—and have family responsibilities. I undertook to work also as a night clerk at the post office. It's been quite a grind for me—a 140-pound ulcer (case) who hasn't been eating. I've handed in my resignation at the post office. I can't keep up that pace. If my wife has to, she'll work. Money problems made it necessary for me to move back to mother's house after I passed the bar—and I, we have been there ever since. Mother now has a bad heart. To complicate things, she's had an ulcer on her right leg for the past ten years. It started after a bad bang on the leg. They know it will never get better, but they say it isn't malignant. From time to time the leg swells up and gives her quite a lot of pain. She's a tall woman, over 200 pounds; she carries a lot of excess weight, really too much, but she's so fond of eating. I take after the little shrimp of an uncle who lived with us after father's death; father himself was on the short side. My sisters are big. But I fill up so easily. I have a queer quirk—want to see something left on the plate. I have been talked to about food by friend and foe, by family and wife. But food is not appealing to me. I've survived on milk over the last five years."

PSYCHODYNAMIC IMPRESSIONS

Long-standing intense dependency has been a striking feature of this patient's emotional life. The defenses against this have been principally in the form of overactivity and denial, and have not succeeded in adequately containing the basically oral needs. Eating and digesting have been functions which have become emotionally charged and sensitized since childhood, with a somatization response focused on the gastrointestinal tract. Father appears as a distant figure, but is principally associated with recollections of disturbances in eating, severe pain, weight loss, and finally death due to stomach cancer during the patient's oedipal years. Two younger sisters represent rivals for the mother's attention, but the mother herself is remembered in a highly ambivalent light. She paid special attention to his feeding during early childhood but later was often away from the home, leaving him lonely and hungry. The hostile aspect of the ambivalence toward her and mother surrogates such as his wife is activated when current environmental circumstances accentuate his dependency needs. Stress situations have extended over a considerable period of time and have included competitive involvement, separation from home and mother who now has a chronic leg ulcer, need to maintain two jobs at the same time, and most recently, wife's pregnancy and arrival of the first baby. The latter situation, with attention obviously being withdrawn from him by his wife, a nurse, especially reinforced his strong oral needs. Under these conditions, an intense and rather primitive type of hostility was activated in him, insufficiently discharged through affective and ideational channels, and consequently diverted to a somatic target. This was the stomach, whose functions appear to have been previously sensitized to emotional stress.

PHYSICAL HISTORY

This patient was admitted with a history of intermittent postprandial epigastric gain, beginning 10 years ago. X-ray studies on several occasions allegedly revealed a duodenal ulcer. The pain continued relatively unabated through the years, but the patient lost little or no time from work and was not hospitalized in recent years until the present. He has rarely gone over a month without symptoms, in spite of his following an excellent dietary program, with frequent, interval feedings. For six to nine months prior to entry, the epigastric pain increased in severity, kept the patient awake many nights, and commenced to radiate through to the back. Banthine and other antispasmodics were of little help. No history, however, of obstruction, hemorrhage, or perforation. The patient had always been a very active person, and recently had started to practice law as well as continuing night work as a postal clerk. Past history reveals perforated appendix about eight years ago; otherwise noncontributory.

PHYSICAL EXAMINATION

During examination the patient was tense and hyperactive. The entire examination was negative except for moderate tenderness in the right upper quadrant of the abdomen with some tenderness on percussion over the right posterior chest.

LABORATORY DATA

Hemogram revealed hemoglobin 15 g with hematocrit of 46 percent. White blood cell count varied from 18,000 on admission to 9,900 two weeks later. Nonprotein nitrogen: 33 mg; chlorides: 95 mEq; CO_2 combining power: 24.7 volumes/100cc. Urinalysis negative.

ROENTGENOGRAMS

Gastrointestinal series: a large duodenal ulcer was clearly demonstrable.

HOSPITAL COURSE

Patient was initially treated with bland diet, bed rest, antispasmodics and sedation. During the first four days, there was no response at all. Consequently, on the fifth hospital day, constant gastric suction was begun and continued for three days during which time he was given parenteral fluids. This afforded considerable relief which continued for several days after the constant suction was omitted. Diet was gradually increased to a Gastric III, and after a week on this diet, during which time the patient was asymptomatic, he was sent out on leave of absence.

While at home he continued to follow a strict diet, but despite this, had an exacerbation of pain so that he had to return to the hospital after five days. The consensus was that the patient's condition was "intractable" and that he possibly also had some posterior wall penetration. He was seen in surgical consultation and gastrectomy was advised. One month after his original admission, a subtotal gastrectomy with anterior gastroenterestomy was done under continuous spinal anesthesia. The patient did well postoperatively, except for a persistent headache which initially failed to respond to caffeine sodium benzoate, dramamine, codeine, abdominal binder, and special fluid replacement. On the seventh postoperative day, the headache was much improved. The skin sutures were removed, the wound was well-healed. The patient was tolerating a six-meal bland diet quite well. Several days later he was discharged.

DISCHARGE DIAGNOSIS

Duodenal ulcer, intractable. Treated surgically by subtotal gastrectomy with anterior gastroenterostomy, improved.

COMMENT

A special clinical procedure was employed early in the patient's treatment. He was put on constant gastric suction and parenteral fluids, which seemed to afford him considerable relief from symptoms. While this procedure seemed to affect physiological functions beneficially, its psychological significance for the patient and, in turn, its impact on his psychophysical state should not be overlooked. First, being in a hospital and away from outside stresses and responsibilities could be helpful in relieving tensions. The considerable and skillful nursing attention he received might have been for him a source of much-needed emotional supplies. The suction, apart from its mechanical effect, could also have had a particular psychological significance for the patient. If stomach contents symbolically represented for him offending (human) objects, their removal might bring an emotional relief which in turn would be reflected somatically. There is the further possibility that still other symbolisms of a sexual nature were also involved in the intubation procedure.

Clinical and laboratory procedures have both a realistic and symbolic significance for the individuals that undergo them. It is a well-known fact that some seemingly healthy (at least physically) young males may faint when a venipuncture is about to be done. Acute anxiety associated with an activated sexualized fantasy of being attacked may cause the syncope. Of course, a hypodermic needle and syringe are a hypodermic needle and syringe realistically, but the use of these instruments on some individuals may have an unrealistic, symbolic meaning for them. A patient in analysis had his routine annual physical checkup one day in his internist's office. The examination proceeded without incident until examination of the prostate was begun. The patient became faint and almost "passed out." In a subsequent analytic hour he referred to the procedure in the form of a slip—"when I had the gynecol . . . I mean, prostate examination." This passive-feminine man brought in further associations linking the procedure with a homosexual assault; he had had occasional masturbatory fantasies of playing the role of the (anally) receiving woman in homosexual relationships. Under the influence of neurotic factors, nongenital areas may become sexualized, insertion of instruments into various orifices may have a sadistic significance, medication may be seen as poisonous, and so on.

Margolin (1951) in an intensive study of a 22-year-old, Negro college girl with gastrostomy found that organ functioning is markedly influenced by unconscious mental processes and stressed that this must be taken into consideration in physiological and pharmacological experimentation during which psychological stress can be or is evoked. The individual's psychological reactions can affect the physical data being collected. In this patient, studies were made of her gastric motility, color of gastric mucosa, volume of gastric secretion, hydrochloric acid and pepsin concentrations. The subject's emotional reactions to her physical manipulation and instrumentation were found to have significant unconscious components: (1) The cleaning and handling of the gastrostomy was both pleasurable in a definitely erotic way and also frightening. This phenomenon has been observed in patients with colostomies and ileostomies. (2) In interviews, when intense oral fantasies occurred, casting the interviewer in the role of a mother figure being devoured, the gastric secretions welled out of the gastrostomy, soaking dressings, clothing, and couch. The more conscious content was the need to be taken care of, but the significance of the unconscious counterpart was that of an unsatiable appetite. (3) As hostile impulses varied in origin, aim, and object there were concomitant changes in the physiological activity of the stomach, ranging from synchronous to random, asynchronous fluctuations. Margolin feels that observation–interpretation of patterns of gastric activity is like the analysis of very young children unable to communicate verbally in an effective way. It is similar to a nonverbal symbol of communication.

CASE 14

CHIEF PRESENTING SYMPTOM	Pain in stomach
SENSORIMOTOR CONFIGURATIONS	Sensory configurations
	Pain, temperature, interoceptive
	Associated with feelings of deprivation, sensitivity to separation, and competitive tensions
	Motor configurations
	Gnawing, tearing out
	Linked to activation of intense hostility at frustration of powerful oral needs by mother and mother surrogates, with subsequent strong guilt
SOMATIC IDENTIFICATION	*Father* Size, cancer of stomach death, patient age six (Direct, organ constitutional)
	Mother Ulcer pain of right leg for 10 years
	Uncle Size
SENSITIZED ORGAN SYSTEM	Gastrointestinal—stomach
STRESS (*surface meaning*)	Competitive involvement at school, in military service with separation problems, work overload, and most recently wife's pregnancy and arrival of first baby

STRESS (*dynamic significance*)   Reinforcement of oral dependent needs, generating intense hostility, added to competitive hostility

DEFENSES   Overactivity
Denial

AFFECTS   *Intensity*   *Pathway of expression*

Anxiety   ++   some ideational plus somatic equivalents

Depression   +++   some affective and ideational, somatization

Hostility   +++   slight ideational, somatization

OTHER FACTORS   Long-standing intense dependency—oral needs
Trauma of father's death—oedipal years
Ambivalence toward mother

HOMEOSTATIC SHIFT(S)   Activation of oral dependency needs inadequately defended, causing shift to marked somatization response

DIAGNOSIS   Duodenal ulcer, intractable. Treated surgically by subtotal gastrectomy with anterior gastroenterostomy, improved

case 15

Cerebral Embolism in an Uncommunicative Patient

Patient is mute, unresponsive to mild stimuli. He is in bed, with eyes closed and left leg drawn up. Occasionally he puts his left hand under his head, scratching. An interview was not possible.

DIAGNOSIS

Rheumatic heart disease with mitral stenosis, mitral insufficiency, auricular fibrillation, and left cerebral embolism.

CASE 15

CHIEF PRESENTING SYMPTOM	Mute patient
SENSORIMOTOR CONFIGURATIONS	No data
SOMATIC IDENTIFICATION	No data
AFFECTS	Patient mute
DIAGNOSIS	Rheumatic heart disease with mitral stenosis, mitral insufficiency, auricular fibrillation, and left cerebral embolism

case 16

Sore Throat: Symbolism of Body Organs

CHIEF PRESENTING SYMPTOM

Sore throat.

BRIEF ANAMNESIS PSYCHODYNAMICALLY INTERPRETED

The patient's severe sore throat and hoarseness make for a brief interview: Soreness is at first connected with fever and a general feeling of uneasiness one week before admission. The next associations deal with chest operations done in the recent past and most specifically with one "to fill in a dead space." Intense hostility against doctors "because they're bunglers" is revealed in the content. The associations then refer again to his throat and to enlarged tonsils. These have not been taken out because the doctors said about them: "Let the dead rest." This second reference to "dead" leads eventually to associations about the patient's deceased parents. Both died when the patient was nine years old. The father died first, of a disease of the lungs, probably pneumonia. "He was awfully sick for just a short time with fever and chest pain." The mother had "woman's trouble," was operated on "down below," and shortly thereafter died, also. Thus the space in the chest and the two tonsils are referred to in the verbal associations of the patient in such a way as to suggest they are symbolic somatic representations of parental figures. These body areas have been "objectified" or "personified" in the patient's thinking.

The symptom of sore throat then leads to connections with pain in chest, first experienced several years ago. An anniversary association follows. Two years ago almost exactly, the patient had been hospitalized for pain and night sweats. A shadow and a cavity were found in the X-ray of the chest. This, however, was preceded by an appendectomy: "They (doctors) took them (appendix) out too soon." The figure two appears several times. Two doctors who had been buddies of his back in elementary school advised the operation. The appendix thus also appears in the patient's think-

159

ing as an objectified organ expressed in the plural sense and a symbolic somatic representation of the parental figures. There are associated recollections of a deep sense of loss—of feeling weak, helpless, and alone, as a child. There were seven children, and he was the second youngest. An older sister took over the care of the family, and there were "rough times." The appendectomy was followed by chest pains and loss of strength—a somatic recapitulation of the patient's reaction to his parents' deaths.

The interview ended with references to soreness, irritation, and chronic marital difficulties, more marked since he has been out of work and especially in the week prior to admission when his wife threatened to leave. There are no children. Here the patient's intense hostility is only poorly masked by a smiling facade.

PHYSICAL HISTORY

This is the patient's third hospital admission, this time with chief complaint of sore throat of two days' duration. The patient had been originally hospitalized two years ago for moderately advanced pulmonary tuberculosis, bilateral; a right thoracoplasty was subsequently performed. He was again hospitalized two months before the present admission for repair of a chest wall defect. The present history revealed two days of severe sore throat with difficulty in swallowing, fever, and chilly sensations, but no shaking chills. A chronic cough, productive of a small amount of sputum, remains unchanged from the past.

PHYSICAL EXAMINATION

Temperature 102°F. Pulse 100. Blood pressure 130/82. Patient is a well-developed, well-nourished man in some distress. Tonsils were markedly hypertrophied and reddened, with exudation present in the crypts; the exudate was not confluent. The pharynx was reddened. Chest showed a right thoracoplasty scar with two drains in place in the right axilla. Lungs: Post-tussic rales at the right apex; left lung was negative. The remainder of the physical examination was unchanged from previous admissions.

LABORATORY DATA

Hemoglobin 12.4 g with hematocrit 38 percent. Sedimentation rate 31 mm per hr. White blood cell count: 11,950 with 61 segmented cells, 10 band cells, 22 lymphocytes, 5 monocytes and 2 eosinophiles. Urinalysis showed slight trace of albumin, rare white blood cells per high power field and 3 to 5 red blood cells per high power field. Throat culture showed beta and alpha streptococci. Smear and culture for diphtheria bacillus: negative. Sputum for acid-fast bacilli: negative.

ROENTGENOGRAM

Chest plate showed no tuberculosis activity and no change from previous discharge film.

HOSPITAL COURSE

Patient was given a course of penicillin and his temperature rapidly dropped to normal and remained so. He was seen in consultation by ENT service after his tonsillitis had cleared; they felt that tonsillectomy should be deferred at this time. The patient was discharged, to return for follow-up to thoracic surgery clinic.

DISCHARGE DIAGNOSES

1. Acute follicular tonsillitis and pharyngitis, treated, improved.
2. Pulmonary tuberculosis, moderately advanced, reinfectious type, bilateral, inactive, Class IV.
3. Wound defect of the right lateral chest wall secondary to thoracoplasy. Unchanged, untreated.

COMMENT

In the individual's thinking an organ or organ system may become a symbolized internal representation of an external object (person) emotionally significant for him. This will occur particularly under conditions when the object has been lost or loss is threatened. Then a narcissistic regression occurs in which psychological processes are mobilized in an attempt to recover or hold on to the lost object via recollected sensorimotor configurations originally (in early childhood) linking it with a particular body part. Thus, references to body areas and parts may appear in a patient's associations in a personified or objectified form. When a particular organ becomes a focus of attention and particularly if it is involved in a disease process, it may be referred to as "she," "he," or "they," representing the significant family figures or their surrogates. This usually occurs without the patient's being aware of the connection.

CASE 16

CHIEF PRESENTING SYMPTOM   Sore throat

SENSORIMOTOR CONFIGURATIONS   Sensory configurations

Pain

Associated with recollections of losing both parents within a short time of each other, and frustrated efforts to get lasting substitutes, especially through marriage

Motor configurations

	Operative interventions
	Linked with hostility toward doctors who are described as failing to restore his physical integrity and, symbolically, his sense of wholeness
SOMATIC IDENTIFICATION	*Father* Lung disease death, patient aged nine (Direct, organ constitutional for earlier illness—TB)
	Mother "Female trouble" operation, same time
SENSITIZED ORGAN SYSTEM	Respiratory—lungs, nasopharynx
STRESS (*surface meaning*)	Chronic—a continuing marital crisis; most recently wife has threatened to leave him; job-finding difficulties
STRESS (*dynamic significance*)	Threat of being left by wife (representing a parental figure), mobilizing intense hostile dependent feelings
DEFENSES	Smiling facade

AFFECTS	*Intensity*	*Pathway of expression*
Anxiety	+	Ideational
Depression	+++ chronically exaggerated	Somatization, some ideational
Hostility	+++ chronically exaggerated	Somatization

OTHER FACTORS	None elicited
HOMEOSTATIC SHIFT(S)	Additional intensification of hostility insufficiently defended against by previous defensive alignment
DIAGNOSES	a) Acute follicular tonsillitis and pharyngitis, treated, improved; b) Pulmonary tuberculosis, moderately advanced; reinfectious type, bilateral, inactive, Class IV; c) Wound defect of the right lateral chest wall secondary to thoracoplasty, untreated, unchanged

CLINICAL MATERIAL FROM ANOTHER CASE

A patient being treated for a bleeding peptic ulcer kept referring to his stomach as "she." When he found the symptoms of gnawing epigastric pain to be particularly disturbing, he talked about how much trouble "she" (the stomach) was giving him. He was an only child, with a deeply ambivalent attachment to his ailing mother with whom he lived, though he was now a man of 40. He had never married and after some desultory attempts at dating, had led a rather restricted social life, spending only occasional evenings out "with the boys." He had recently been promoted in his job and with the assumption of new responsibilities had become anxious about his ability to work. Though he tried to act independently, he found himself once again having to turn to his mother for guidance and advice, being at the same time resentful that he needed to do so. His ulcer, which had been quiescent for years, again began to trouble him. The epigastric pain and bleeding could not be controlled by a medical regimen and a subtotal gastrectomy was done. During convalescence from surgery, the patient kept remarking that his stomach symptoms had disappeared, but he wondered why he now had begun to have severe headaches which he also referred to as "she," without being aware of its significance. This physical manifestation had not been present for many years, in fact, since childhood, when it had followed severe temper tantrums. His mother had had attacks of migraine when he was growing up, but had been free of them for some time now. No organic basis was established for the patient's headaches. Surgical intervention had in fact removed most of his stomach, which had been the seat of physical pathology. However, it had also been a target organ for psychological tensions which had not become significantly modified as a result of the operation. He was still locked in an activated dependency conflict with strong ambivalence toward his mother. It could be postulated that the emotionally significant object, symbolically represented in the stomach, had been eliminated in the psychological sense, also. But this state of affairs was a temporary one only. Another internal representation, also somatic, had been substituted via the headaches. The important object had been somatically relocated.

The development of new symptoms following gastrectomy has already been referred to (Browning and Houseworth). It may be further noted here that of the 30 patients so treated, a follow-up 12 to 18 months later revealed that a total of six had developed migraine headaches.

case 17
Stomach Pain and Depression

CHIEF PRESENTING SYMPTOM

Stomach pain.

BASIC ANAMNESTIC EXCERPTS

"This trouble began about two and a half months ago. I first noticed it in the middle of my stomach. I had pain there and would throw up. I noticed my weight going down, and I must have lost about 30 pounds. I've been feeling wonderful since getting into the hospital and being on a milk and cream diet.

"The pain can be sharp—so sharp that I feel nauseated, or it can be grinding and dull, and that has the same effect. I didn't know what it was. My wife told me to get examined on account of the weight loss. You see, my father has cancer, and it might be going through her mind that I could have it, too. He has cancer of the bowel and was operated on about three months ago. Before that he was having trouble moving his bowels, and then he had terrible pains. He told me that he wouldn't want to go through such pains again. The doctor didn't tell him he had cancer. Since the operation he's been at home, feeling better and trying to take it easy. As I remember it, he just started to feel quite sick about nine months ago. He hasn't been well for quite a few years with sugar diabetes. It was first discovered when I was away overseas. He was put on a diet and insulin. He'd never been sick before, worked 45 years in one place, becoming a foreman in a rubber factory."

There is a reference to financial stress: "If my wife hadn't suggested it, I wouldn't have taken the time off to come into the hospital. It's tough living—we need money, and if I'm away from work, there just won't be any. I've been an assistant manager at a restaurant for the past three years, before that I did factory work. But there hasn't been much money in it. I've been married three years, and we have a little baby—a boy 16 months old. I've been working right up to the day I came into the hospital, except for three days I took off when I was throwing up so much that I felt weak and dizzy if I stood up."

164

Previous illnesses or fears about being sick or physically defective are recalled and to some extent minimized: "I was never on sick call in the service. The only time I was in a hospital before was for tonsils when I was 18 years old. I was in high school then, studying hard and got a little run down, so the doctor told me that the tonsils, which were swollen, should come out, and then he gave me iron injections because the white corpuscles outnumbered the red. But that wasn't anything to be concerned about, and I was soon alright. As a youngster I had measles—I remember the rash and very soon after that I had mumps; my face was all swollen up. My mother took care of me. I was a healthy, active kid, otherwise, always liked sports like football and baseball. I was heavy then, but now I'm the smallest in weight of anyone in the family outside of my two sisters. My two brothers both weigh more than me. I'm the youngest; they used to tease me about being the baby. I always had a good appetite. Right now I just have coffee and cigarettes. I've stopped eating in the last three or four months, but here, since I've come in, I'm hungry all the time."

A hostile theme is next introduced: "Before the baby, my wife was always baking and cooking. Now it depends on her mood. If she's in a baking mood, there'll be pies and cakes. Otherwise, I can't get anything out of her. But the baby is really thriving; he now has the weight of a two and a half year old boy and gaining all the time. My wife now weighs more than me, and she maintains her weight, too." There is a further elaboration about weight. "Father's weight is now down to 130, and he used to be over 200. When I came back from overseas, he already had diabetes; he had lost so much weight, I hardly knew him. He seemed to have shrunk down from a big, strapping man, the way I remember him when I was a child, to half that size."

Now a guilt theme appears: "I blame myself, I blame the stomach trouble on eating too much fried food, taking in stuff that wasn't good for me, and being greedy about it. I first started as a cook in the restaurant and used to grab a little here and there while working. Before you know it, you're eating all the time. Now I've gotten to be in the management side, but the hours are too long, and there are too many responsibilities. It makes me feel uneasy and uncertain. I never had the greatest confidence in myself. I'd rather leave this job and go back to sheet metal work, something I learned when I was in military service."

PSYCHODYNAMIC IMPRESSIONS

Underlying inferiority feelings and dependency needs, long associated with thoughts of being the baby, and now the smallest, of the family, have been activated by multiple stress factors. These are the impending loss of his father and the loss of his own special status (as baby) with his wife, being displaced by the arrival of their first child. In addition, there are the demands of his job which pays little in return. These dependent trends have been defended against in the past by compensatory athletic activities and interest in "manly" work. These defensive maneuvers have been supplemented by denial, projection, and rationalization as his anxiety and guilt have mounted in recent months. These feelings are closely related to his concern about his masculinity and his hostility toward his wife—a phallic mother figure—and toward his child—a sibling surrogate who displaced him in her affections. In addition, there is a strong emotional reaction to the impending loss of his father. These implementations of defense appear to have become insufficient, and a conversion reaction with gastrointestinal manifestations has been added to them. The father, with whom there now appears to be a particularly strong somatic identification, has changed from a powerful, strapping, responsible man to a dependent, weak, shrunken figure who needs to be cared for. The patient fears this may be his own fate—the activation of old dependency needs and fears of physical inferiority. He seems for some months already to have been in mourning for his father's impending death. Hostility seems recently to have been accentuated, but tends to have some affective discharge.

PHYSICAL HISTORY

This patient was admitted with a chief complaint of recurrent bouts of epigastric pain, the most recent beginning four days before hospitalization. Two and a half months ago, he noticed the gradual onset of dull but fairly severe midepigastric pain, without radiation. The pain lasted a half hour, then would recur every few hours and lasted altogether about three days with several episodes of vomiting. Milk would relieve the pain somewhat, but Amphogel taken at the suggestion of friends did not help. Following this episode the patient had anorexia and then recurrence of pain and vomiting for one day two weeks later. Meanwhile, anorexia continued and patient lost 25 pounds. Pain recurred four days ago and was associated with vomiting, similar to the initial episode. There was no hematemesis or melena. Patient is an assistant restaurant manager, working extremely hard of late. The father is living, age 69, has carcinoma of the bowel, and diabetes. Mother is living and well, age 69, also. One brother has diabetes. The patient's general health has been good. He is myopic and has had some decrease in hearing of the left ear with some tinnitus for the past two years.

PHYSICAL EXAMINATION

Temperature 98.8°F. Pulse 80. Blood pressure 120/70. Weight 136 pounds. Patient is a well-developed, thin, white male in no distress who did appear to have lost considerable weight. The physical examination, including neurological, was within normal limits.

LABORATORY DATA

Hemogram, serology, and urinalysis were negative.

ROENTGENOGRAMS

Chest film and gastrointestinal series were normal.

HOSPITAL COURSE

The patient was put on a Gastric I diet on admission; this was changed to a Gastric III the following day, and a bland diet four days later. Informal supportive psychotherapy was instituted by the doctor in charge. The patient gained three pounds while in the hospital and was completely symptom-free. He was discharged after being in the hospital one week.

DISCHARGE DIAGNOSIS

Observation for peptic ulcer. No disease found. Condition: improved.

COMMENT

This patient's chief symptom is stomach pain which is accompanied by anorexia and weight loss. These are not manifestations of an organic illness but rather are somatic equivalents of a depressive reaction. The pain represents a somatic identification with his sick father and a physical expression of his reaction to the impending loss of this emotionally important figure for him. Mourning may antedate actual death if the fatal illness is chronic and lingering as it is in this case. The patient is going through such a grief reaction, but the psychological elements are less obvious than the physical. The hospital stay, brief though it was, seems to have been a helpful interlude interrupting the further progression of the emotional disturbance, particularly because of the excellent relationship the patient developed with his doctor.

Adamson and Schmale (1965) noted that 45 of 50 patients studied after their admission to an acute psychiatric service reported "giving up" as a final affective response to a significant loss which took place before the onset of the episode of illness. The most conspicuous general difference between this group and those hospitalized for medical reasons appeared to be that the former gave the impression they had had "difficult and unrewarding" emotional and interpersonal experiences for years. This was not characteristic of the medical patients.

CASE 17

CHIEF PRESENTING SYMPTOM	Stomach pain
SENSORIMOTOR CONFIGURATIONS	Sensory configurations

Pain

Associated with many losses, particularly father's impending death, and with hostility toward wife seen as frustrating maternal figure

Motor configurations

Activity

Linked with need to deny fears of physical defect and concern about manliness

SOMATIC IDENTIFICATION	*Father* Weight loss due to cancer of bowel, recent (Direct)
SENSITIZED ORGAN SYSTEM	Gastrointestinal—stomach
STRESS (*surface meaning*)	Father's impending death; newly born baby; job and financial problems
STRESS (*dynamic significance*)	Anticipated loss of father, increased dependency feelings together with activated hostility at their frustration
DEFENSES	Overcompensatory athletic activities and interest Denial Projection Rationalization

AFFECTS	*Intensity*	*Pathway of expression*
Anxiety	+	Ideational, somatic equivalents
Depression	++	Ideational, affective, some somatization
Hostility	++	Ideational, affective, some somatization

OTHER FACTORS	Troublesome conscience
HOMEOSTATIC SHIFT(S)	The usual defensive alignment disrupted by stress, causing a mild to moderate somatization reaction. A more favorable shift caused by psychological effect of hospitalization
DIAGNOSIS	Observation for peptic ulcer. No disease found. Result: improved

case 18

Nausea, Flank Pain, and Recurrent Psychological Losses

CHIEF PRESENTING SYMPTOM

Nausea.

BASIC ANAMNESTIC EXCERPTS

The symptom of nausea began five weeks before admission. "When I get this nauseating feeling, it's like I'm going to pass out. One night I had a terrific pain in the right side. I called a doctor who thought it was a kidney stone. I then went down to another hospital where they told me it wasn't a stone but an infected prostate, and they didn't admit me. But a short time later, I again felt nauseated, worse than before. I was about to take a bath and got a severe chill and back came the pain. This time I went to a hospital where they kept me four weeks and said I did have kidney stones after all. One night there my legs went numb. It was as if the pain had worked down from my stomach. It was a paralyzing numbness which left my left foot but not my right. Then my left arm went numb. Now I've got pains in my right leg. I'd like to be able to walk a few steps, go to the toilet, and get a few things. But I'm afraid I can't hold myself up."

Another symptom cluster next appears: "I've had a terrible itching in the last few days. I scratch so much my skin gets red, my hips, thighs, shoulders, wrists. Four days ago while sitting up to scratch, I fell out of bed." There is a return to symptoms involving the extremities: "My legs aren't numb any more, but I can't use them too well. I can move my right arm, and can move and bend my leg, but not the toes—and I still can't put all my weight on it. I'd like to be able to get up and around, and I've been asking about physical therapy."

"Before this present sickness began I used to get dizzy spells; my eyes would get blurry, and I couldn't see straight. That nauseating feeling would come on quite a bit before, also. While working in the course of an eight-hour day, my feet would get tired from standing all day long . . . I'm in a leather finishing outfit. I match colors and mix the chemicals which they apply." Next are references to a concern about eating: "If I had a small breakfast and a small meal at noon, I'd feel better than if I went home or out for a big lunch . . . I wouldn't feel ambitious, just want to rest after a big meal." There is again emphasis on fatigability: "If I had a restive night, I'd be worn out in the morning, and the whole day would be ruined because of that tired feeling. It's been like that for the past six months. When I stand on a cement platform, my feet bother me more than on a wooden platform. My feet got so bad that when I'd walk, they'd get puffed up, I'd feel exhausted and feel like passing out. Also, on climbing stairs I would feel so nauseated; just like passing out. I've noticed in the last year or two, if I overexert myself, I can cause myself to hemorrhage from the mouth. There's a pinkish color to the sputum, not a rich red.

"I feel pretty good in the summer. The winter is bad. In the cold weather, walking against the wind, I get headaches and sinus pains. In the summer, of course, I don't wear so many clothes and don't carry as much weight. I have a little boy; if he wanted me to pull him on a sled, I couldn't do it. If I should have to walk up a hill, I'd get so exhausted. I've felt this tiredness now for the past nine years. Before that I played in all sports. I'd hardly ever go home to rest. When I was so active, I needed my eight or nine hours of sleep so I'd go to bed pretty early. I used to like to sleep. I never smoked or drank much. I didn't like it. Smoking cigarettes would get me short-winded, and I didn't like the taste of it. So I started a pipe. I always felt I was never of age to drink. My folks would never allow it— that is, going out to the barroom with the fellows. If I came to your house as company, I'd drink a cordial. My folks are from the old country." (At this point in the interview, the patient became aware of a sensation of pins and needles in his feet.)

"I used to work on a farm summers between school. It was healthy work—nine hours a day. My folks were strict. I come from a big family of five girls and four boys. I'm the second youngest. My father died when I was 16. There are no cripples in the family. He died of a heart condition—suddenly in New York while working in a restaurant. He had been in the trucking business and used to do hard physical work. Then he had to switch jobs because his heart went bad. Mother's sickly, in a convalescent home. She had a shock eight months ago which paralyzed her right side. She had complained a lot about dizziness and tiredness before her shock. They say she'll be all right, but it'll take time. She can use her foot a little, but can't really walk yet. She was always a hardworking woman. When the kids were young, she got a job in a factory to help support the family, and she'd think nothing of going out and chopping wood for fire. We had to get along the best we could with her away so much."

Again there are references to himself, to his health, this time to sore throats, with difficulty in swallowing and colds every few months. At age 13 he had a tonsillectomy and at age 18 an appendectomy. The themes of a defective body with losses of body parts and an overall preoccupation with body integrity are repeated.

PSYCHODYNAMIC IMPRESSIONS

An intense self-preoccupation is manifested principally in bodily or physical terms. Objects other than the patient appear late in the interview and then only rather briefly. There are not only many associations to the patient's current incapacitated state, but also references to past anxieties activated by operations leading to loss of body parts (tonsils, appendix). Extremely dependent needs and feelings of physical inferiority, defended against by attempts to keep busy and mobile, have again become activated as the patient's physical capacities have decompensated, making such defense no longer possible. There is evidence to suggest a rigid, strict upbringing and considerable guilt, particularly brought on by his insatiable oral needs. Hostility toward other objects appears only once in the context of parental strictness, and the patient at that moment experiences the physical sensation of pins and needles in his right foot; mother's paralysis was on the right. Multiple symptom clusters, involving various body systems, appear in shifting order. However, the extremities, with associated references to both motility and painful paresthesia, are the focus of the patient's preoccupation. They give way only temporarily to other areas—vision, respiratory and gastrointestinal systems. All symptoms are closely identified with those referred to as occurring in one or the other parent, so that somatic identification with the parents is striking, especially with mother who has more recently been ill and incapacitated, and with whom the patient is in regular contact.

PHYSICAL HISTORY

The patient was transferred here from another hospital for further treatment of severe right flank pain. Eight years before, a heart murmur had been discovered, although there was no definite history of rheumatic fever. For the past few years he has noted increased exertional dyspnea. There has been intermittent ankle edema at night for the past year, and he had noted tightness and occasionally pain in the chest after excess activity. He had been put on digitalis and other unknown medication by a local physician for the past six months. Two and a half months ago, he developed sudden onset of severe right flank pain, radiating to the right groin, with some difficulty in passing urine. There was no hematuria, burning, or dark urine. He was admitted to another hospital where the pain subsided the following day, and there was no further difficulty with urination. Physical examination on admission there was reported negative except for right flank tenderness. An intravenous pyelogram, cystoscopy, and retrogrades were performed, but revealed only a slight delay in emptying of the right kidney. Urinalysis revealed specific gravity 1.028, 1+ albumin, and 3 red blood cells per high power field. Twenty-four hours after admission he was noted to be fibrillating and was digitalized. He ran a spiking temperature curve for two weeks from the time of admission, and then the temperature leveled off to normal. A tentative diagnosis of subacute bacterial endocarditis was made, but repeat blood cultures were sterile. He was treated with massive doses of penicillin as well as dicumarol. The hemoglobin was 83 percent, white blood cell count 15,750 with 74 polymorphonuclear leukocytes. Sedimentation rate varied between 21 and 52 mm. Cerebrospinal fluid examination was negative.

About three weeks before his present admission, he developed sudden onset of numbness, coldness, pallor, and cyanosis of both legs, followed by swelling of the legs, greater on the right. He was able to feel the numbness move gradually down the right leg to the toes. He was given an injection for the severe pain, and by the following day, all symptoms had subsided in the left leg, and those in the right leg began to diminish. Two weeks before admission, he again developed swelling, coldness and pallor of the right leg, this time extending from the feet to just above the knee. Following this there was persisting, mild numbness of the right foot. One week prior to admission, he was found by his wife, lying on his side in bed, confused, unable to speak coherently, and unable to move the left leg and arm. There has been a gradual disappearance of confusion and a slow return of ability to speak, but he still does not realize that there is no motion in the left leg, still has poor memory, and at times is incontinent.

PHYSICAL EXAMINATION

Vital signs: normal. Patient appeared slightly pale, lying quietly in bed, unable to move left extremities. He was oriented but memory was somewhat impaired, and he was confused as to temporal relations and proper sequence of events. He was not aware of his inability to move the left leg. Mouth deviated to the right when opened; food particles present in left buccal chamber; tongue not atrophied and protruded to left side. Lungs: diminished breath sounds; fine and inspiratory moist rales posteriorly at left base; otherwise clear to percussion and auscultation. Heart: not enlarged; PMI palpable in fifth intercostal space at midclavicular line;

rate irregular at 72 to 76 with occasional extrasystoles; sounds of good quality; P-2 louder than A-2; forceful apical impulse but no definite thrill; loud M-1; late rumbling diastolic murmur at apex, with no definite presystolic accentuation. Dorsalis pedis pulses were palpable bilaterally but stronger on the left; no posterior tibial palpable on the right; both popliteals and femorals equal; right toes slightly cooler than left. Neurological: residuals of old left cerebrovascular accident with mild spasticity, hyperreflexia, Babinski and Hoffman present on the left. In addition to the left hemiplegia, the right ankle was fixed in plantar flexion at 100°.

LABORATORY DATA

Urine: specific gravity 1.020 with negative albumin and sediment. Hemoglobin 12.4 g, hematocrit 41 percent, sedimentation rate 13 mm per hr. White blood cell count 16,000 with 80 polymorphonuclear leukocytes, 18 lymphocytes. Serology negative. Nonprotein nitrogen 30. Urine cultures: Staphylococcus aureus, coagulase negative; alpha streptococci. Blood cultures negative on three determinations.

ROENTGENOGRAMS

Films taken in recumbent position. Chest: heart enlarged and the configuration suggests mitral valvular disease; left auricle enlarged elevating the left main bronchus, and there is an enlarged pulmonary artery. Slight vascular engorgement. Findings consistent with rheumatic mitral valvular disease. One month later, X-ray showed definite and moderate decrease in the size of the heart compared with previous examination, but the degree of pulmonary congestion remained approximately the same.

ELECTROCARDIOGRAM

On admission showed auricular flutter–fibrillation with auricular rate of 380, ventricular rate of 82; otherwise normal. Repeat one week later showed reversion to normal sinus rhythm with ventricular rate 86, PR interval .22, QRS .08. Large P waves and prolonged PR interval interpreted as probably quinidine effect.

HOSPITAL COURSE

Shortly after admission, conversion of the patient's auricular fibrillation to normal sinus rhythm was attempted with quinidine; 0.2 g was administered every 2 hours for 5 doses, followed by 0.3 and 0.4 and 0.5 g supplied at the same dosage on succeeding days. Conversion was achieved, and the patient has since maintained a regular sinus rhythm on a dosage of 0.3 g quinidine every 6 hours. He was otherwise treated with a low-salt diet and digitoxin, 1 mg daily. There was an occasional afternoon temperature rise to 99.6°F, but no other febrile episodes. A short, blowing diastolic murmur was heard at the base several weeks after admission. On one occasion the patient complained of left upper quadrant pain, at which time a slightly tender spleen tip could barely be palpated on deep inspiration. The major portion of his hospitalization was devoted to rehabilitation with physical and corrective therapy because of his left hemiplegia. There was a gradual but marked increase in mobility and muscle strength in both lower extremities, but only a slight increase in the left upper extremity. He was ambulated and taught self-care activities.

DISCHARGE DIAGNOSES

1. Rheumatic heart disease; auricular fibrillation; mitral stenosis; congestive failure, Class II B; treated, improved.

2. Multiple embolic phenomena, secondary to No. 1; untreated; improved.

3. Cerebral vascular accident, involving branch of right middle cerebral artery with left hemiparesis; treated; improved.

4. Probable embolus, right renal artery and right iliac or femoral arteries.

COMMENT

Severe organic disease is here accompanied by intense self-preoccupation, particularly with physical symptoms. How extensively and at what time each symptom appears within the patient's awareness is related not only to structural changes and dysfunction of physical disease, but also to psychological determinants. These involve the patient's emotional response to his illness both in a global sense and in less marked variations that may occur from day to day. Additionally, they include his reactions to other stress and to the various people who are emotionally significant for him, including those who are involved in the care and treatment of his sickness.

Chambers and Reiser (1953), in their study of emotional stress in the precipitation of congestive heart failure, refer to previous work which indicates that such stress may be accompanied by measurable changes in pulse rate, stroke volume, cardiac output, peripheral resistance, and arterial blood pressure. Furthermore, emotional tension is related to interferences in coronary circulation, the intrinsic cardiac conduction mechanisms and efficient recovery from exercise. It is pointed out that when other than only catastrophic events are considered as stress, and routine life situations may at times symbolically represent stressful factors, then emotional elements will be seen to contribute, more frequently than had been considered previously, to episodes of cardiac decompensation. It was found that the nature of precipitating events was remarkably uniform in 19 cases. These situations involved (1) those leading chiefly to feelings of rejection and loss of security and (2) those leading chiefly to feelings of frustration and rage. In 4 of 5 patients selected for long-range study, it was thought that emotional factors were more important than organic factors in precipitation of congestive failure. Similarly stressful experiences had been encountered by many of the patients earlier in their lives, but at a time when myocardial reserve had not been so limited and then the stress did not break the circulatory equilibrium. With progression of cardiac disease, increasing loss of cardiac reserve, stressful events had increasingly greater impact in disturbing the circulatory equilibrium.

CASE 18

CHIEF PRESENTING SYMPTOM	Nausea
SENSORIMOTOR CONFIGURATIONS	Sensory configurations

Pain, interoceptive, tactile, temperature

Manifested in marked preoccupation with self and close identification with parental illnesses, and associated with guilt over intensified oral needs

Motor configurations

Activity

Expressed in terms of working, walking, falling, and easy fatigability, and associated with great concern over physical integrity

SOMATIC IDENTIFICATION	*Father*	Sudden heart disease death, 15 years ago (Direct, organ constitutional)
	Mother	Right-sided paralysis from shock eight months ago (Direct, organ constitutional)

SENSITIZED ORGAN SYSTEM	Cardiovascular Respiratory Extremities Gastrointestinal
STRESS (*surface meaning*)	Mother's illnesses—most recently a "shock"
STRESS (*dynamic significance*)	Deeply dependent needs activated through mother's recent illness and potential loss

DEFENSES		Overcompensatory activity with mobility especially emphasized Massive denial

AFFECTS	*Intensity*	*Pathway of expression*
Anxiety	++	Some ideational, some somatic equivalents
Depression	+++	Somatization
Hostility	+++	Somatization

OTHER FACTORS	Intense body narcissism Oral needs marked Rigid upbringing; marked guilt
HOMEOSTATIC SHIFT(S)	Activated depressive and hostile affects inadequately defended against by denial, with compensatory activities no longer available. Marked regressive shifts with further impact of hostile energies on the already vulnerable and malfunctioning cardiovascular system
DIAGNOSES	a) Rheumatic heart disease; auricular fibrillation; mitral stenosis; congestive failure, Class II B, treated, improved; b) Multiple embolic phenomena, secondary to a), untreated, improved; c) Cerebral vascular accident, involving branch of right middle cerebral artery with left hemiparesis, treated, improved; d) Probable embolus, right renal artery and right iliac or femoral arteries

FOLLOW-UP DATA

INTERIM NOTE

After the patient was discharged from the hospital on leave of absence, he failed to return and was not readmitted again until almost three years later. In the interim, no new symptoms developed, although the patient continued to have a slight speech impediment and residuals of a left hemiparesis. He had been working irregularly one or two days a week, first on the outside and then later "taking in" some "simple" work at home, and finally not working at all. Alcoholic intake had been increasing and had become considerable. Another child had been born into the family. Wife recently had become ill, nature of the illness being unknown. It was evident that stresses in the patient's environment were building up.

Approximately three years following the hospital admission already reported in detail, the patient entered the hospital again because of nausea and weight loss. He remained in the hospital only briefly and the chief findings there were residuals of a left hemiparesis with symmetrical involvement of the left-sided motor groups except the face. Also noted was beginning development of leukoplakia of the mucous membrane overlying the hard palate. There was no evidence of congestive failure and the rheumatic heart disease did not appear to have progressed particularly. He became rapidly asymptomatic in the hospital and was discharged shortly back home. Within a couple of months he was again admitted with complaints of nausea, vomiting, diarrhea one day prior to entry. As before, no basis was found for this condition. He became rapidly asymptomatic again.

During this stay additional information about his home situation was obtained. This indicated a rapid and severe deterioration was taking place there. His wife had become increasingly sicker. The patient had been drinking very heavily, was constantly demanding attention from his wife, arguing and fighting with her. The wife felt very discouraged. Bills were piling up and their financial situation had become precarious. The wife's sister was trying to help out, but relationships between the patient and his in-laws had become terribly strained.

Within a few weeks after discharge the patient was readmitted once more to the hospital with the same complaints as previously. This time a significant change in his physical condition could be noted. There was rapid atrial fibrillation not responsive to increased digitalization, intractable congestive failure, and presumptive evidence of recurrent pulmonary embolization. The patient was placed on the seriously ill list. One Monday morning—a month after hospitalization—the patient who had been responding favorably to the treatment and was "now" being readied to leave the hospital, possibly for a nursing home, read in the newspaper that his wife had died over the weekend. The differences with his in-laws had become so great that they had not informed him of this tragic event. The patient became extremely agitated, blaming his in-laws. He signed out of the hospital against medical advice to attend his wife's funeral.

Eighteen hours later he was brought back to the hospital by relatives. His chief complaint at this time was shortness of breath.

PHYSICAL EXAMINATION

Revealed a thin, well-developed, white male, appearing chronically ill, orthopneic, sitting up in bed with clearly evident venous distention of the neck. Temperature 97°F. Pulse 100 to 120, apical. Respirations 26 per minute. Blood pressure was not obtainable. Chest: increased PA diameter. Heart: enlarged to anterior axillary line with rapid atrial fibrillation. There was dullness 3 cm below the right costal margin. The lower extremities were mottled, cyanotic, with edema to the knees.

LABORATORY DATA

Hemoglobin 13.7 g; hematocrit 51 percent; white blood cell count 10,500 with normal differential. Urinalysis: specific gravity 1.013, 2+ albumin, few white blood cell per high power field. Nonprotein nitrogen 44 mg. Chlorides 88 mEq, potassium 5.9 mEq, sodium 116 mEq, CO_2 20 mEq. These figures for blood chemistry began to rise in the next week.

ROENTGENOGRAM

Chest: Slight increase in size of heart over previous admission, with evidence of interlobular nodular edema.

ELECTROCARDIOGRAM

Atrial fibrillation with frequent ventricular extrasystoles.

COURSE

The patient was continued on a regime of digitalis, periodic injections of mercurials, and a low-salt diet. For several weeks there was little change clinically with persistence of intractable congestive failure and rapid atrial fibrillation. The patient died suddenly on the twenty-fifth hospital day.

DIAGNOSIS

Rheumatic heart disease; auricular fibrillation; mitral stenosis; congestive failure.

POSTMORTEM FINDINGS

Respiratory system: (1) pulmonary edema; (2) obliterative fibrous pleuritis, right; (3) hydrothorax, left.

Cardiovascular system: (1) idiopathic myocardial hypertrophy with mural organizing thrombi (old to recent), myocardial fibrosis, dilatation of right and left ventricles, and congestive failure; (2) organized thrombi in auricular appendages; (3) subendocardial fibroelastosis of i.v. septum; (4) atherosclerosis of aorta, slight.

Liver: (1) passive congestion, marked; (2) cardiac cirrhosis, slight.

Genitourinary: (1) infarct, recent, left kidney.

Spleen, lymph nodes, marrow: (1) normoblastic hyperplasia of vertebral marrow; (2) hemosiderosis of vertebral marrow, slight.

Miscellaneous: (1) ascites; (2) edema of lower extremities and scrotum.

FINAL COMMENT

As far as can be ascertained, this patient's environment had become relatively stabilized for about three years, as had his physical condition. However, alcoholic intake had begun to increase, suggesting an attempt to compensate for increased oral needs. Then, after this period of time, the equilibrium was disrupted with the development of illness in the patient's wife and her increasing inability to meet his simultaneously increased demands for her attention and care. She had become a critically important object, representing a maternal figure for this intensely narcissistic and extremely dependent patient. It should be noted that the wife was not mentioned in the original interview. Omission of important objects in a patient's associations can also indicate a disturbance in relationship, but in a different fashion than verbalized material would. As the wife's illness introduced the complicating factor of frustration, it may be assumed that the patient's ambivalence, his potential for aggressive buildup, and concomitant guilt were mobilized. The disrupted equilibrium could no longer be reestablished, despite more reliance on alcoholism and some half-hearted help from relatives. A rapidly developing psychophysical regression began to manifest itself. This was evident in the repeated hospitalizations where the presenting symptoms—mostly gastrointestinal—were found to have no basis, rapidly subsided, and it seemed clear that hospitalization was having more of a psychological than directly medical effect. The patient in this way was able to remove himself from the very difficult home environment and, at the same time, his dependent needs could at least be partially and temporarily satisfied. Just prior to his last hospitalization, the home situation had deteriorated still further, wife had become sicker, and this time the patient's physical condition showed a definite change for the worse. After this hospitalization, he still responded enough to be considered for discharge to a nursing home. Then, suddenly, his wife died and the patient left against medical advice to attend her funeral. This produced a further sharp disruption of psychophysical equilibrium. It would seem that the mourning period that the patient then went through was highly pathological, with aggression turned inward, guilt, and a sense of helplessness escalating to critical levels. Affective and ideational outlets were blocked off, psychotherapeutic or related efforts to unblock them unavailable, so that the full impact of the patient's highly disturbed emotions were directed against an already malfunctioning soma.

case 19

Gastrointestinal Symptoms in a Loss-sensitive Patient

CHIEF PRESENTING SYMPTOM

Sick stomach.

BASIC ANAMNESTIC EXCERPTS

There is an immediate interconnection of presenting symptom with a liver condition when the patient was yellow (jaundiced) and had to be hospitalized for a period of five months while in military service. The next associations are references to a period six months ago, when he lost his appetite and some weight, although ordinarily he is a big eater. Then a further elaboration of stomach symptoms follows: "I've always had trouble with gas on my stomach. I've found that the only way to relieve it is to take a walk. Sometimes I throw up—just phlegm or liquid stuff, but nothing solid. (Further sensory specifications about vomitus not given.) After some foods, fried or heavy, I get indigestion, a sour stomach, and then everything tastes sour. At times it burns in my stomach."

"It began late last summer after my vacation. I started to lose weight, having been always 180. I just couldn't eat. I switched from cold sandwiches to hot soups on advice of my doctor. That made me feel better for a while. It sort of warmed me up inside. My arms went down (in size). I used to have a stomach on me, and it disappeared." Again there is reference to the illness eight years before, turning yellow, having no appetite, being nauseous, all related to a little escapade, not specified but having to do with "something improper" occurring in the hot desert while overseas in military service.

The associations now develop further around eating: "I've just had coffee, never ate breakfast for the past five years. It seems as if I'm just not hungry when I first get up. If I loafed around for a couple of hours at home, I might get an appetite. But here I'm ready to go after several days of gastric diet; that was pretty rough—all those sauces and creams. I once ate desserts, but when I left home, I gave them up and haven't had them since, even though my wife, who's a good cook, is after me all the time to eat them."

The wife, who is the first object to appear in his associations, is further described: "I've been married 10 years. Our little girl will soon be six. My wife had a tough time having her, and there's been nothing since. She had a Caesarean section and lost a lot of blood. She hasn't menstruated right since. Two years ago she started to hemorrhage for three days and had to go to the hospital to be scraped out. She had to have three transfusions. When the baby came, it lodged in such a way that if it had been born normal, it would have broken its neck. The child now has such big tonsils that they will have to come out in a couple of weeks."

The associations now shift to losses in the past: "When I was five years old, my father and mother died within a week of each other, leaving me and two stepsisters and a stepbrother from father's previous marriage. I don't know what mother died of; father had pneumonia. I was in a run-down condition then, lost weight, and had to be in a sanitarium for a year. I was then brought up by my mother's sister—an aunt—as a state ward. She had no children of her own. We didn't get along well because I wouldn't eat regularly. She became sick with cancer when I was 18, and she looked terrible and sunken in. She was always in bed, couldn't eat well, just hot soup and stuff. Finally she hemorrhaged and never came out of it. I left home then and shortly afterward went into the service."

Returning to the present, the patient's associations again allude to difficulties between himself and his wife. These have been increased ever since her pregnancy. She is tense and irritable. He also refers to tensions at his job, where he has to work very hard and isn't appreciated, either.

PSYCHODYNAMIC IMPRESSIONS

The patient was, in a sense, his mother's only child, i.e., through her second husband. The stepsiblings were much older than the patient. Mother was already sickly during his early childhood and died when he was only five years old. Within a week he sustained another serious loss—that of his father. A long period of anorexia, weight loss, and hospitalization followed these major traumatic events. Thereafter, he remained a generally tense, high-strung person who was frequently preoccupied with body integrity and concerned about physical defects. When his aunt took him in as an orphan, he became her only child also. His relationship with her was highly ambivalent, disagreements between the two often being focused around eating functions. When, after some years, she became ill with cancer and died, this led in the patient to a reinforcement of somatic and psychological identifications with women.

The pregnancy of his wife seems to have triggered a regressive but not fixed shift in psychological equilibrium. The new baby was seen as a rival for his wife's maternal affections. This coincided with the patient's eating difficulties, repeated with his wife as with his aunt, and before the wife's postpartum physical complications, mutual irritability and tension adversely affected their relationship. Strains at work, where he also felt he gave all and got little in return have added to his increased dependency needs and activated hostility. The aggressive elements however are modified by a strong libidinizing influence; his strong feminine identification is marked by sexualized elements appearing in the associations as pregnancy fantasies.

PHYSICAL HISTORY

This patient was admitted with multiple complaints of "morning sickness," nervousness, and gassy stomach of six years' duration. He stated he had been nervous for many years. He has also had a variety of gastrointestinal difficulties, including "sick stomach" in the morning with occasional vomiting; always "loaded with gas" and passing flatus; also sour eructations. Six years ago, a gastrointestinal series was done, and the patient was informed that it was negative. Five years ago, for reasons not known or clear to the patient, he had several electrocardiograms. He knows of no heart condition or cardiac symptoms. More recently, he has become extremely nervous and noted a loss of appetite with weight dropping from 180 to 160 pounds.

PHYSICAL EXAMINATION

Well-developed and well-nourished male, obviously tense, but in no distress. Temperature 98.6°F. Pulse 80. Blood pressure 170/90. Teeth are carious. Heart showed a Grade I apical systolic murmur. Lungs were clear. Abdomen was soft and non-tender. Skin: there were numerous firm, cystic masses near the right ear, back, face, and numerous scars of previous lesions; on the legs were discrete maculopapular lesions.

LABORATORY DATA

Admission urine showed 1+ albumin with 20 to 25 white blood cells per high power field. Admission blood studies were negative, including the serology. Repeat urinalysis showed no albumin and no cellular elements in the sediment. Urine culture grew out Staphylococcus aureus, coagulase negative. Nonprotein nitrogen, serum anylase, and liver function tests were all within normal limits. Stools were guaiac negative.

ROENTGENOGRAMS

Chest film and gallbladder series showed no abnormalities. Gastrointestinal series was negative except for some spasm and coarse folds in the region of the descending portion of the duodenum.

HOSPITAL COURSE

The patient was afebrile throughout. On a regimen including a soft diet with interval feedings, sedation, antispasmodics, and antacids, he quickly became asymptomatic. On the twelfth hospital day, an old drained furuncle in the left axilla showed signs of inflammation and swelling. The patient was started on penicillin by injection and dry sterile dressings for three days, and was then discharged with instructions to take oral penicillin for an additional three days. The initial elevated blood pressure fell rapidly to normal by the third hospital day and remained at normotensive levels.

DISCHARGE DIAGNOSES

1. Somatization reaction, manifested by gastrointestinal symptoms, treated, improved.
2. Furuncle, left axilla, treated, improved.

COMMENT

The presenting symptom in this case is associated with a number of sensory clusters including visual, taste, and temperature percepts, as well as motor referents expressed in terms of losing, getting rid of, and walking. They provide recollective links with the past. The sensory percepts are associated with loss of parents and aunt, reflecting long-standing and intermittently activated dependency needs. They also are linked with a strong tendency toward feminine identification. The motor configurations symbolically represent his concern about his masculinity, his not being appreciated at home or at work, and are connected with his activated hostility toward depriving and rejecting parental figures. Recently, all these trends have become activated in his relationship with his wife, especially during and subsequent to her last pregnancy. In a sense, the patient continues to act out the role of being his mother's only child, and threats of losing his position activate a marked depressive response which is reflected largely in physical rather than psychological manifestations, although no organic disease has been discovered. The depression is reinforced by remaining guilt related to improper sexual behavior while in military service.

CASE 19

CHIEF PRESENTING SYMPTOM	Sick stomach
SENSORIMOTOR CONFIGURATIONS	Sensory configurations

Visual, interoceptive, taste, temperature

Related to many losses, especially parents and aunt, and associated with dependency needs, strong feminine identification and symbolized pregnancy fantasies

Motor configurations

Losing

Expressed in throwing up, not being appreciated, threatened work status, and connected with activated hostility toward authority figures

SOMATIC IDENTIFICATION	*Father*	Sudden death of pneumonia, patient age five
	Aunt (mother surrogate)	Cancer of stomach death, patient age 18 (Direct, ? organ constitutional)
	Wife	Uterine hemorrhages, and difficult delivery, recent years
SENSITIZED ORGAN SYSTEM	Gastrointestinal	
STRESS (*surface meaning*)	Work tensions and marital problems, wife's pregnancy	
STRESS (*dynamic significance*)	Fears about adequacy as a man and concomitant activated dependency needs, new baby seen as displacing him in wife's affections	
DEFENSES	Attempt to ingratiate by giving all Projection	

AFFECTS	*Intensity*	*Pathway of expression*
Anxiety	++	Affective, ideational, somatic equivalents
Depression	++	Ideational, some affective, some somatization
Hostility	++	Ideational, some affective, some somatization

OTHER FACTORS

Trauma of mother's death—patient age five, followed by death of father in a week. Marked sensitivity to loss. Deeply established dependency needs

HOMEOSTATIC SHIFT(S)

Dependency and activated hostility requiring further somatic channels of expression, but somatization modified by strong libidinal drives

DIAGNOSES

a) Somatization reaction, manifested by gastrointestinal symptoms, treated, improved;
b) Furuncle, left axilla, treated, improved

case 20

Chronic Epigastric Discomfort: The Stomach as Target Organ

CHIEF PRESENTING SYMPTOM

Stomach trouble.

BASIC ANAMNESTIC EXCERPTS

"I've had stomach attacks for quite a while. My stomach used to keep turning over on me, and I used to keep vomiting. This past year I haven't been feeling too bad—until recently when my doctor told me I ought to come down here and get a thorough checkup and X-rays. I might need surgery.

"I couldn't keep anything down. Cramps would start here in the pit of my stomach and keep rolling back. They'd double me up. After I'd vomit, I'd feel good for an hour or two. Then my stomach would start bothering me some more. I would eat things to try and quiet my stomach down. That irritated it all the more. So the doctor told me to just drink milk and since then I haven't vomited. I sure didn't like those cramps. It felt like something was in there rolling my stomach right upside down. She'd tighten right up, and I'd vomit, and then I'd feel relaxed. It would feel like stones rolling through my insides, making noises. After spending a few days in bed at home, I'd feel better and go back to work.

"Once I was back at work, I was able to keep going for three weeks, and then my stomach started bothering me again, and this time I had to come in here. I'm a hoisting engineer. I had just started to work a month ago, the day before my illness kicked up. I had been laid off for months before that, and was home all winter. The work I was doing was to take care of one of the pumps that was draining out the water, though I usually operate shovels and cranes. That's what I mean by a hoisting engineer. When I wasn't working, I was at home. I ate good, slept good up to the first day I went to work. It was rainy that day. We didn't really work—just hung around the garage. It was the second day I went in that I started feeling lousy right away in the morning. I started getting these cramps. The next day I vomited. So I went to bed and stayed there for three days. Then I returned to work and was alright until about four days ago.

"Back about five years ago, that's when it really bothered me. I had pain under my ribs on the right that went through to my back. When I was overseas, about eight years ago, I first noticed my stomach hurting me and the vomiting. I remember having gas pains in high school. However, my stomach pain didn't get severe until I was overseas. Then it used to be a concentrated pain in one place. This time it seems more like a rolling, rocking thing all the way up and down. Overseas I found things rugged, different from back home, couldn't get used to it. Finally they put me in a hospital, took X-rays but couldn't find anything in my stomach. They gave me insulin treatments for a week, and then sent me back to duty. I don't know what the purpose of the insulin was. But when I went back to my outfit, I wasn't there more than a couple of weeks when I started feeling the same all over again. I was hospitalized again, and then I came back home. I tried to get as much rest and sleep as I could and felt pretty good for a year. When I got really sick again four years ago, it was after I broke up with a girl I had been in love with; she left me for another fellow. Then two months later they took X-rays and found an ulcer. I went on a diet and from then till recently I felt good.

"I've heard an ulcer is a bruise in the lining of the wall of the stomach or intestine. It's the hydrochloric acid that gets in there that irritates it so much. The vagus nerve contains the acid. When they operated on the stomach, they used to sever the vagus nerve. Anyhow, my father used to have ulcers about 15 years ago. I remember when he had that first attack of pain. That was one summer when my mother, brother, and sister went to Europe. I spent that summer with my father at the Cape. I was about 15. He worked on the Cape Cod Canal when they were dredging it out. He had to be on a milk and cracker diet then for a month. I stayed with father because I was supposed to go over to Europe the next time, but it never came (laughing). Anyway my father got an ulcer, so I got one, too.

"Ulcers come from nerves, I read. Like you're driving an automobile and somebody steps out suddenly in front of you. You get a tightening. Everytime you get excited, you get a tightening and the nerve shoots off acid. The overamount of acid in your stomach can't be taken care of by your system, and that's where it starts to eat away. I'm nervous (laughing) —to a certain extent. Restless. Lots of times I'm doing something, and it doesn't go right, I get mad. I've always been more or less that way. Never easygoing or being able to take things as they come.

"I remember different incidents. Lots of times my mother would start yelling at me for something I did, and I used to jump right up and yell back at her. My stomach would get upset and I'd throw up or have belly-aches. My brother—when we were kids—he'd do something and I'd get mad. I'd whale the hell out of him. He's four years younger. My brother used to be smaller than me until he reached high school. After that he was a pretty big boy, and I never fooled around again (laughing). I remember once I booted him so hard in the pants that it picked him right up and knocked him to the floor. My father said: 'The next time you hit that kid, I'm going to whale the hell out of you.' After that I held my temper in."

Work is again referred to: "I was advised a long time ago not to over-work. But you got to work for a living. I've been married less than a year. Right now my wife is still working. If a child should come along, she's got to leave work, and I've got to do the supporting, don't I? I found out in the service the harder you worked for somebody the less thanks you got. I couldn't get a promotion because I was in the hospital four months. After working my head off, I got nothing. When I was single, I didn't worry about working or not working. I always lived with my folks and they took care of me."

PSYCHODYNAMIC IMPRESSIONS

The associations concerned with stomach symptoms are largely ex-pressed in motor terms, particularly related to the theme of retention and ejection. The implications go far beyond references to eating and food; they involve symbolically the patient's dependent needs, his emotional ties to key people in his life, and his hostile tendencies (need to get rid of offending objects) especially evoked by frustration and competition. Evidence can be noted of sibling rivalry with younger brother, especially for mother's affection. Ambivalence toward mother herself or mother surro-gates (wife) is marked, with the hostility often activated by disappoint-ment of his infantile expectations. Father appears in several roles: the severe parental figure who forces suppression of the patient's powerful hostile impulses, but is himself susceptible to physical incapacity under certain conditions, and then becomes an object of somatic identification for the patient, in terms of stomach ulcer. Though the stomach has been a target organ for many years, the first severe physical reaction did not occur until the patient was overseas in military service. At that time his homesickness, activated dependency needs, disappointed expectations of promotion, and escalating hostility apparently found insufficient discharge through idea-tional and affective channels. Somatic pathways then were utilized for expression of the patient's expanding emotional difficulties. Subsequently, with the return to civilian life, environmental stresses continued to be re-flected in a now customary somatic response. These stresses included leaving a regressively comfortable position, as bachelor living with his parents, for marriage and new responsibilities, and undertaking an unfamiliar job. The marriage, for a while, permitted a continuation of passive dependent tendencies—with his wife working—and with him at home. However, pressures from her about having a child, together with his being forced to assume more of a "grownup's" role produced the most recent decompensation. This increased the hostile impulses directed toward the disappointing or frustrating objects—wife (mother figure) and boss at work (authoritative parental surrogate).

While there is a rather clear sexual symbolism in the associative links with his stomach symptoms, this is overshadowed by aggressive elements. On a number of occasions in the associations, the stomach is personified, referred to as if it were a human object, a "she," a maternal figure who is frustrating and rejecting, and, in turn, an object of the patient's hostility.

PHYSICAL HISTORY

The patient first noted epigastric pain and vomiting eight years ago while in military service overseas. The presence of a duodenal ulcer was not definitely established, and apparently he was given subcoma insulin. Four years ago he had recurrence of severe epigastric pain with vomiting, and at one time blood was seen in the vomitus, but no tarry stools were noted. He was put on a six-meal bland diet and improved in the next few years with only occasional mild symptoms, easily relieved by antacids. On returning to work a month prior to entry, the patient again developed symptoms, became constipated and vomited for three days. He was treated with belladonna and diet without much relief, and on X-ray a question of partial obstruction was raised. Five days prior to entry, there was recurrence of gnawing pain and two days later, after eating chicken broth and a sandwich, the patient began to vomit all foods, including milk. He denied weight loss, hematemesis, or melena. He was not awakened by the pain at night, and only occasionally noted radiation of the pain to the back.

PHYSICAL EXAMINATION

Vital signs normal. Weight 174 pounds. A husky, well developed man in moderate distress, complaining of abdominal pain. Examination within normal limits except for abdomen: moderate epigastric and right upper quadrant tenderness was elicited.

LABORATORY DATA

Hemoglobin 16.4 g, hematocrit 48 percent. White blood cell count 7,800 with normal differential. Urine essentially normal. Nonprotein nitrogen 47. Two stools were guaiac negative. Serology negative.

ROENTGENOGRAMS

Chest film negative. Gastrointestinal series revealed grossly and persistently deformed duodenal cap and a crater 3 to 4 mm in size on the greater curvature side; no appreciable residual on five-hour film.

HOSPITAL COURSE

On admission the patient was aspirated and a residual of 300 ml was obtained. He was started on two ounces of milk every hour during the day and every three hours during the night, and given banthine, 50 mgm every six hours. Aspirations for the first two days in the hospital produced varying amounts of milk, but it was learned that the patient had not obeyed instructions and that he had drunk milk almost up to the time of aspiration. He rapidly became asymptomatic, however, except for dry skin and tongue and some hesitancy of urination, which were felt to be due to banthine. A Gastric II diet was started three days after admission, and a Gastric III five days after admission. The patient continued to do well, had no pain and no evidence of obstruction and was discharged eleven days after admission.

DISCHARGE DIAGNOSIS

Duodenal ulcer, active, treated, improved.

COMMENT

This patient recalls having gastrointestinal symptoms at least 15 years before the present hospitalization. These were generally mild and transient. Then, eight years ago, while he was in military service overseas, he had severe stomach complaints, but no organic disease was found. Instead "a nervous condition" was diagnosed; he was treated with subcoma insulin rather unsuccessfully, and finally had to be discharged from the service. It was not until four years ago that a definite diagnosis of duodenal ulcer was made. A period of at least 11 (and most likely more) years had elapsed before organic disease finally developed in a clinically detectable sense. During this interval the patient's physical symptoms had indicated quite unmistakably that the principal somatic discharge pathway for his emotional tensions, specifically his oral-dependent needs, was the stomach. In other instances these indicators of the potential target organ are neither so prominent, clear-cut, or long-lasting. Instead they may involve several organ systems or body areas, be less well-defined and shorter in duration, or not even within the patient's immediate awareness. Nevertheless, when accessible, they should be considerd as having some usefulness in locating the site where future organic disease may develop in a given individual.

F. Alexander (1950) has considered that *prolonged* frustration of oral–receptive needs is specific for the development of peptic ulcer. Two psychodynamic patterns are described. In one, these needs, though repressed, continue and lead to gastric hyperfunction, i.e., hypersecretion and hypermotility. In the other, frustration of the needs leads to an intense hostility which causes guilt and anxiety, and in turn an overcompensatory effort at being active and successful which finally only activates the oral dependency. This is then followed by gastric hyperfunction. Since such psychodynamic patterns can be found in other diseases, Alexander added a constitutional factor to his specificity hypothesis. Garma (1953) has further elaborated these concepts by suggesting that the psychological mechanism of introjection is involved. The content of the patient's infantile fantasies is concerned with the incorporation of a mother who has frustrated her child, and with her subsequently attacking it from within. Grinker and Robbins (1954) have subjected the specificity hypothesis to critical evaluation and rejected its application not only in the case of peptic ulcer but for all physical illness. Schur (1955) has also found fault with Alexander's formulation, particularly from the standpoint that it does not include the role of the ego functions.

CASE 20

CHIEF PRESENTING SYMPTOM	Stomach trouble
SENSORIMOTOR CONFIGURATIONS	Sensory configurations

Pain, interoceptive, auditory

Associated with intense dependent needs, concern about separation from emotionally significant objects, especially mother, and pressures linked with assuming adult responsibilities

Motor configurations

Tightening, ejecting

Connected with marked hostility toward frustrating, disappointing, and competitive figures

SOMATIC IDENTIFICATION	Father Chronic pain from stomach ulcer for 15 years (Direct, organ constitutional)
SENSITIZED ORGAN SYSTEM	Gastrointestinal—stomach

STRESS (*surface meaning*)	Difficult adjustment while in military service overseas More recently work tensions and marital difficulties
STRESS (*dynamic significance*)	In service, homesickness with increased dependency needs, disappointment in expectations of reward by promotion, with escalating hostility More recently, increased fears of inadequacy as a man, frustration of dependency needs
DEFENSES	Rationalization

AFFECTS	*Intensity*	*Pathway of expression*
Anxiety	++	Ideational. somatic equivalents
Depression	+++	Some ideational, somatization
Hostility	+++	Some ideational, somatization

OTHER FACTORS	Sibling rivalry Ambivalence to mother and surrogates (wife) Father threatening—forcing containment of hostile impulses Secondary gain
HOMEOSTATIC SHIFT(S)	Neurotic tendencies manifested more and more via somatic pathway
DIAGNOSIS	Duodenal ulcer, active, treated, improved

case 21

Stomach Pain in Remission with Rapidly Shifting Psychological Defenses

CHIEF PRESENTING SYMPTOM

Stomach pain.

BASIC ANAMNESTIC EXCERPTS

The patient tends to be repetitious and superficial for quite a while in the interview. "I had pains in my stomach. Every time I ate, the pains went away, and then they came back after an hour. My doctor told me I had an ulcer. So I went and had X-rays, and I was told that I had a small ulcer—too small to send me into a hospital, but I received notice to report here today. I thought it could be treated while I was home. I could stay on my diet. I've been on my diet ever since my family doctor told me to. And I haven't had any pain since. The doctor said the ulcer can be cured without an operation if I keep on a diet. When I had the pain, it went right through my stomach. The pain was something like a cramp. It wouldn't leave me until I ate. When I ate, it went away but came back after I ate. When I took my medicine, it never came back."

Asked for further associations to the pain, the patient responds: "It's hard to describe. Like a gas pain in the stomach. You see the X-rays showed I had an ulcer. If I'm just going to stay here to be put on a diet, I can go home and do the same thing. I knew a lot back home that had ulcers—not in my family—but friends of mine. I know a couple more that were operated on because it was very bad. They had perforated ulcers. They seem to be alright now. They can eat anything after that operation. But the doctor says it can be cured by dieting if it isn't too bad. You got to eat creamy foods."

The patient next refers to his family: "My wife and I have three little girls. The oldest is three years, the next is two, and the other is eight

193

months old. My kids are like a ladder. Two we planned on. The other came, but we can't help that. We like that one just as much as the others. It's alright to have a big family if you can support them. I can support three (laughing). It's a money problem. It takes a lot more than it did years ago. Everybody lived on a farm. My mother had ... there's eight living. I was the last one—the baby.... That's what my mother called me—the baby. I have four brothers and four sisters. In those days everything wasn't too expensive, and we got along. My father worked in a mill; he doesn't work any more now, he's too old, 76. My mother is 75. Father worked as a weaver, then as a painter. Mother had a big family to raise— but they came one at a time, so it wasn't too bad (laughing). Even now my folks manage to get along."

The patient's own work is elaborated on: "I do alright. Work on the outside as a roofer for a nearby concern. I always did like carpenter work, even when I was small. All my brothers work at the same thing. I work with one of my brothers now for the same concern. Another brother works for my brother-in-law, who's also in the roofing business. I worked for him until six weeks ago, and then I quit. We couldn't get along (pause). We used to have arguments (pause). About nothing (laughing). He kept insisting everybody else was wrong. Even though he's boss, he could be wrong. Everybody can make mistakes, and he never made any. He claimed he didn't, anyway. Everything you did was wrong, so there were arguments all the time. So I quit to make everything peaceful in the family. I'd be doing something at work, and he'd tell me to do it his way. I just didn't go for that, though I didn't say anything at first. Finally I just told him if he wants it done his way to do it himself. It developed into a sort of argument that just went on and on for quite a while. That's why I quit; I didn't want it to get worse. He's a guy that was always right, never made mistakes. I haven't been on speaking terms with my brother-in-law since I left. He thought I was scared to quit, that I probably wouldn't be able to find any work. I didn't have any trouble getting another job, and we haven't seen each other since. When I quit, they didn't have anybody to do the carpenter work, so he had to do it himself. My own three brothers don't do much carpenter work in roofing. Every time they had something of that sort to do, they used to call me over.

"When I was about 13, I was always making a lot of things that could be used around the house. But I also used to play a lot. Went in for sports—swimming, sledding, skiing. I never had any trouble with my health. Not until about a year and a half ago when I was operated on for appendix. No trouble since. It was the first time I'd ever been in a hospital. Once when I was 18, I was cutting wood, and the axe went right through a branch and hit me on the leg, but I didn't go to the hospital for that."

PSYCHODYNAMIC IMPRESSIONS

There were references to motility in connection with the symptom of pain, as well as references to size and "good and bad" aspects. A persistent connection could also be noted between the idea of cure and the right kind of feeding, that is, the right diet. A theme associated with this and referring to an ability on the part of the parents to care for children was next introduced. The patient talked about big families, his coming from one of such a size, his being called a baby by his mother (he was the last of nine siblings), and his feelings of being devaluated in this role, particularly in relationship to his brothers. It appears that there were attempts to defend himself against infantile, particularly oral-dependent tendencies, by establishing himself as an active, vigorous person who had unique abilities (carpentry) which his brothers didn't have.

In talking about his own family, consisting of wife and three girls, following each other like rungs on a ladder, he indicated that only two were planned for, but hasty protestations follow about how the third one (the baby) is liked. Three children is the absolute maximum for him because he feels that he could not support more. One wonders if there is some projective component involved in his reference to the wanted but unplanned-for child, that is, does he identify himself as having been in such a position once?

It was possible, with some persistence, to finally get behind the barrier of superficiality and rationalization, and then the content that was elicited indicated that the patient had been subject to severe stress situations, first a year and a half before, and more recently, six weeks before admission to the hospital. Both involved his relationship with a brother-in-law described as rigid, overbearing, authoritarian, and finally impossible to work for. At the beginning of this work relationship, there was the development of sudden severe abdominal pain and the patient was operated on for appendicitis. Six weeks before admission and following the accumulation of marked hostile impulses directed inward, the patient developed stomach pain; again the gastrointestinal tract was involved. The patient had handled this hostility in the beginning by trying to hold in his feelings, by trying to avoid arguments, but eventually this became impossible, and yet, even though he engaged in verbal interchanges, very little relief was experienced. Most of the anger could not be adequately discharged through affective pathways of expression.

PHYSICAL HISTORY

Seven weeks before admission, the patient noted the onset of dull epigastric aching when his stomach was empty. The pain was relieved by eating. Four weeks before admission, he went to his local M.D. who told the patient he had an ulcer and put him on a diet with gelusil. The pain disappeared, and he became asymptomatic. He was, however, advised to come into the hospital to have the diagnosis confirmed.

PHYSICAL EXAMINATION

Nasal septum deviated to the right. The heart showed a Grade I apical systolic murmur; no enlargement. There was no epigastric tenderness, and the remainder of the physical examination was negative.

LABORATORY DATA

Serology, blood counts, urine, stools, nonprotein nitrogen all normal.

ROENTGENOGRAMS

Chest and gallbladder films showed no abnormalities. Gastrointestinal series revealed a small duodenal ulcer in the center of the bulb.

HOSPITAL COURSE

The patient was afebrile throughout. He was given a Gastric IV diet with antacids, sedation, and antispasmodics. He remained asymptomatic during his hospital stay.

DISCHARGE DIAGNOSIS

Duodenal ulcer, active, treated, improved.

COMMENT

The patient had become rapidly asymptomatic physically by the time the interview was held. A shifting of defenses was obviously taking place. References to physical symptoms included little in the way of actual sensory perceptions; instead, denial and rationalization of the symptoms were becoming more prominent. The patient was oriented toward going home and away from the hospital, and was thus uninvolved enough so that relatively freer associations about his original physical disability were not forthcoming. However, behind the screen of rationalizations and superficiality it was possible even at the beginning to note certain dynamic components in the content, as far as the symptom of pain in the stomach was concerned. In addition, clear temporal relationships could be elicited between the development of his gastrointestinal illnesses and severe psychological stresses which he was experiencing on each occasion.

CASE 21

CHIEF PRESENTING SYMPTOM	Stomach pain
SENSORIMOTOR CONFIGURATIONS	Sensory configurations

Interoceptive
Connected with repressed, long-standing oral-dependent needs, particularly in relationship with mother and wife

Motor configurations

Activity
Associated with need to appear as a responsible adult, and linked with competitive hostility toward male parental figures

SOMATIC IDENTIFICATION	*Friends* Ulcer, perforated, operated on during recent years
SENSITIZED ORGAN SYSTEM	Gastrointestinal tract—stomach
STRESS (*surface meaning*)	Brother-in-law trouble and need to change jobs
STRESS (*dynamic significance*)	Threat to security, competitiveness with a parental figure, activation of dependent needs and mobilized hostility
DEFENSES	Laughing denial Superficiality Rationalizations Many activities with attempts to prove himself unique

AFFECTS	*Intensity*	*Pathway of expression*
Anxiety	+	Ideational, somatic equivalents
Depression	+++	Some ideational, somatization
Hostility	+++	Some ideational, somatization

OTHER FACTORS	"Baby" of a large family Orality
HOMEOSTATIC SHIFT(S)	First a regressive somatization shift which began quickly to reverse itself, with return to former defensive alignment in which ideational and behavioral elements predominated
DIAGNOSIS	Duodenal ulcer, active, treated, improved

case 22

Gastrointestinal Complaints: Patient's Need for Diagnosis of Organic Illness

CHIEF PRESENTING SYMPTOM

Stomach trouble.

BASIC ANAMNESTIC EXCERPTS

"I've been having it for a year and a half or so. A year ago I went to a doctor who had my stomach X-rayed, and the results were duodenal ulcer, and he put me on a diet. He said that the diet was that I just eat what you feed a nine-months-old baby and stop smoking. Well, I didn't; I cut down on smoking and tried to stay pretty close to the diet, but it seemed that my ulcer was getting worse. Since I've turned into the hospital here, I noticed that I still have gas, but it isn't burning. When I belch or when I used to, it burned all the way up, but now it doesn't. And then another thing is that I've been constipated. Sometimes I won't pass my bowels for about three or four days, and it's usually very, very hard and small and drips out. Sometimes I notice that there's just a slight bit of blood on the paper where I had to force myself to pass it—just very, very slight, that's all.

"Every night lately that I've come home from work, I just get filled up. At night I might have stew. Just as soon as I'd get that in my stomach, I'd fill up, then want to lay down and go to sleep for the night. In fact, I also come home from work at noontime and I lay down, and then my mother would have to wake me up to go back to work.

"There's a lot of gas in my stomach all the time, and I'm constantly burping, and then when I'm at work, I'm passing gas through my bowels all the time. There's burning, a fiery sort of feeling. Also I get a feeling of being filled up." The patient again refers to constipation and gas: "It isn't loud or anything, like little air bubbles are passing through. The

198

movements are very hard, dark, have to be forced out. I used to be very regular when I was in military service. I think much of it was because I had regular meals and everything."

The next references are to preparation of food: "The meals are prepared by my mother. She doesn't have too much imagination, and the doctor told her to make whatever you give to a nine-months-old child. But that wasn't specific enough. She gives me chicken sandwiches. I eat a lot of chicken sandwiches. And stews and macaroni. Those are the things that stand out (pause).

"I used to be a great eater. I drink a lot of milk now. Maybe that has something to do with my weight going up. But I do a lot of exercise, too. I'm an expediter in a manufacturing plant, and I have to walk all over the factory all day long, you know, checking shipments. When I took that job, I thought that it would help with my bowel movements, because I've always heard exercise is good for them. I've been with this company about seven years.

"After I'd been taking baking soda every suppertime, my mother finally told me to go see a doctor. He said I had an ulcer, and he wanted me to go on a diet. When the X-ray was taken, I was told it was a small ulcer. My boss, my supervisor, has an ulcer."

The patient next refers to his family: "I was married a year ago and I have a baby, and my mother and my brother . . . My father died when I was 11 years old. He fell down the cellar stairs and fractured his skull. It was just about Christmas time, and we children and my mother were upstairs decorating the tree. My father came home, put his lunchbox down, went out to feed the chickens or something, and he came back and there was a crash. He tripped and I ran down and lifted him up, and his hands were all blood, and we ran next door and called the ambulance and they took him up, and he died in the hospital that night. It must have been an accident; he was a very healthy man, very big and strong." (The patient becomes tearful.)

"Next month it'll be a year that we're married. We have a four-months old baby (pause). Well, I had to get married. I had been going with her for a couple of years. I probably would have married her anyway, but not so soon. But I got excited a couple of nights. Anyway, now we have a four-months boy. He can eat chopped foods now, I think. Strained food, that 's right, and regular milk—whole milk. No trouble feeding him. A big baby when he was born. My wife had a little trouble, and she had to have a blood transfusion. I don't know why. There's no use worrying about it. It's all over anyway."

There is a further elaboration of worrying tendencies: "I know I used to worry about taking a test in school and things like that. I'd smoke a lot of cigarettes and drink coffee and be kind of worried whether I was going to get a good mark or not. I was studying business administration at college.

"Mother prepares the meals because my wife went back to work after a six-months pregnancy leave, so that she could get back her old job with seniority. While we're away, mother takes care of the child and the cooking. We're not planning any more right now. I'd like to get a little more secure financially; you need to have some money set aside first. Mother's able to do all that at home because she's always liked to keep going. She wants to do something all the time. It's her house. The mortgage was all paid off before my father died. Father worked for a public utility. When he died, there was quite a bit of insurance. Mother spent every penny she had to bring us up and keep us in school.

"After high school I went to work, got called into military service, came out, attended college for three years and returned to work. I took a job in a clothing store. I guess the owner had it on his mind all the time he was going to go into bankruptcy. In the meantime, another fellow he owed some money to came in and said that he was taking over some of the goods, and he'd like to have me work for him because he didn't know what to do with the goods. I had to stay in there all day, and I more or less just grabbed my meals on the fly. I didn't have anyone to relieve me. I worked there from nine o'clock in the morning till six o'clock at night. And as soon as I would bite into a sandwich or something, some customer would come in and I would have to wait on them. And then, too, they used to get me boiling mad. The original owner needed the money so badly that he wouldn't let a customer walk out without buying something. The kind of people that came in just used to get me churning inside. My stomach used to feel like a rock sometimes. So that's what I think is the real cause of it, and I did that for a year, and I don't think I really liked the work five minutes.

"The original owner's wife had ulcers, too. She thought it was just robbing Peter to pay Paul for five years, and she just couldn't stand it, whereas he had a happy-go-lucky way about him, and he said when something like that happened, he'd just think about something funny and start laughing. But me—I couldn't, and she couldn't. I was more or less like her."

PSYCHODYNAMIC IMPRESSIONS

Here also the patient begins not with symptoms but with a diagnosis. When the symptoms are again asked for, there is reference to a recommended baby's diet. After a while, some upper and lower gastrointestinal symptoms are mentioned, but again there is a shift to diagnostic terms and questioning what causes what. Finally, as these resistances are modified, it is possible to learn more about the patient's emotional difficulties.

He has been troubled for a long time by doubts about his masculinity. There are also associated but repressed needs to be looked after. The patient attempts to ward off his concern about himself by intellectualization and overambitious striving. However, decompensation, chiefly in the form of anxiety and lesser depressive reactions, occurs at points of special stress—school examinations, forced marriage, frustrated ambition, problems at work, and financial difficulties. The affects are expressed through various pathways, including somatic equivalents referable to the gastrointestinal tract and concerned with the functions of eating and elimination. This organ system appears to be the most sensitized one, although another psychophysical shift involving the respiratory tract occurred some years earlier; the patient first became depressed and then ill with pneumonia during an anniversary of his father's death, which had been and remains a highly traumatic event in the patient's life. This was evident from the patient's tearfulness when he spoke of the matter during the interview. The latter part of the interview continued to be abreactive in nature, revealing his disappointments and need to settle for a job far below his expectations.

PHYSICAL HISTORY

About two years before admission, the patient noted the onset of a burning sensation in the epigastrium, usually in the evening, starting about one hour before eating, and unassociated with any actual pain—only a "bloated" feeling. Since that time the condition has grown gradually worse. A gastrointestinal series was done a year ago, and allegedly he was told that he had a small ulcer. He states that he was placed on a diet of foods suitable for a baby. The diet afforded him some relief, but more recently his epigastric discomfort returned. He has noted some increased fatigability. There has been no weight loss and no history suggestive of bleeding, obstruction, or perforation.

PHYSICAL EXAMINATION

A rather tense young male who was "belching" frequently. Vital signs normal. There was slightly reduced hearing bilaterally. The remainder of the physical examination was negative.

LABORATORY DATA

Essentially negative, including hemogram, urinalysis, serology, and examination of stools for occult blood.

ROENTGENOGRAMS

Chest film: negative. Gastrointestinal series revealed only questionable deformity of the duodenal bulb. Gallbladder studies: negative.

HOSPITAL COURSE

Patient was afebrile throughout. He was placed on a Gastric III diet with interval feedings, sedation, antacids, and antispasmodics. On this regimen the burning epigastric sensation disappeared, although he still complained of a "bloated" feeling for a few days. The patient was told that he had no organic disease, although he was advised to continue taking antacids and antispasmodics because of the relief they afforded.

DISCHARGE DIAGNOSES

1. No gastrointestinal pathology found.
2. Anxiety reaction, mild, treated, improved.

COMMENT

This patient does not have organic disease. Yet he ascribes his physical symptoms to an ulcer. This diagnosis may have been given him by one of the doctors who treated him before his hospitalization. It may also have been mentioned only as a possibility and could then have been misinterpreted by the patient to be his actual condition. In any event, many patients who have physical symptoms but no organic illness find it difficult to accept emotional disturbance as the most likely basis for these manifestations. In part, this may be due to the lingering stigma attached to emotional illness, and also to the misconception that physical symptoms due to physical disease are real, and those which are not are imaginary. These attitudes are not necessarily only those of the individual with the symptoms, but also may be shared by his relatives, friends, employer, members of various community agencies, and even by some doctors. Considerable reinforcement for such reactions in patients thus may come from outside themselves. However, an essential factor in the persistence of these responses is the patient's own need to avoid facing his emotional difficulties. Consequently, in certain individuals there may be a tenacious insistence that the physical manifestations can only be the result of an organic disease process. They will be displeased with any other explanation and may go from doctor to doctor until they find one who agrees with them.

CASE 22

CHIEF PRESENTING SYMPTOM	Stomach trouble
SENSORIMOTOR CONFIGURATIONS	Sensory configurations

Interoceptive, temperature, visual

Associated with doubts about his physical integrity and that of parental figures with whom he identifies, anxiety in stress situations, and repressed needs to be nurtured

Motor configurations

Working, resting

Linked with getting filled up, forcing out, eating and elimination, and connected with overambitious striving to prove his adequacy

SOMATIC IDENTIFICATION	Father	Accidental fall, death due to skull fracture, patient age 11
	Boss	Stomach ulcer recently (Direct)
	Wife	Difficult delivery, hemorrhage requiring transfusion recently
	Employer's wife	Stomach ulcer recently (Direct)

SENSITIZED ORGAN SYSTEM	Gastrointestinal Respiratory
STRESS (surface meaning)	Forced marriage with complicating pregnancy, frustrated ambitions, work and money problems A previous stress was an anniversary reaction—father's death
STRESS (dynamic significance)	Increased doubts about his masculinity
DEFENSES	Rationalization Intellectualization Overcompensatory ambition

AFFECTS	*Intensity*	*Pathway of expression*
Anxiety	+++	Ideational, affective, somatic equivalents
Depression	+	Ideational, some somatization

Hostility   ++   Ideational affective, some somatization

OTHER FACTORS   Anal references
Troublesome conscience

HOMEOSTATIC SHIFT(S)   Relatively minor in direction of somatization

DIAGNOSES   a) No gastrointestinal pathology found;
b) Anxiety reaction, mild, treated, improved

case 23

Pain in Back and Extremities
Related to Psychological Stress

CHIEF PRESENTING SYMPTOM

"Arthritis."

BASIC ANAMNESTIC EXCERPTS

"I have arthritis, doctor. Bothers my legs a lot. It's in my neck right now. I had this nine years ago. They tell me it was arthritis inside the sacroiliac joints. It affected my sciatic nerves. My left leg got to bothering me so bad that I couldn't work. Last July, I couldn't use a wrench with my left arm, so I changed doctors. Got X-ray treatments and they helped me. It wore off about a month ago, I'd say. I did have it in the military service. Since it came back, it's in my legs and not in my shoulders. But my neck is very sore. Since I got in here, my leg don't bother me. My back bothers me around four o'clock in the morning. I get up, take a shower, and wait for chow. I have a good job, and I want to go home.

"I've taken aspirins. They gave me a lot of them, and they made me sick. My ears were ringing. I went so far that I was getting dizzy, real sick to my stomach. Last night I stood it as long as I could, and then went over and asked the nurse for something to make me sleep. She gave it to me. This morning she told me there was a standing order, if I got pains like that, they should give me something."

When asked to elaborate on the pain: "I don't know what pain feels like. All I know is it hurts, aches. It hurts so much that you just can't stand it (pause). Haven't had pain like that. I've been cut, and I've been stitched, but it's not like this. Pain in the neck gets worse just laying down. If I'm lucky, I can get through the night. Won't bother me, till about four o'clock in the morning. Then it'll wake me up. I get up early anyway. Never sleep late.

"When I was small, I had everything, but never had nothing like today. My mother told me I nearly died of pneumonia when I was about

205

four years old, but I've worked ever since I was 12 years old, made my own way. My father died at the age of 35. He suffered a lot from pain. He had been operated on for an ulcer. My mother was about seven months along at that time. I can just remember him barely (patient grimaces with pain). He left me and my two older sisters. The oldest one worked in a grocery store. I had a grandfather that was pensioned from a railroad. We made it—very hard, of course, but we all stayed together until I was 16. When I worked, I would go from five in the morning until eight, then go to school all day, then work from four till nine at night. Saturdays and Sundays, too. It was quite a schedule (laughing). My mother also worked so hard keeping us together. We're all very close."

There are references to the nervousness of a sister and also his own wife: "That's my next oldest sister. They were thinking of giving her some shock treatments on the outside. My wife has been in the state hospital a couple of times. That's why I say outside. This doctor my sister was doctoring with said she might have to have shock treatments if she didn't straighten herself out. But she's not had any to this time. I guess she's able to take care of her family. . . . My own wife has been in the state hospital twice within the last four years. Nervous breakdown, I guess. Lost an awful lot of weight. I got a psychiatrist to come out and see her. I stayed with her for a week—day and night. She'd want to go for a ride, and we'd go. She'd think someone was watching her, and she'd want to take all the stuff with her. I had the old-fashioned idea about these hospitals, and I hated like hell to put her in one of those. Finally I had to. She spent six months there; they didn't want to turn her loose. But she was hard at me to get her home—so I took her home. She went in there again January this year, 7th or 11th, and she came out on her birthday which was April 25th. Now wait—I'm sorry. It was a year ago. (April 25th was the date of the patient's own hospitalization.) Anyway, we're talking about her—how about me (laughing)?

"We've been married about ten years. She's complained a lot about pain, especially in her stomach. She's had an operation here (right breast) for a small tumor of some kind, and now she got another over here (left breast), and I'm trying to get her to go, but she's frightened, afraid of hospitals. You can't blame her, of course. There are no children. I've been checked, and I'm sterile. We tried to straighten that out, but she was in the state hospital. When she got out, we went to see our doctor. He told me not to have children. Her sickness may be hereditary—or something. So we just told my wife I was sterile—so as not to worry her. I never had no venereal disease in my life. Was never hurt.

"When I was in military service, I hated working on a minesweeper, but what could you do? Once I was dropped to the bottom in a diving suit to untangle cable that got twisted in the screw. After I came up my ears kept hurting. It gradually wore off, about when I was set to leave the service. I can't stand cold in my ears today, but I don't know that that caused it. I do a lot of hunting in the fall and winter, and before I go out, I'll stuff my ears full of cotton. They never bother me any more, if I keep them damn holes filled up.

"I can't sit around. I've got to keep doing something. Work after my job. Always have. My job is repairing shoe machinery. They don't pay so much, although I get by. It's a secure job. I've never been laid off since I've been there. I like to have a free hand in what I do. I don't want anyone pushing me. At work they told me if this arthritis bothers me so much, they'll give me another job. That's the kind of people they are. Nice.

"I don't care to mix too much. By mixing I mean joining clubs, going to parties. My wife doesn't, either. We stay home a lot. When I was a kid, I had no time for sports or athletics. You had to work to survive. I got the work habit (laughing). Keeps you out of trouble (laughing)." The interview ends with a laughing reference by the patient that he's probably a little nuts.

PSYCHODYNAMIC IMPRESSIONS

The first part of the interview is characterized by the patient's use of diagnostic and medical terms. Patients with a chronic disease, or who for other reasons have been frequently examined or hospitalized, and those who have read extensively in the medical literature, may exhibit such an early associative response. In any event, in this patient, the extremities, neck, and back are the sites of incapacity. As the interview continues, pain appears as a chief complaint. Defensiveness about being hospitalized, suggestive of an underlying, strong, infantile need to be taken care of, is prominent. Another expression of this defensiveness is found in the extraordinary range of activity the patient has felt impelled to engage in over the years, warding off opposite trends—the feeling of physical and particularly sexual inferiority (his sterility). In addition, the development of somatic illness has been complicated by secondary-gain factors, especially in relation to his job. When the patient is able to elaborate on the symptom of pain, the associations lead in a variety of different directions to its being unbearable, to being cut (physical castration), to being "nuts" (mental castration), to immobility and fatigue (loss of physical capabilities), to a need to balance tremendous pressures, perhaps by a chronic spastic set in certain parts of the musculoskeletal system, especially the back. These pressures appear in the associative connections not only as physical, but also symbolic of chronic situational tensions. The latter in-

clude his wife's chronic, severe mental illness and its effect on their marriage
and on him personally.

An early, severe childhood illness apparently left a deep emotional
imprint in him about his own physical capabilities. This was followed by
another traumatic experience—the death of his father from an ulcer operation—a loss only partially made up by the presence of a grandfather, with
whom the identification appears principally in the form of extreme activity.
Mother and older sister had to work and often were not at home. Environmental pressures during childhood and adolescence in the form of financial
distress and hardship were dealt with in a driving, active fashion—through
work. The emotional pain of those early years is reflected by an increase in
physical pain during the interview itself, as the relevant childhood memories
emerge.

In military service, he was unhappy in his assignment, and developed
pain in his ears, apparently without organic basis.

Anger and resentment, related to many situational stresses, have had
no real affective pathway of discharge. At times, the patient tries to deny
his troubles by "laughing it off."

PHYSICAL HISTORY

The patient first began to develop aching pains in both thighs, consisting of a tired, hurting pain, nine years ago while in military service. This
has recurred at various intervals, lasting from one day to one week, with
questionable relief when sitting or lying. About one year after the onset,
the patient noted aching pain in the right lower back, which occasionally
was severe enough to completely prevent motion of the extremities and
kept him awake. For this he received diathermy to the legs and back, with
no definite relief. The condition remained unchanged until the year prior
to admission, at which time he began to notice soreness in both shoulder
blades, again at recurring intervals, and occasionally bad enough to prevent
all motion of arms. No relief was obtained with medicines, injections, or
diathermy. In July of the previous year, the patient visited a specialist who
took X-rays, did a sedimentation rate, and told the patient he had Marie-
Strumpell's disease. Following this he received nine X-ray treatments with
no immediate improvement. However, one month later, he started to experience great relief, with only moderate residuals of occasional soreness in
the back, shoulders, and pleuritic pains in both sides of the chest. Just
previous to his admission he had recurrent stiffness of the back and neck
which came and went for one- or two-day intervals. There was associated
tenderness in these areas. He had, however, been able to work steadily and
get relief from the worst symptoms fairly readily with two aspirins taken
every four hours when necessary. He had never noted any pain, swelling,

redness, or tenderness in any of the peripheral joints. He claimed to sweat a great deal, especially on the palms, and became easily fatigued. There was occasional weakness of the left leg, and then especially he would feel he could not support his weight. There was no fever or chills, no weight loss or malaise. Past history, systems review, and family history was noncontributory, except that the patient for the last eight years had been bothered by recurrent rashes on his penis consisting of small, white pimples which would ulcerate and form scabs. These would occur at intervals of about two weeks. There was accompanying severe pruritus.

PHYSICAL EXAMINATION

Temperature 98.6°F. Pulse 74. Respirations 14. Blood pressure 150/90. The remainder of the physical examination was negative, except for (1) tenderness over the upper lumbar spine; (2) pain on dorsiflexion of the back with no obvious limitation of motion; (3) pain on dorsiflexion of the neck with slight limitation in all planes; (4) pain on passive internal rotation of the thigh; (5) the chest expansion was diminished to a maximum of 2″.

LABORATORY DATA

Serology negative. Hemoglobin 14.2 g. Sedimentation rate 15 mm per hr. White blood cell count: 8,950 with 66 percent polymorphonuclear leukocytes. Urinalysis was negative as were stool guaiacs. Nonprotein nitrogen: 33. Fasting blood sugar: 84.

ROENTGENOGRAMS

Chest, both shoulders, and the lumbar spine revealed no abnormalities. However, films of the sacroiliac joints revealed loss of cortex over the lower portion of those joints with an associated sclerosis in the adjacent iliac bone. On the left the lower cortical margins were also indistinct, and there was slight para-articular bony condensation. The picture was thought to be consistent with rheumatoid arthritis.

HOSPITAL COURSE

While in the hospital, the patient was essentially afebrile. The arthritis consultant suggested a diagnosis of rheumatoid spondylitis in view of the X-ray changes. Accordingly, the patient was treated with aspirin throughout the day, Sayre traction to the neck for 30 minutes, followed by infrared and massage to the neck, low back, and buttocks, with active and passive neck and postural low-back exercises. Under this therapy, plus the addition of a neck brace between tractions, the patient gradually became asymptomatic, except for occasional soreness in the shoulders. He was discharged with instructions to continue the exercises, neck traction, and bed boards at home and return for follow-up in one month.

DISCHARGE DIAGNOSIS

Rheumatoid spondylitis, treated, improved.

COMMENT

The patient's chief complaint was "arthritis," with associative references to pain and muscle tension in various parts of the musculoskeletal system. Muscle tension may be noted by clinical observations of spasm, stiffness, or weakness in the individual's posture and walk. Electromyography adds data about the electrical potential of various muscles, when no gross abnormalities can be clinically observed. Gottschalk et al. (1950), studying rheumatoid arthritis, found it possible to make predictions about psychological tensions being present or absent, from physical recordings of muscle tension changes. They felt that such physical tension in rheumatoid arthritis tended to be reduced during the course of psychoanalytic therapy.

In another study which compared ulcer patients and those with rheumatoid arthritis, Cleveland and Fisher (1960) noted that while the presence of marked hostile feelings was not unique in arthritis, some of their defensive maneuvers might be. They found that the arthritic tends to report rather intense physical activity earlier in life, shows a preference for the out-of-doors, and in some there is a close temporal relationship between giving up vigorous activity and the onset of arthritic symptoms. They point to space motility as a possible central point for conflict. At one or another period in the lives of these patients, motility in space serves as an outlet for aggression, but later, following the illness, there may set in a characteristic limitation of mobility and a number of these individuals become unusually interested in cooking, household duties, and the like, which tend to confine them physically. Cleveland and Fisher felt that the arthritic emphasizes the "containing and protecting character" of his body image exterior, while the ulcer patient tends to visualize a body boundary which is "relatively weak and vulnerable." They considered these to be "not mere reflections of symptom discomfort, but basic styles of orientation toward body and environment." Furthermore, the defensive patterns in the arthritic heavily involve reaction formation, whereas the ulcer patient projects his resentment. Still other comparisons note that the arthritic in fantasy "buttresses his body wall, seeing his body and inner feelings as something to be contained and controlled, and is offended by those who don't react likewise." On the other hand, the ulcer patient "sees the body wall as violated and vulnerable, expressing many literal oral fantasies reflective of much dissatisfaction . . . with others."

CASE 23

CHIEF PRESENTING SYMPTOM	"Arthritis"
SENSORIMOTOR CONFIGURATIONS	Sensory configurations

Pain

Associated with great concern over mental and particularly physical integrity, and reflecting reactions to situational tensions

Motor configurations

Activity

Linked with extraordinary work schedule since childhood, serving as defense against inferiority feelings and also as pathway of expression for intense aggressiveness, which is blocked by chronic spastic musculoskeletal set, resulting in relative immobility and increased dependency feelings

SOMATIC IDENTIFICATION

Father	Death due to ulcer, in patient's childhood
Wife	Breast tumor operation recently and in immediate future

SENSITIZED ORGAN SYSTEM   Musculoskeletal system

STRESS (*surface meaning*)   Wife's mental illness—chronic

STRESS (*dynamic significance*)   Frustration, feeling of being trapped, continuing sense of unrelenting pressure, concern about manliness and ability to cope with environmental difficulties

DEFENSES

Laughing denial
Rationalization—intellectualization
Marked overactivity
Reaction formations

AFFECTS	*Intensity*	*Pathway of expression*
Anxiety	+	Ideational, some affective and somatic equivalents
Depression	++	Minimal affective and ideational
Hostility	+++	Minimal affective and ideational, somatization

OTHER FACTORS	Secondary gain
	Severe childhood illness
	Death of patient's father
	Troublesome conscience
HOMEOSTATIC SHIFT(S)	Regressive to a marked somatization reaction which has become relatively set
DIAGNOSIS	Rheumatoid spondylitis, treated, improved

case 24

Chest Pain, Alcoholism, and Resistance to Psychotherapy

CHIEF PRESENTING SYMPTOM

Pain in chest.

BASIC ANAMNESTIC EXCERPTS

"Mostly in my chest, sharp, very sharp for the past year. Tired feeling, like pins, pinpoints, then it starts across my chest. I get these tiresome pains in my neck: It starts off on the left side of the neck, goes to my head, stays there about 20 minutes until I get my mind off of it. Mostly when I'm sitting, doing nothing, or if I'm standing up working, standing up a long time. I can't drive a car—if I move quickly the prick will come, very sharp. It's a short pain, comes and goes. Sometimes it gets so I can't stand up, have to grab hold of something, otherwise I might keel over. Anything can bring it on. For five years I've had it, about once every six months. Then I can't have anybody around me, can't talk to anybody. It started six months ago. Before, it was once every six months. Now it's every day almost, every other day. I went to some doctor who gave me pills to kill the pain. As soon as I stopped taking the pills, it came back. I had X-rays taken and nothing showed there. As long as I'm taking the pills, they kill the pain. When I stop after a few weeks, the pain comes back, and I keep on getting it. That's why I'm in here.

"I first thought it was heartburn. I thought it might be a cigarette cough, but now I get it even if I don't smoke. At first I believed it was my heart, but while I was overseas they took X-rays and said it was alright. I was in the South Pacific in the medical corps. I started out working in surgery, but I got into trouble staying out late, so they put me in the kitchen as a punishment. But I liked the kitchen, so I stayed there the rest of the time. My first work was on a surgical ward, and I didn't like it because I couldn't stand the sight of blood. Couldn't stand the sight of anyone throwing up or anything like that.

"I had these pains even before I entered military service, but they weren't severe then, like a heartburn. I was driving a big cement truck, and it was a strain to handle it. When I was going to grammar school, I used to have, I don't know if it was arthritis. I couldn't walk for six months. I was about 13 years old then. I felt the pain, mostly at night, in my knees. The doctor prescribed stuff to rub on, and it went away by itself. Mother rubbed the stuff on me. I had similar pain nine years ago. I was going overseas, and on the boat I got that same pain in my back and arms, couldn't raise my hands over my head. The doctor prescribed the same thing—I could tell by the peppermint smell. One of the ward boys rubbed it in. The only other pain I had was from appendix when I was 17. I was on a Conservation Corps job, away from home. I was working out on a road, when all of a sudden I keeled over and they brought me to a hospital.

"My father's pretty sick now. He's had this arthritis or whatever it is. His legs bother him, and so do his arms and back. He's been sick maybe about 15 years. He can't stand the pain any more, it's so bad. He's still working, and even though he's sort of shut up, he won't quit. The doctors don't know what it is themselves (sighing). They said it was rheumatism, arthritis, and that's all he got from them, so he's just given up going.

"I've got five sisters—all healthy, inside, I mean outside their marriage sicknesses—you know, having babies, they got sick from that, otherwise they've always been healthy. I'm the only boy (pause). Father is the only sick one, outside of me (smiling, pause). But I keep working like he does.

"Right now I'm a band saw operator. I've been at this job six months. Before that I was in a cotton mill, but I needed more money so I asked the boss. He said if I didn't like the job to find another one. So I did. I have a good paying job now. It's just that nobody wants to keep it because it's awful dusty. It's also tiresome because you've got to stay in one spot. You can't get enough fresh air, even if you open the windows. Some people say that a dusty place is the easiest place to get T. B. or whatever it is. They say dust is bad for lungs, so they're scared to work on it. It's a night job so that I'm away from home all night. My wife—well, there's nothing she can say about it. I'm the boss in the house, since I got married 10 years ago.

"We've got a boy eight years old and a daughter, three. The boy is pretty sickly—got bronchitis I think, always crouping and coughing up phlegm, complaining his chest hurts him. He's been that way now since the day he was born. Always sickly. He had adenoids, too, born with them. We had to wait until he was four years old before we could get them out. This bronchitis or whatever you call it—he's always had it. But the girl is healthy. We've tried everything for the boy, spent a lot of money on doctors, but they can't do anything about it. They say he may grow out of it. It gets specially bad in damp weather. Another thing bothers him then. That's his right foot; he broke it when he was three."

The wife is next referred to and in a disgusted tone of voice: "After having the baby, she was sick, something the matter with her stomach. Lately, she's been getting very nervous, mostly on account of me more than anything else. She worries about the pain in my chest, and she worries about the way I holler at the children, and the way l holler at her and can't get along with her. When I'm home, I can't stay home. I guess it's more worry about the way I feel about my chest than anything else. Can't stand anybody around me then. I just lose control. I hope I can be helped like they did my wife's brother. He had lots of pain from ulcers and from a boil or something inside his rectum. They did a good job on him with surgery."

PSYCHODYNAMIC IMPRESSIONS

It is clear that the patient has basic feelings of insecurity, which are often so great that he cannot face his responsibilities, especially since marriage. Passive–dependent needs, however, appear rather clearly to have been powerful and operative already early in his life, activated particularly by separation situations. There also seem to be somewhat more disguised feminine tendencies: As he grew up he felt surrounded by his five sisters, keenly missing his father who was frequently absent. Currently he compares himself with his sick father whose musculoskeletal system is involved. The patient's reaction to his own chest symptoms is also reflected in his concern about his oldest boy who has chronic lung trouble and accompanying chest pain. The symptom of chest pain is multidetermined, having a variety of symbolic meanings, some bisexual and others representing an objectification of the irritating and frustrating people he is in contact with —his wife, children, father, all his troubles with employers, and the authority figures that he did not mention.

Previous illnesses are associated with activated dependent needs and a strong secondary-gain factor. Hostility is marked and rather openly discharged through affective channels.

Retrospectively, although the patient brought up a number of environmental stresses in the interview, he omitted the one connected with his being on court probation and also did not indicate in any way that he had been drinking heavily to the point of having been arrested for drunkenness. The shifting of dates referable to the onset of his pain may have represented an attempt to cover up this aspect of his current situational difficulties.

PHYSICAL HISTORY

For the past five years the patient has noted sharp, lancinating type of pain located in the left anterior chest, which begins in an area just above the left nipple, proceeding across the left chest to the right. Pain is sharp, knife-like, lasts only ten seconds, and in the past six months has appeared to increase in frequency and severity. Pain occurs at rest as well as on exertion, but turning of the left shoulder and body toward the left appears to aggravate and cause the onset of pain. In addition, for the past few years, patient has noticed headaches located in the occipital and sub-occipital area, described as a drawing or tightening sensation. Sensation lasts for about 20 minutes and spontaneously subsides. This difficulty occurs usually in the afternoon when patient is at work. In the past three months he has noticed increasing nervousness and tremulousness. He and his wife have noted also great irritability during this period of time. Appetite is fair to good, but there has been no change in it. He has lost about six pounds in the three months prior to admission, sweats excessively, but this has been true all his life. He prefers cooler weather. System review and past history are essentially noncontributory.

PHYSICAL EXAMINATION

Vital signs normal. A well-developed, well-nourished male in no acute distress, but apparently apprehensive and tense. There was a fine tremor to the outstretched hands. Thyroid was palpable but was not thought to be enlarged. The remainder of the physical examination was negative, except for a right lower quadrant abdominal scar.

LABORATORY DATA

Serology and urinalyses negative. Hemoglobin 16.6 g with hematocrit 54 percent. Sedimentation rate: 1 mm per hr. White blood cell count 8,700: 35 segmented cells, 25 band cells, 38 lymphocytes, 2 monocytes. Basal metabolism rate: +16. Cholesterol total 256 with cholesterol esters 176. Cerebrospinal fluid examination: negative.

ROENTGENOGRAMS

Chest, skull, cervical and dorsal spine negative.

HOSPITAL COURSE

Patient was afebrile during his hospital stay. Aspirin gave some relief from pain. A social service consultation revealed that the patient had had a number of arrests for alcoholism and was currently on probation for his part in connection with a robbery two years ago. The patient refused psychotherapeutic intervention and was discharged improved symptomatically.

DISCHARGE DIAGNOSIS

Passive–aggressive reaction with somatic components and anxiety in a dependent individual.

COMMENT

Secondary-gain factors are prominently involved in this case. The patient not only uses his physical symptoms as a rationalization for avoiding his responsibilities to his family but also as an excuse for alcoholism and a means of escaping legal consequences. Psychodynamically his physical complaints represent conversion symptoms; however, the more serious aspects of the illness would seem to lie in the realm of his addictive tendencies and difficulties with the law. Thus the physical symptoms appear against a background of deeply dependent needs and superego pathology suggestive of psychopathic traits. Alcoholism, psychopathy, and secondary gain make a formidable combination to deal with in psychotherapy. Such patients seldom are motivated sufficiently to undertake treatment of their emotional difficulties. The development of such motivation requires specially skilled work on the part of the referring agency, social worker, or physician, as well as the consulting psychiatrist. When there are relatively more accessible physical manifestations such as the conversion symptoms noted in this case, it is sometimes possible to enlist the patient's interest and curiosity about these, especially if they produce a degree of suffering, with some likelihood of then favorably influencing the patient in the direction of a therapeutic relationship. Unfortunately, in this case there was outright refusal on the patient's part, and before further intervention could be tried, he left the hospital. In any event, when physical symptoms or illness occur in addicts or psychopaths, the motivation of these patients is apt to be considerably influenced unfavorably by the secondary-gain possibilities that may develop, or favorably if enough suffering is present. However, even under distressing physical conditions, the desire to get well may be interfered with by the uncontrollable craving for the addictive substance, or else by a pressing (though unconscious) tendency to interpret the physical suffering as a form of punishment calculated to relieve superego tensions.

CASE 24

CHIEF PRESENTING SYMPTOM	Pain in chest
SENSORIMOTOR CONFIGURATIONS	Sensory configurations

Pain, tactile, visual, interoceptive

Associated with a variety of symbolic meanings, some bisexual, and others representing irritating and frustrating figures in his life

Motor configurations

Activity

Linked, though insufficient and unstable, with defenses against feelings of basic in-security and passive–feminine tendencies

SOMATIC IDENTIFICATION		
	Father	Painful joints for 15 years
	Child	Bronchitis for eight years (Direct)
	Wife	Stomach sickness for eight years
	Brother-in-law	Painful ulcers and rectal trouble for years

SENSITIZED ORGAN SYSTEM	Respiratory
STRESS (*surface meaning*)	Job troubles; wife's illness and nervousness Unmentioned—trouble with the law
STRESS (*dynamic significance*)	Increasing dependent needs, then frustration, attempts to ward off depression by alcoholism
DEFENSES	Rationalization Denial Addictive tendencies

AFFECTS	*Intensity*	*Pathway of expression*
Anxiety	++	Ideational, some affective, somatic equivalents
Depression	++	Behavioral (concealed), ideational, some affective, little somatization
Hostility	++	Behavioral (concealed), some affective, little somatization

OTHER FACTORS   Orality marked
Feminine tendencies
Secondary gain
Superego pathology

HOMEOSTATIC SHIFT(s)   Addictive, behavioral patterns basically maintained with only mild to moderate somatization response

DIAGNOSIS   Passive–aggressive reaction with somatic components and anxiety in a dependent individual

case 25
Chronic Ulcer Symptoms: Difficulties in Following Medical Advice

CHIEF PRESENTING SYMPTOM

"Ulcer."

BASIC ANAMNESTIC EXCERPTS

The patient's first associations are couched in diagnostic and medical terms. The medicines have not seemed to do any good, and the patient is thinking of an operation. His illness has cost him a lot of jobs, and he has to support a family of seven children. He is disgusted with the whole business and believes an operation would put him on his feet and enable him to hold a steady job. The most recent recommendation of his family doctor is that he have surgery because of the hemorrhages that had already occurred.

When asked again about his symptoms, the patient responds as follows: "I get heartburn and pains running through the center of my stomach. I have a heck of a lot of pain and gas all the time. I'm forever burping. When I'm lying on my back, sleeping, I'd wake up with pains all through here—up and down. Lots of times sitting up would do it because then lots of gas would come up and relieve the pain. The pain is aching more than anything else. In the past year, I've had a shooting pain, knife-like. I don't have it all the time. It hits me like a knife right in the pit of my stomach. If I'm doing anything, it'll break me right off short. I don't feel like moving when it's there. It lasts only a minute or it seems like a minute to me, then it'll go away and I'll be alright (pause, patient grimaces). That's a little one I'm having right now (pause). When the pain is dull, then the stomach's just uneasy all the time; it's uncomfortable. I get heartburn after I eat. It's a burning sensation, but a drink of soda relieves it."

Nine years ago, he had been home on a furlough and had felt well, but on his return to camp, he first noticed epigastric discomfort: "I went on sick call with it. They gave me little CC pills to take, for indigestion or something. Then came the first hemorrhage—suddenly. I was in the hospital three times in four months. The last time I had two hemorrhages and two blood transfusions while I was in the hospital." He was then put on limited service and shortly thereafter discharged: "They finally threw me out. I had some hemorrhages a short while later. I went to the hospital and wanted to be operated on at that time, but it wasn't done, and I got disgusted with the waiting and asked to be discharged. When I got back home, I went on straight milk and got straightened out for a while. But the moment I go back to work, it goes right off again. A diet is difficult with seven kids. I can't ask my wife to set one table for them and one for me. I always have to string along, except when my stomach goes on the blink. Then I don't eat anything. She doesn't go out of her way to knock me off the diet. Where it can be kept in bounds, she keeps it in."

Before the onset of the stomach symptoms, the patient had never been to see a doctor except once when he split his wrist: "I was 15 and was chopping wood. A big crossbeam came down across my wrist, split it open. So I went upstairs and my mother put a bandage on it and the doctor clipped it. My father gave me heck about it. Told me I shouldn't have been chopping with the axe that way. Then the next week he went down and did the same thing and split his hand open (laughing)." The incident was fixed in the patient's mind because his father gave him "so much hell" for it. This appears to be a screen memory involving castration and retaliation fantasies—in relation to the father. Another accident, four years ago, is next recalled: "I got hit in the back by a car while I was walking. The car came right across the road and hit me. I had to go to the doctor for heat treatment."

The patient next brings up his otherwise good health and good appetite as a youngster. He was the youngest of seven children. When the patient was four, he was the only child at home, since all the others, grown up, had already left. The father is now 83, so that he was approximately 53 when the patient was born. Further references to father follow: "He worked up to the time he was 80 in a paper mill. I could never work there. Three years ago he fell in the mill and hurt his leg. They retired him because of water on the knee. He spent 35 years in that sulphur smell. Once was enough for me."

There follows a reference to there always being plenty to eat, then to fluctuations in weight during sickness. His weight has gone up in the past four months. He was laid off one job four months ago and took another job as salesman on the road, selling TV, radios: "I got too nervous. My stomach went to pieces. I started being bothered pretty heavy on my stomach. I don't know if it's the tension of trying to make the sale or what. It made me nervous. It all reacted on my stomach. So I haven't worked since this last time, just collected unemployment insurance. I just help my wife around the house.

"With the crew she's got, she can stand a little help. Seven kids. We've been married nine years. They came one after another. We tried the rhythm system and it didn't work. We tried everything else, and it didn't work; she'd still get pregnant. Anyway, she can't have any more. She lost the last one at six months. She hemorrhaged and was in the hospital a couple of times within a month. She may go to the hospital this fall to be operated on. The doctor says she could stand a rebuilding job, set everything back in their proper positions."

The next references are to his parents: "Mother is 73. She's had high blood pressure this past year. This winter she had a pretty bad cold, and got bronchial asthma. She'd never been sick before. I worry about her health." At this point the patient fingers a long scar on his face, and he is asked about it: "I fell on a nursing bottle when I was learning to walk, when I was a year old. They tell me I tripped over the doorstep, and a doctor sewed me up. They had just taken the stitches off, when my sister took me out, and I tripped and fell again and split it open. It got filled full of sand, so they had to go and scrape it off and sew it up again."

Again the patient's thoughts return to the matter of an operation for his stomach condition: "I've thought of it for years. The doctor now thinks where all the medicines have been exhausted, surgery would be the best thing. If it's not there, and I feel better and can go on a job to work steady, it's worth it. The pension is the least of my worries because in the past 10 years I've lost more money than the pension will even give. The ulcer has cost me more than it's worth by a long shot. All these hemorrhages require an operation." (The somatic identification with his wife reappears quite clearly.)

PSYCHODYNAMIC IMPRESSIONS

Here again the presenting symptom is in the form of a diagnostic term, and the early associative connections are in largely medical terms. There is a persistent focus on operation as the cure. These developments occur against a background of chronic symptoms and illness referable to the upper gastrointestinal tract. Pain appears finally as the chief symptom. It is connected with situational stress—the inability to hold jobs and the responsibility of providing for a large family. Pain is further linked with hospitalization and hemorrhage in the past.

The patient, the youngest of seven, had a special status in the sibling constellation—being separated by 12 years from the next oldest. He was left alone at an early age with mother, and became a focus of her considerable, overprotective attentions. He was a feeding problem and had many stomachaches as a child.

Original onset of ulcer symptoms was connected with highly traumatic separation experiences. As the years went by, the somatic manifestations became chronic, due to multiple exacerbating situational factors—the increasing financial burden and the many children, one after another, despite every effort to prevent childbirth. More recently, tensions associated with a selling job were reflected in the highly sensitized stomach with exacerbation of symptoms. Another recent precipitating factor was a six-months' pregnancy lost by his wife when she hemorrhaged badly.

Chronic intense hostility, severe guilt, shunting of affect discharge to somatic pathways are other psychological factors that can be noted in the interview material.

PHYSICAL HISTORY

The patient first noted sharp epigastric pain and heartburn thirty minutes after meals 10 years ago, while in military service. A month after the onset of these symptoms, he had his first episode of hematemesis and melena and was hospitalized but not transfused. Within two months he had two more episodes, the last requiring transfusion. He was discharged from service 10 months after the onset. Two years later he was hospitalized for hematemesis and melena, again transfused, but X-rays for the first time were said to show duodenal ulcer and supposedly had shown it again since that time—the last one two years prior to admission.

Since that time he had had frequent symptoms of pain, belching, and weak, shaky periods relieved by food and frequent episodes of vomiting—necessitating a straight milk diet. He felt that his symptoms were worse in spring and fall. He had been under the care of his private physician for seven years and was given diet, antacids, and antispasmodics. He could not afford to stay on the diet, and had had no interval feedings. He began to use soda bicarbonate extensively. He had not been employed during the four months prior to admission, partly because of ulcer symptoms. He had gained about eight pounds during this period. Reason for hospitalization at this time was that the patient had suggested surgery on several occasions to his physician, who had always acquiesced, and the patient felt that the time had come for him to be operated on.

PHYSICAL EXAMINATION

A well-developed, well-nourished white male in no apparent distress. Except for hyporeflexia in the lower extremities and blood pressure of 106/66, the remainder of the physical examination was negative.

LABORATORY DATA

Hemogram, serology, urinalysis, stool guaiac, blood chemistry serum amylase, and total protein within normal limits.

ROENTGENOGRAMS

Chest plate and gallbladder series revealed no abnormalities. Gastrointestinal series showed equivocal changes interpreted as deformity of the duodenal bulb. A repeat gastrointestinal series was interpreted as: stomach negative but duodenal cap is grossly and persistently deformed without definite evidence of crater; the rest of the duodenum and proximal jejunum are negative.

HOSPITAL COURSE

On admission the patient was placed on a Gastric II diet, antacids, antispasmodics, and night feedings. He continued to have dull pain plus occasional heartburn intermittently relieved by milk. The patient was seen at medical–surgical conferences, and there was general agreement that he should have surgery because of his total inability to manage his ulcer medically and the long history of ulcer symptomatology. Report from previous hospital indicated that at that time no definite ulcer, only a slight irregularity of the duodenal cap, had been demonstrated. With repeat gastrointestinal series showing gross deformity of the cap during the present hospitalization, the problem was further discussed with the gastrointestinal consultant, who concurred in the recommendation for surgery. The patient was then transferred to the surgical service where a subtotal gastrectomy and gastroenterostomy was done under spinal anesthesia, with uneventful postoperative course.

DISCHARGE DIAGNOSIS

Duodenal ulcer, chronic, treated surgically, improved.

COMMENT

The patient's protestations directed against receiving a pension are in the form of various rationalizations which include blaming medical personnel and previously prescribed treatment for not effecting a cure and thus forcing him into a financially dependent position. However, the patient's emotional dependency and insecurity existed a long time before the development of his ulcer, though this physical state now both reflects his psychological problems and is a source of secondary emotional reactions. The question can be raised whether the patient was able to follow medical advice and treatment recommended to him. The difficulties which many patients encounter in following treatment programs prescribed by their physicians is well known. Such problems become especially evident when the regimen is to be adhered to for any prolonged period of time, as in chronic physical illness. There are drugs to be taken, diets to follow, rules about exercise and rest, and various physical procedures. What is often overlooked, or at least not understood, however, are the emotional factors which play a significant role in the individual's behavior. Some patients who follow medical recommendations meticulously are apt to be rather obsessive–compulsive in their character structure. Others are wrapped up in themselves and their illness, and keep a most careful check on their state of health, including all aspects of treatment. Those of the latter group, whose hypochondriacal preoccupation is mixed with doubts and underlying distrust of the doctor, will frequently discard one physician and the treatment he prescribes for another. Other patients consciously and unconsciously sabotage the regimen which has been suggested, for different reasons. Sometimes, limited infantile masochistic needs are gratified in this way, or a more serious self-destructive tendency is acted out. The patient does not follow the medical advice because of strong, emotionally and irrationally determined needs to hurt himself. In other instances, stubborn contrariness, an acting out of infantile rebellious tendencies, may interfere. Then, of course, there is always the additional possibility of the advantage to be gained through illness, the secondary gain which may symbolically represent the help, protection, and right to privileges which the patient emotionally needs as assurance against what for him would be the threat of rejection and abandonment. Whenever difficulties arise in the successful implementation of a treatment program, time and effort spent in trying to discover and understand (at least to some extent) what psychological components are involved will often be in the patient's best interests.

Another aspect of this patient's case is his insistence on having an operation. Without question, certain reality elements are behind his demand. However, these are not the only determinants. This patient has intense hostility and concomitant guilt feelings. This discomfort from the ulcer and its incapacitating effect, real and exaggerated, seems, however, to have become insufficient to adequately contain the guilt. Another means of dealing with superego tensions may then be through persistence of ideational systems concerned with the cutting out of the organ which is so highly symbolized and emotionally invested.

CASE 25

CHIEF PRESENTING SYMPTOM	"Ulcer"
SENSORIMOTOR CONFIGURATIONS	Sensory configurations

Pain, interoceptive

Associated with early feeding problems, frequent stomach symptoms as a child, separation experiences, and current responsibilities of providing for a large family

Motor configurations

Activity

Linked with physical trauma, symbolic associations of castration by and retaliatory hostility toward father, as well as anger at frustration of oral-dependent needs, with accompanying guilt

SOMATIC IDENTIFICATION	Father	Painful leg, water on the knee, three years ago
	Wife	Difficult recent pregnancy with hemorrhage (Direct)
	Mother	High blood pressure, asthma

SENSITIZED ORGAN SYSTEM   Gastrointestinal tract—stomach

STRESS (*surface meaning*)   Inability to keep job with consequent financial troubles; wife's illness requiring operation
Much earlier—problems of adjustment in military service

STRESS (*dynamic significance*)   Activation of inadequacy feelings and deeply dependent needs; wife's inability to fulfill his infantile expectations

DEFENSES   Rationalization, projection
Humor

AFFECTS	*Intensity*	*Pathway of expression*
Anxiety	+	Some ideational and affective
Depression	++	Some ideational, somatization
Hostility	+++	Some ideational, somatization

OTHER FACTORS   A feeding problem in childhood
Secondary gain
Severe superego

HOMEOSTATIC SHIFT(s)   Regressive toward marked and relatively fixed somatization

DIAGNOSIS   Duodenal ulcer, chronic, treated surgically, improved

case 26

Anorexia in a Patient with Markedly Unstable Psychophysical Equilibrium

CHIEF PRESENTING SYMPTOM

Inability to eat.

BASIC ANAMNESTIC EXCERPTS PSYCHODYNAMICALLY
INTERPRETED

The interview was brief because of the patient's marked anxiety and depression.

The inability to eat, more noticeable in the two weeks before admission, is associated with several episodes of vomiting, but nothing usually comes up, except some blood-tinged mucus. There is also frequent cough and pulling sensation in abdomen and easy fatigability. The patient has connected his symptoms with ulcer—he has heard about this illness from friends.

In associating to this symptom cluster, the patient brings up his mother's illnesses. Twenty-six months ago she developed pneumonia and had to be hospitalized. Her chief symptoms then were severe, persistent cough, extreme fatigability, and weakness; here a definite somatic identification can be noted. Following recovery from this illness she was well until four months ago when she began to complain of back pain while sitting on a piano stool. The patient, who is single and lives at home with his mother and two younger brothers, urged her to seek medical advice. Finally one doctor treated her for several months without success and without taking X-rays. Another doctor took X-rays which showed that the edges of her backbone were "eaten away." One month ago she lost her appetite, and two weeks later she was taken to a cancer hospital. The somatic identification and temporal relationships involving separation are again quite clearly connected with the onset of and particular kinds of symptoms developed by the patient.

The patient next associatively recalls that, several months after his mother's original illness with pneumonia, and actually then two years before his present hospitalization, he developed severe vomiting and had to be hospitalized. At that time X-rays were not taken. He remembers being given a sleeping pill, and then he "blew as high as a kite," had hallucinations in which he saw lights and heard rasping noises, and wanted to run from the hospital. He was committed to a state mental hospital where his mental symptoms subsided and he was discharged at the end of a 30-day commitment.

The patient then indicates that except for a period in military service, he has always lived at home, never cared much for girls, and never went out with them. The very close attachment to mother is quite apparent, though not verbalized. He is the oldest of four siblings, there being a married sister who lives away from home. His father died when the patient was 14. This occurred while the father was doing rescue work during a flood and his boat tipped over; the body was never recovered. The patient had always been a finicky eater and recalled that some time after his father's death this tendency became quite marked. His mother, then, had to go to work as a schoolteacher, and shortly thereafter the patient himself went to work. He has held a number of nonskilled jobs, has brought his earnings faithfully home to his mother, and has sought little social life outside the home.

PHYSICAL HISTORY

The patient stated that for the week and a half prior to admission he had completely lost his appetite. Just prior to this, his mother was hospitalized because it was discovered that she had carcinoma. Patient states that he ate practically nothing for a week and then, three days prior to admission, he vomited four times in the period of one hour, bringing up a quart of material altogether. The first two times, the vomitus was yellowish–white in color and contained no food particles. The third time he brought up about half a cup of bright red blood. Associated with the vomiting was epigastric burning distress which has persisted to the present. There was no recurrence of vomiting and the patient was able to take milk without distress. Two years prior to admission, the patient had a similar attack of vomiting, lasting two days. He was hospitalized for a few days but had a psychotic reaction for which he was committed for 30 days. During the two-year interim to the present, he had no gastrointestinal complaints but felt easily fatigued. There was no history of constipation, diarrhea, change in bowel habits, blood, or melena.

PHYSICAL EXAMINATION

Revealed a very apprehensive, tense, markedly nervous, well-developed, well-nourished white male in no acute distress. Vital signs normal. The physical examination was within normal limits.

LABORATORY DATA

Hemogram, sedimentation rate, serology, urinalysis, and stool guaiacs: negative.

ROENTGENOGRAMS

Chest and gall bladder series negative. Gastrointestinal series: stomach normal in appearance, not enlarged, and nothing to suggest previous existence of obstruction. The duodenal bulb was normal in outline, but contained very large and irregular mucosal folds with no definite ulcer crater demonstrable; the appearance of the bulb was considered definitely abnormal and suggested inflammatory changes possibly productive of edema. A six-hour film showed no retention.

HOSPITAL COURSE

Patient was afebrile during his hospital course. He was started on a Gastric I and rapidly increased to a Gastric IV diet, following which his symptoms promptly disappeared. He was seen in formal consultation by the psychiatric service; it was noted that his symptomatology appeared to be exacerbated by extreme tension and anxiety brought on by situational stress. The patient did not wish psychiatric treatment and was discharged on a six-meal bland diet with antacids and antispasmodics.

DISCHARGE DIAGNOSIS

Duodenal ulcer, treated, improved.

COMMENT

The patient elaborates his own symptoms relatively little, but does describe his mother's physical difficulties much more freely. His identification with her is marked, and this is currently reflected in the symptom of anorexia. When a patient is so emotionally involved with another person, associations about such an individual may be disguised references about the patient himself. Much earlier in childhood, the patient had been a finicky eater with frequent stomach upsets which persisted as he grew up, often becoming linked with emotional disturbances. In addition, during puberty, he had had a severe depressive episode following the sudden loss of his father who accidentally drowned.

Two years before his present illness, the patient had reacted sharply when his mother was suddenly hospitalized with pneumonia. His symptoms were first physical, reflecting the sensitized response of the stomach which had become a principal target organ during emotional upsets. Then, as his stomach symptoms were subsiding, he had a sudden, acute psychotic episode. The gastrointestinal symptoms disappeared as the mental illness reached its peak. The psychosis in turn was of short duration, and he had recovered from it at the end of his 30-day hospital commitment. Such marked changes in psychophysical equilibrium have already been described in some detail in Case 6.

Paneth (1959) reported two cases of duodenal ulcer in which there was an alternation between the physical symptoms and psychosis, the former subsiding as the latter developed. A connection between the two conditions is suggested by similarity of psychodynamic factors contributing to the production of the ulcer and the content of the psychosis. The intense dependency needs become much more manifest in the psychosis. Attempts to compensate for these needs, when unsuccessful because of activation due to the continuing presence of the disturbing figure (mother or mother image) or efforts to disengage from this person, cause further regressive shifts from fantasies that food is harmful and symbolizes mother, to delusions of being poisoned by the mother image. The delusion takes over, as it were, the expression of the same dependent needs which formerly found an outlet through the ulcer.

It should be further noted here that less dramatic and intense shifts from physical to psychological manifestations, and vice versa, can also occur in a given episode of illness. In several ulcer patients seen in psychotherapy, as somatic symptoms subsided, feelings of depression became manifest. On the other hand, certain obsessional patients, whose rigid psychological defenses are beginning to be loosened by the therapeutic process, may then experience physical sensations or symptoms which had been absent when they started treatment.

The patient's current physical illness also began in close temporal relationship to his mother's hospitalization, this time for cancer. His own disability now manifests itself chiefly in somatic form. His affective response, except for some indications of anxiety, appears to have been blocked off. The patient's relationship with his mother had been a very close one and had existed with little modification for a long time until her recent illnesses. Such enduring intensity of a specific object relationship, should it be suddenly disrupted, makes for the possibility of severe psychophysical repercussions. This could be physically or emotionally disastrous for the patient if the significant object is permanently lost and no adequate substitute found.

VARIABLES

CASE 26

CHIEF PRESENTING SYMPTOM	Inability to eat
SENSORIMOTOR CONFIGURATIONS	Sensory configurations

Interoceptive

Associated with feeding problems in childhood, very close attachment and identification with mother, and marked separation reactions

Motor configurations

Ejection

Linked with vomiting, coughing, and symbolically expressive of the intensely hostile aspect of the ambivalent relationship with mother

SOMATIC IDENTIFICATION   Mother   Acute pneumonia with marked fatigability, two years ago; Stomach cancer with spinal metastasis, four months ago

SENSITIZED ORGAN SYSTEM   Gastrointestinal basically—stomach
Respiratory

STRESS (*surface meaning*)   Mother's illnesses

STRESS (*dynamic significance*)   Threat of loss of mother to whom there is a very close attachment, activating intense passive–dependent trends

DEFENSES   Denial
Projection

AFFECTS   *Intensity*   *Pathway of expression*

Anxiety   +++   Affective, ideational, some somatic equivalents

Depression   +++   Somatization, some affective

Hostility   +++   Somatization

OTHER FACTORS   Marked orality and feminine identification
Superego pathology

HOMEOSTATIC SHIFT(s)   Severe regression to psychotic state two years ago, following mother's first illness, with subsidence of somatization response focused on gastrointestinal system; currently, reactivated somatization

DIAGNOSIS   Duodenal ulcer, treated, improved

case 27

Eye Trouble, Endocrine Dysfunction, and Psychotic Episode

CHIEF PRESENTING SYMPTOM

Eye trouble.

BASIC ANAMNESTIC EXCERPTS

The patient's immediate associations are to being out of military service for the past six years and having lost 40 pounds in that time. The next references are to a state of nervousness during this interval: "I've been more than nervous. The only thing that gives me peace and comfort is to go away from the house and kids. However, being alone in a room here in the hospital is something I couldn't take; it's better for me that I'm on the ward with others."

Then he refers to the eyes: "There's a tiredness in them that makes it hard for me to see. When I was in military service, it was very hard for me to awaken in the morning. When I was a kid, I used to have disturbed sleep, nightmares, jumping out of bed and running around. Mother would come in as she does now sometimes and startle me so, that I almost poked her. I'd get the feeling of being tangled up in the blankets and feeling trapped.

"I was a medical corpsman and remember seeing soldiers being blown up by dynamite. I had to pick up pieces of human beings, couldn't stand looking at them, didn't want to stay in the medics. Finally I was transferred to truckdriving."

Once again there is a shift to the theme of getting away: "My greatest ambition is to leave the city—so I won't have relatives coming in and out telling me what to do and how to live my life, especially my mother. She dominates and interferes. She makes me unhappy whenever she's with me and my own family. Mother divorced father when I was 10 years old, and I haven't had a father since then. My wife comes from England, and Mother seems to think she doesn't do things like Americans. But with three kids, how can she? Mother criticizes her and calls her sloppy. We have enough trouble as it is. Our youngest was born seven months ago, had pneumonia, and was hospitalized for almost three months. Mother's a gossip, a busybody; she has to know our plans and it's none of her business. She just won't find any interests outside of us. She stays cooped up in her room and won't go out and find friends of her own. I don't want to account to her for all my actions because then your life isn't your own. I think she's a paranoid because she thinks we're talking about her all the time. My wife is a good cook and a good housekeeper. I can cook good, too, because I learned to do it myself when I was left home by Mother while she went to work after she was divorced. You see, if I didn't cook, I didn't eat. I remember that I was boarded out part of this time; but the woman who was supposed to take care of me kept me restricted. So finally I went back to my own home."

There now follow some references to his father: "He was a shoe-cutter but was often out of work. He was such a nervous person himself because of his own bad childhood: His own parents ate butter while they gave their kids lard. Today he doesn't weigh 110 pounds (the patient's weight). I've been told he's had a nervous breakdown." The associations next refer to a benevolent (idealized) father figure in the person of a high-ranking Army officer: "This colonel took a liking to me and I to him. A lieutenant cracked me up in a jeep, and the colonel punished him and promoted me."

The theme of activity follows: "I've never slowed down in my life. When I was 18, I started working. All I have to do is see how something is done once and I can do it. I've learned to take things apart and put them together. When I was in the service, I was the only one who could handle and take apart big trucks. I've jumped from moving trains and trucks without getting killed because I'm a good judge of distance. I could get those trucks through the tightest places without scraping any paint. I've maneuvered enormous tractors into hatches." The associations are suggestive of sexualized material, but also contain elements of grandiosity.

Again there are references to the eyes: "I've started to read a little. Once I get started, I go right through a book. At one time I read hundreds of books, interesting things, scientific and not childish." There follows more boasting about being able to put an automobile engine together without having taken a course: "I'm a mechanic of all trades. I've always enjoyed taking things apart and putting them together. I can change the performance of a car, just did it on my own. I find after taking things apart and putting them together, I know more than they've specified in the plans." With the grandiosity there is now a euphoric response: "I feel I have the ambition and courage to push way ahead.

"I haven't pushed myself too much in the last five months. My last job was in an ammo depot, loading and unloading five-inch shells. Before that I worked in a gas station but found I couldn't stand on my feet—they're flat. That was one reason I was put off the job. I've been trying to get arch supports and some false teeth." More exaggerations follow: "Ten years ago I had two extractions. My mother came up that morning, and when she saw me, she said my mouth was out on each side. These teeth had long roots, winding around and crowding each other. They had to strap me and the dentist had to put a foot against my chest to get the teeth out. They were really stuck in there. Some years later, a private dentist had no trouble taking some other teeth out. Now I've been trying to get them replaced. It isn't helping my indigestion any without having teeth to chew."

There are further references to work and to mother: "Before I was in military service, I went to bed early and got a good night's rest; mother taught me that. I wasn't out with the kids in the street at night. Mother herself had a tough time all her life. She's worked in many shops. She'd give me a piece of steak once a week and go without it herself. I lived with her in a three-room apartment until I went into service. I'd be alone all day. Right now I live in three rooms with my family. The dampness has ruined the furniture, and it put the baby into the hospital with pneumonia, when we lived in this summer camp last year. At least now where we are is dry and clean. But money is our big problem."

Again the theme of wanting to get away and see different things appears: "There's no fun looking at the shoe factories in the town where I live. They're dark, dreary buildings along the side of the road, with dirty water discharging into the river. I like to see nice, clean, painted buildings. I don't like old, dark, brown colors. I'd like to take a trip around the country and see different things. I specially would like to go to New Hampshire where father lives and see how they live there."

There follows a rambling discourse of likes and dislikes: "I don't like wild horses, monuments, and airplanes, but I do like boats. What I want to see, I see. During the time our ship was sailing from New York harbor, I determined to see the Statue of Liberty. Everyone was supposed to be in the hold. We were going out under secret orders. But I got on deck. There were no guards around, and you were forbidden to be on deck because of security regulations. I had never seen it before, and I wanted to see it face to face, this statue that represented freedom."

PSYCHODYNAMIC IMPRESSIONS

There are clinical indications of a possibly severe regression in the offing: grandiosity, euphoria, rambling, and at times confused stream of thought suggest that a break with reality may be near. The content of the interview, focused around the presenting symptom of eye trouble, reveals ever increasing tension related to multiple stress situations which the patient would like to avoid either by physical separation and activity or by not seeing what is going on.

A key relationship is the one with mother. It is highly ambivalent with the emphasis on negative aspects. She is represented as a dominating, interfering figure in the present; one of her obsessional concerns is cleanliness. In the past the patient had little opportunity for healthy identifications with a male figure. He was alone with his mother for years and was left by her or boarded out because she had to work. Considerable hostility appears in connection with these early relationships seen as separations and rejections. Father, too, is recalled as a figure who abandoned him, and is seen in a devaluated light and also as a deprived person. The longing for a benevolent, protecting, giving father figure is quite clear.

Activity is indicated as a basic defense against deeply dependent needs. However, its adequacy for this purpose is no longer sufficient in the light of accumulating stresses.

Sexualization of certain activities can be noted particularly in the references to the eyes. They may be involved in forbidden looking, associated with guilt and the possibilities of punishment and retaliation. The latter, in part, are represented by castration themes which appear in the associative connections. At other points in the interview, the eyes seem to have a symbolic, phallic meaning as well as symbolically representing organs which are incorporative, i.e., take in objects.

Recent events involve financial stress, close living together under adverse conditions, the baby's prolonged illness and hospitalization, ever growing tensions with mother, mounting hostility, and ever pressing needs to free himself from domination and from responsibilities. Cumulative traumatic factors have broken the existing psychic equilibrium and set in motion a regressive shift which is in the direction of somatization. Enormous aggressive energies, no longer having sufficient discharge pathways through other means, are being directed against the soma. There is, however, an even more ominous note in the turn toward grandiosity, euphoria, and confusional tendencies, which suggest a still further regressive shift toward possible development of a break with reality.

Note: The anticipated further severe psychological regression occurred a few days after the patient was interviewed. The preliminary indicators of grandiosity, euphoria, and intermittent confusion became much more manifest and more extensive, so that the patient's condition, while improving physically, deteriorated mentally; in fact, as the thyrotoxicosis remitted and the auricular fibrillation reverted to a normal rhythm, the psychotic manifestations clinically became more and more pronounced. There then appeared loosely organized and fluctuating delusional systems and intermittent visual hallucinatory experiences in which the central theme was represented by hostile maternal figures who were constantly after him, criticizing him, accusing him of perverse sexual interests, as well as of being a greedy, animal-like creature who wanted to eat everything up. A considerable degree of anxiety developed when these more bizarre psychotic manifestations appeared. The patient kept peering at walls, ceilings, and in corners, as if in response to the hallucinatory experiences. This clinical picture gradually changed. The first symptoms to disappear were the overt paranoid ones, and then there was a diminution in the confusional tendencies. At the end of approximately a month, the psychotic episode had subsided.

PHYSICAL HISTORY

This patient entered with chief complaint of weight loss and nervousness of several months' duration. His story was rather difficult to obtain as the patient was somewhat confused. He had been "nervous" for about eight years, and for the past six months his mother had noted an increased swelling in the region of the thyroid gland. He has been overactive and has eaten about 10 meals a day during this time. There has been a moderate increase in exertional dyspnea, and he has had two pillow orthopnea for two months. There has been increased fatigability. Details of family and past history were difficult to obtain from the patient. However, it was apparent that the home situation was fairly complex and had been stressful for the patient.

PHYSICAL EXAMINATION

Revealed a well-developed, thin, exophthalmic, anxious, hyperactive young white male. There was a coarse tremor of the hands. The hair was soft and silky. Temperature 98°8F. Pulse 100. Respirations 18. Blood pressure 160/85. Thyroid gland was diffusely enlarged and there was a palpable thrill and an audible bruit. The cardiac rate was totally irregular. There was a marked Grade III systolic murmur over the entire left anterior chest, transmitted to the carotid arteries. The heart was thought to be slightly enlarged beyond the midclavicular line by percussion. The hands were warm and moist. There was evidence of generalized muscular wasting. The patient was edentulous. The remainder of the physical examination was essentially within normal limits.

LABORATORY DATA

On admission, hemoglobin 11 g, hematocrit 41 percent, white blood cell count 7,850 with a normal differential. Initial basal metabolism rate was

+61. Urinalysis and serology were negative. Total cholesterol was 148 and cholesterol esters were 94. Stool guaiac: negative.

ROENTGENOGRAMS

Chest normal.

ELECTROCARDIOGRAM

Showed auricular fibrillation.

ELECTROENCEPHALOGRAM

Within normal limits.

HOSPITAL COURSE

During the early part of the patient's hospitalization, he eloped twice, seemed mentally confused, and had amnesia for his second elopement. He was transferred to the closed psychiatric ward for an observation period. Medical regimen of radioactive iodine, propyl thiouracil, digitoxin, sedations, multivitamins, and high calorie diet was instituted. Basal metabolism rate gradually fell to +28. Auricular fibrillation reverted to normal sinus rhythm of 90. The psychotic episode subsided after a month, and the patient was discharged in the care of his relatives.

DISCHARGE DIAGNOSES

1. Thyrotoxicosis, treated, improved.
2. Toxic psychosis, treated, improved.

COMMENT

Here is another instance of shifting psychophysical equilibrium on an extensive scale. A major physical illness remits under the influence of medication as a major psychotic episode develops. In considering the background of this dramatic change, a number of clinical details stand out. The patient was a highly nervous child. His father was himself a very tense person who had a psychotic break early in the patient's childhood. As the patient grew up, overactivity, particularly that of a counterphobic kind, became a chief line of defense against the development of anxiety. This psychological equilibrium was upset by the patient's traumatic combat experiences, leaving him for almost eight years markedly tense, irritable, and somewhat depressed. This chronic emotional reaction was maintained by environmental stimulus nutriment, in the form of recurrent stress which became particularly marked and cumulative in the last six months before hospitalization. Massive aggressive energies accumulated and, being blocked from sufficient discharge via affective, behavioral, and ideational pathways, turned inward with impact on the endocrine system, specifically the thyroid. Why this system and organ were target sites is not clear. There are no references, either in the anamnestic interview or physical history, which suggest a past somatic involvement or constitutional factor affecting the endocrine system. In any event, the somatic response was of such a depth and severity that a serious thyroid dysfunction developed over a period of a few months. Secondary emotional responses to the hyperthyroid condition and its side effects complicated the clinical picture so that not only physical but mental components were prominent. Once proper medical regimen was instituted, the physical manifestations began to ameliorate, but at first, no improvement could be noted in the mental symptoms. Rather, these increased ominously and precipitously, but then ran only a short course.

Thyroid function and psychiatric illness have often been linked together (Gibson, 1962), but the exact nature of the relationship is relatively obscure. Some 250 cases of patients, most of whom had an affective disorder, have been compiled by Richter (1957). A somewhat detailed history of a 50-year-old female patient who developed a psychotic agitated depression two months post thyroidectomy has been described by Libow and Durell (1965b). Triiodothyronine treatment was accompanied by recovery from the psychosis, but after it was stopped a recurrence of the psychotic symptoms took place. This coincided with a marked increase in thyroid-stimulating hormone secretion. It was suggested that there is a specific relationship between the neurophysiological processes associated with psychosis and those involved in thyroid gland function.

CASE 27

CHIEF PRESENTING SYMPTOM	Eye trouble
SENSORIMOTOR CONFIGURATIONS	Sensory configurations

Visual, interoceptive

Associated with loss, destructiveness, nervousness, and an ambivalent relationship with an interfering and domineering mother

Motor configurations

Looking, getting away, working

Linked with forbidden sexualized and hostile impulses, avoidance of traumatic stress situations, longing for benevolent, protective father, and defenses against deeply dependent needs

VARIABLES

SOMATIC IDENTIFICATION	*Father* Underweight recently (Direct)
SENSITIZED ORGAN SYSTEM	Thyroid Eye Brain
STRESS (*surface meaning*)	Financial problems, adverse living conditions, baby's illness, tension with mother
STRESS (*dynamic significance*)	Feeling more and more dominated by mother, with reactive intense hostility and need to free himself from her, and increasing inability to cope with his oral-dependent needs
DEFENSES	Overactivity Projection

AFFECTS	*Intensity*	*Pathway of expression*
Anxiety	+++	Ideational
Depression	+++	Ideational, affective opposite (euphoria)
Hostility	+++	Somatic, ideational, with shift to maximal ideational, behavioral, and diminution of somatization intensity, and then reversal once again

OTHER FACTORS	Abandonment by father; mother frequently absent in childhood Longing for benevolent, protective father figure Oral incorporative tendencies are marked; also present are anal and phallic sadistic elements, and voyeuristic–exhibitionistic trends
HOMEOSTATIC SHIFT(S)	Increasingly severe regression reaching critical level, with development of marked somatization response which is temporarily insufficient to contain enormous aggressive energies, resulting in psychotic episode and diminution in physical symptoms. Followed after a month by subsidence of psychosis, and continued but diminished somatization
DIAGNOSES	a) Thyrotoxicosis, treated, improved; b) Toxic psychosis, treated, improved

FOLLOW-UP DATA

Following discharge, the patient continued on the medical regimen instituted at the hospital. When seen in follow-up six months later, his physical improvement had been maintained and there was no evidence of any psychotic symptomatology. The patient revealed that before his hospitalization his mother had herself been ill, had had several small shocks, but couldn't seem to slow down. Her eyes had become quite "bad." He now wondered when she would have her next stroke. In the meantime, with help from several social agencies, his financial affairs had become somewhat straightened out. His wife was now pregnant for the fourth time.

A period of six years elapsed before the patient was seen again in the thyroid clinic. He had returned for a checkup "to see how things were after all this time." Actually he had few symptoms, chiefly referable to what he called a "nervous stomach." At this time he was euthyroid. Four more children had been born, the youngest just two months ago. The patient had a modest but steady job. He had been able to separate himself more from his mother's influence and presence.

When seen two years later, the patient was still euthyroid and relatively free of symptoms except for vague, mild, long-standing abdominal distress.

case 28

Epigastric Distress, Surgical Intervention, and Chronic Neurosis

CHIEF PRESENTING SYMPTOM

Burning sensation in stomach.

BASIC ANAMNESTIC EXCERPTS

"I find that when I eat something like bacon or a piece of chocolate candy—I'll get a burning sensation. It felt as if I wanted to get it up, but it wouldn't come up, and I'd take something like bicarbonate of soda, but that burnt me at the same time and left a kind of lousy taste. My landlady mentioned a powder that I've found very sweet and soothing, and that did the trick for a while. But I've had this burning again, the last few days it was very uncomfortable." Burning is then further associated with gas, oppression, and burping which affords temporary relief. "My wife does the cooking and does a lot of frying. That fried stuff doesn't agree with me. If it's acid or bitter or fried, I get that burning.

"I never sit down to a man-sized meal. I have a small appetite." He is small in stature and has an effeminate manner. "I don't like liver or lamb. I like steak, but I don't like it medium, even though I know meat eaten with blood in it is good for you, being nutritious. I don't like fat, either. Maybe it's all from childhood. If you always kept away from certain stuff and had your own way in what you wanted to eat, then you could be the same way as you grow to manhood. I've been a small eater from way back. Take my brother. He's a big, robust person. He loved oatmeal. I remember when we were kids, he would eat tremendous bowls of it and love it. I couldn't eat that stuff for all the tea in China. But I had to eat what was put in front of me, so I wasn't catered to then. I wanted to eat cold cereal, but mother forced me to eat hot (burning) oatmeal though I hated the taste of it. My own five-year-old daughter pecks at the food today. I have to force her to eat, but I don't use the methods of years ago.

"The way I treat my child and the way my mother treated me pertaining to food is entirely different. I hope she did it for my good. She gave me just so much time to eat it or else. Maybe it was stubbornness to a certain degree that I couldn't get it down. No matter how hard I tried it would make me sick, and I'd want to gag. Well, if I didn't eat, I'd get a whack, so you ate because you feared a licking. I wouldn't do that to my child. If I see the kid actually gag on it, I know damn well she can't eat it, but if she's just eating little by little, and it's getting on my nerves, I say to her: 'I don't want you to talk again until you're through eating.'

"My wife can eat anything no matter how you fixed it. She could have steak for breakfast. Just the thought of coming out of bed in the morning and smelling steak—well, see you later, dear" (the hostility is hardly disguised).

The wife's pregnancy is next associated to: "This baby is very close to her bladder. She had a fall, took a tumble a couple of months ago. I think the baby dropped a little quicker that it should have. Other than that she's very healthy, just complains of being restless, can't sit too long. She carries it all in the rear, way down and in the back, so that her behind sticks out, like a secretary's spread. But she's a very small person." There are further references to the fall: "She could have hurt herself seriously, probably lost the baby. Until I can get those concrete steps put down, it wouldn't be too good an idea for her to step out of the house by herself. I worry about it, afraid she might trip. Right now she looks big and that's rather funny for a short, petite girl like a Dresden doll. She's just a good little housewife, that's all I can say." (Again there is hostility, thinly covered over by flattering references.)

The patient recalls several operations: "I've had my eyes operated on; they were cut open, what is it, the coronary or cornea was cut. Ten years ago I had my appendix out, and oh, yes, two years ago my gallbladder was removed because of gallstones."

References to the family come next: "Father is a very large man. Both my brother and sister, who are at least eight or nine years older than me, are over six feet. But my mother is small like I am. Brother and father are big eaters, too. I guess I'm just different. They're big and I'm little."

Further associations to the symptoms of burning sensation and gassiness follow: When I was in the hospital a couple of years ago, they said I might have a septic (peptic) ulcer. Maybe my work has something to do with it. I work in the laboratory, assisting with autopsies. When the head fellow is away, off duty, I sew them up. Then there's glassware and stuff like that in the laboratory that has to be sterilized. I've been there eight months. Before that I was an attendant on the paraplegic ward. Let's understand each other. I didn't come in because I was sick. It was that burning sensation over the weekend. I can do a day's work as well as you can right now. I may not have an ulcer. If certain foods don't agree with you and give you that uncomfortable burning feeling, I thought that was symptom of an ulcer. It was when I had my gallbladder out. I came in then for the same thing I'm here for now. Afterwards, they didn't put me on a diet, but let me eat anything I wanted. But after the operation I still felt the same way and have had those symptoms since then."

PSYCHODYNAMIC IMPRESSIONS

Food and eating are central preoccupations. The symptom of burning sensation is prominently related to eating. It is, in turn, closely associated with sensory clusters involving taste and temperature, and also with references to motility—expressed as "going down" and "coming up" in the upper G.I. tract. They are tied in with right and wrong, with temptation and consequences thereof. A sought-for idealized maternal figure appears very early in connection with these themes, but then references to the past reveal clearly the early establishment of conflicts with regard to eating, particularly in reference to his own mother, who is pictured as noncatering, strict, dominating, and forcing.

Rebellious, defiant attitudes are also linked with eating, but these tend to be largely expressed in the form of passive resistance. Hostility toward women is only thinly veiled in terms of the feeding situation and includes his wife and her treatment of their daughter in this regard. He identifies in this context with the mistreated child. There is, however, also further evidence of hostility toward his wife, especially in relation to her pregnant condition, with anticipated loss of her attentions to his infantile needs. This hostility again is only thinly covered over by defensive protesting assertions to the contrary.

The patient's major identification is a passive feminine one, now particularly revealed in activated pregnancy fantasies. There are indicators of his early strong feelings of inferiority in relation to his father and siblings—especially an older brother—because of his own small size. The patient's concern about his manliness has been further accentuated by three operative interventions, seen in part as both castrations and more deeply rooted narcissistic losses. Hostility now seems to achieve a certain affective discharge, particularly in thinly veiled sarcasm, but whether such pathways have been sufficient in the past is questionable. There may be a shifting spectrum of affect block and affect discharge. Anxiety about work is intermittently evident.

PHYSICAL HISTORY

This is the patient's third admission. He was first seen two years ago, at which time he complained of epigastric distress, weakness, and nervousness. At that time a study revealed a solitary gallbladder calculus which was removed at operation. Although the operation was done, it was felt that his symptoms were due to psychosomatic difficulties. He was seen again a year later for much the same complaints, and at that time a gastrointestinal survey was negative. He continued to have much the same symptoms, and at present complains of epigastric distress and sour eructations which occur 10 to 15 minutes after eating. These are often relieved by baking soda or equivalent. The patient also has morning nausea and anorexia. The day preceding admission, the epigastric burning was more severe than usual, and he regurgitated some reddish material which he felt resembled blood. The only other symptom of any note is that of heaviness of the scrotum for which he wears a supporter.

PHYSICAL EXAMINATION

Weight 123 pounds. Vital signs: normal. The patient is an apologetic young man who does not appear in acute or chronic distress. The physical examination was essentially negative.

LABORATORY DATA

Urinalysis normal. Serology negative. White blood cell count 7,000 with a normal differential. Hemoglobin 13.6 g on two occasions, and hematocrit 43 percent and 45 percent. Three stools were negative for occult blood.

ROENTGENOGRAMS

Chest plate and gastrointestinal series were within normal limits.

HOSPITAL COURSE

It was felt again that the patient's symptoms were entirely on a functional basis and that there had been no bleeding, since the patient had no anemia and all stools were guaiac negative. The patient was reassured about his condition, advised to take antispasmodics and sedation as needed, and discharged.

DISCHARGE DIAGNOSIS

Somatization reaction, gastrointestinal; treated, improved.

COMMENT

When this patient was previously hospitalized, according to the records, a solitary nonobstructing gallstone was found, apparently bearing little relationship to the patient's symptomatology then. He had been complaining of vague epigastric distress, weakness, and nervousness. Although an operation was performed, again according to the records: "It was felt that the symptoms were due to psychosomatic difficulties." It seems that surgical intervention had been on an "elective" basis. It not only failed to relieve the patient's symptoms but tended to further fixate his attention on and preoccupation with eating, digestion, and his gastrointestinal tract, an already highly sensitized organ system. Recent emotional crises, involving his new, tension-producing work in the pathology laboratory, and also his wife's current pregnancy, further reinforced this fixation. During this present hospitalization the patient appears to have formulated a new physical illness to explain his persisting gastrointestinal symptomatology. He refers to this new illness, not by chance, as "septic" ulcer, instead of peptic.

Irrespective of how the final decision to operate may be made, once surgical intervention has occurred in a case such as the one described above, the groundwork has been laid for serious psychophysical complications. If an organ has been removed, then persisting symptomatology may often be rationalized by both physician and patient as being due to "adhesions." At other times a "phantom organ" may become the site of the disturbing sensations; it is as if the original organ had not been removed. Thus, by a psychological process of denial, the original symptoms are perpetuated. In still other instances a substitute body area, closely related to the first one, becomes the focus of the patient's concern. Finally it is possible for an entirely different organ system to become involved in the somatization process, as has been described in a previous case. In such "somatic solutions" there is very little, if anything, that can be found in terms of physical signs, laboratory studies, or even on exploratory laparotomy, which will account for the symptomatology. The dysfunction that produces the symptoms is not due to any organic changes that are detectable. These patients may soon convince themselves as well as their physicians that another operation is needed to "correct the condition." Some individuals may thus undergo surgery an amazing number of times, without pathology of any significance being found. In a general sense, the symbolic meaning of such procedures for the patient may be that of punishment for expiation of intense, persisting guilt feelings, or that of sexualized masochistic gratification, or else an extraordinary way of getting attention.

CASE 28

CHIEF PRESENTING SYMPTOM	Burning sensation in stomach
SENSORIMOTOR CONFIGURATIONS	Sensory configurations

Interoceptive, temperature, taste

Associated with food and eating, references to right and wrong in relationship to mother seen as noncatering, strict, and forcing, leading to patient's reactive stubbornness, resentment, and anticipation of punishment

Motor configurations

Going down, coming up, working

Linked with passive–feminine identification, pregnancy fantasies, feelings of inferiority in relation to father and siblings, and need to show manliness

SOMATIC IDENTIFICATION	*Wife*	Sustained fall during pregnancy recently
	Mother	Small size

STRESS (*surface meaning*)	Job difficulties and wife's pregnancy
STRESS (*dynamic significance*)	Activation of passive–feminine tendencies, with mounting anxiety and need to deny this; concern about anticipated loss of wife's attentions to his infantile needs
DEFENSES	Rationalization Tendency to project Denial

AFFECTS	*Intensity*	*Pathway of expression*
Anxiety	++	Ideational, some affective, some somatic equivalent
Depression	++	Ideational, some affective
Hostility	++	Affective, ideational, some somatization

OTHER FACTORS	Rebellious, defiant attitudes since childhood
HOMEOSTATIC SHIFT(s)	Insufficiency of ideational defenses causes need for further defensive supplementation by a mild to moderate somatization response
DIAGNOSIS	Somatization reaction, gastrointestinal; treated, improved

case 29

Emotional Conflict Associated
with Endocrine Dysfunction

CHIEF PRESENTING SYMPTOM

Jumpy nervousness.

BASIC ANAMNESTIC EXCERPTS

The interview is begun with an emphasis on feeling better, although for about six years the patient has tended to be jumpy, nervous, tense, tired, excessively perspiring, and having to urinate once or twice a night. "The main thing is being jumpy. If someone toots a horn at me, I jump, but it's less than it used to be. There's been also a great loss of weight, but I've gained it back. I've been up and down, up and down, ever since I've got out of the service. Building up my weight has been a slow process. I'm dying to get back home, because I have some little children, and I'm sure it's not too bad a case."

A temporal factor is next introduced: "I noticed when I came back from combat I couldn't stand seeing things scattered around. I had to place things just so. Everything in my locker had to be just right. Aboard ship it was the same way. The fellows used to ride me—because I used to smooth off my bunk all the time. It wasn't like me at all. Anyway, that seemed to be the first thing: Everything had to be organized just right, or I felt sensitive and irritable. When I came home, my parents noticed that I was shaking. I myself then became aware that if I were writing a letter, my hand would start quivering. If I'm standing for a long time, my legs start quivering all over the place. My hands would shake if I lit a cigarette. Then my weight began to go up and down. I never seemed to be satisfied, and I'd always be hungry, even though I had the equivalent of five meals.

"I was a husky kid even in high school. I played baseball, hockey, football; I loved the contact. I also liked golf. Since my troubles began, I have difficulty in holding the club or putter steady. If I hold the club too long, my hands start quivering; I can't hit the hole just right and keep

missing it. As a youngster I loved rough games. I was always pretty rugged."
There follow references which suggest castration anxiety. "When I was
five, I had my tonsils out, was in a hospital overnight with a terrible pain
in my throat and very scared. When I was about eight, they gave me diphtheria serum—I was allergic to that and almost died from it. I broke out
all over, with big splotches, had a terrible time swallowing, and felt weak.
Later I had to carry a certificate so that doctors wouldn't give me horse
serum. But I wasn't really frail or always sickly. I also had scarlet fever,
but that was just before I graduated from college. The sickness went all
through the school, and this was a bad epidemic just when final exams
were coming up. I had been studying very hard, and my resistance was
way down. Everybody else was the same way; I suppose that's why half the
fellows got it. I remember being hot and flushed but didn't have it bad
at all. Some of the fellows were awful sick."

The next references are to the health of his family: "My Dad is
extremely healthy, but my mother has high blood pressure and a bad heart.
She was quite well until 10 years ago. Now she gets dizzy spells. The whole
thing has made her very nervous and jittery. I have two brothers. The older
one has a little heart murmur—nothing serious; it sort of flops over and
makes him nervous. He's gone to a doctor and was told to cut down on
smoking, which he used to do excessively. Now he's taken up a pipe. My
younger brother is fine."

The patient refers to an auto dealership he and his brother have just
taken over: "I used to sell men's clothing and at the same time I managed
two theaters up in Vermont. I enjoyed that very much. But then the
opportunity came for me to go in with my brother, so I came down here.
At this other work, I was busy but I didn't exactly kill myself. My brother
knows I have this tendency to put everything into my work, so he's made
me take it easier. One thing I don't enjoy is work at night because I want
to be home with the family.

"I have two little boys, and we expect a third baby in a couple of
months. My wife contracted polio five years ago but came out of it O.K.
We'd been married only a year and didn't have any children then. I
thought she'd be on crutches for years. But just a few days after she came
home she put the crutches away. The whole thing gave me a big scare
then. I used to still give her exercises for her legs every morning. Her legs
were unsteady and shaky. But by the time she had her first baby she was
all better."

The patient now elaborates on his own condition: "I'm not worried
about it. But my wife is concerned about the quivering in my legs and my
abnormal appetite. I don't worry about physical things. I try to talk
calmly and be relaxed. I enjoy meeting people, selling, and look forward

to work every morning. I may get a little irritated or cross sometimes when things don't go just right, but I don't think that's abnormal. Everybody gets cross. It seems to be only when my weight's down, that I get upset and growl at the people working for me. When my weight's up, I act better."

PSYCHODYNAMIC IMPRESSIONS

While the patient briefly focuses on his symptoms, there is a much stronger tendency to deny any concern over them, and in conjunction with this denial he projects such concern onto his wife. There are suggestive temporal connections which point to situational factors which have acted as stresses. One in particular was his wife's illness with poliomyelitis and the temporary paralysis of her legs—to which it appears that the patient reacted as if it were for him a major traumatic event. Before that, his mother's growing disability had already been evident for some years. It would seem that a concern about the incapacity of the important female figures, threatening him with loss of their maternal interest, touches on a rather deeply covered-over dependency. This has been defended against particularly by an overcompensatory activity which also served to provide some means of escape from disturbing thoughts and feelings. There are indications that his family responsibilities have weighed heavily on him and have tended to activate a sense of physical inferiority, especially in comparison with his father, against which he has tried constantly to defend himself. Somatic identification is with the female figures. An obsessional core became evident at about the time of his military service, and the manifestations indicated a need to guard against impulses to be disorderly and disobedient. Hostility is deeply defended against, and there appears to be an affect block of strong proportions which may at times be broken through, with some resultant affective discharge. The hostility is evidently generated by frustration of activated dependent needs. Here the presence of the little children, with another on the way, has to be considered as an irritant. Similarly, competitive striving, both with father and older brother figures, is a source of hostile feelings. Patient's symptoms are also connected with some symbolized associations which indicate fear of failing sexual prowess and related castration anxiety.

PHYSICAL HISTORY

The patient was admitted with a history of nervousness for six years prior to hospitalization. One year ago, due to tremor of hands and feet, together with a 10-pound weight loss despite a ravenous appetite, heat intolerance, and palpitation, he consulted a local doctor who did a metabolism test and told him he had an overactive thyroid. He was treated with several kinds of pills—white and pink, then pink alone for four months, following which he felt greatly improved. However, intermittent periods of irritability continued and because of that, together with persistent nocturia, he came in for alleviation of these symptoms.

PHYSICAL EXAMINATION

Temperature: 97.8°F. Pulse: 92. Blood pressure: 158/64. The patient was a well-developed, well nourished male in no acute distress. Head, eyes, ears, nose, and throat negative. There was no enlargement of the thyroid gland. Heart and lungs were negative except for sinus tachycardia. There was a fine tremor of the extended hands. Skin was moist and warm. Physical examination otherwise negative.

LABORATORY DATA

Admission blood and urine studies were negative. Basal metabolism rate was +38 and +34. Radioactive iodine uptake was 80 percent in 24 hours. Protein-bound iodine tests were 10.3 and 9.6 micrograms percent. Cholesterol was 207 mg percent.

ROENTGENOGRAMS

Chest: negative.

ELECTROCARDIOGRAM

Negative except for sinus tachycardia.

HOSPITAL COURSE

The patient was treated with a dose of radioactive iodine of 2.35 millicurie 10 days after admission. One month later on a follow-up visit, basal metabolism rate was +30. However, symptomatically he was greatly improved, appetite was normal, and he was sleeping well. He was again sent on leave of absence to return for follow-up.

DISCHARGE DIAGNOSIS

Hyperthyroidism without evident goiter, treated, improved.

COMMENT

The patient's hyperthyroidism has to be considered against an emotional background of long-continued worries, annoyances, disappointment, and anxiety. There are also the references to the throat and swallowing, associated with surgical and medical experiences and emotional trauma during childhood. The current presenting symptom is one which is closely identified with the mother's own symptomatology, and to some extent with the wife's previous illness. These are both persons to whom the patient had marked dependency ties.

The considerable literature on emotional factors in thyrotoxicosis from the time of Parry's description of the disease in 1925 to approximately the late forties has been covered by Lidz (1949). He described disruption of patterns of intense dependency needs and reactivated problems of unresolved sibling rivalry as precipitating factors in hyperthyroidism. There was emphasis on the feeling of hopelessness and helplessness experienced by these patients if they lose a sense of their own importance.

In 1950, Lidz and Whitehorn wrote further that, when emotional disturbances are discovered to be profound, even though not necessarily in dramatic ways, the onset of hyperthyroidism will be found to be preceded by emotional stress in over 90 percent of cases. They felt the common factor was an intense emotional reaction to disruption or threat of disruption of the dominant interpersonal relationship, attachment to mother —especially in women. The emotional trauma was not simple, brief, or accidental, but a chronic, continuous stress involving this relationship. Ham et al. (1951), in a definitive paper on thyrotoxicosis, proposed that the disease symptoms can be meaningfully understood as the organism's responses to early experiences of development characteristic for these patients. Observations on 24 cases revealed the following specific dynamic pattern: Frustration of dependency needs and persistent threats to security (including exposure to death) in early life lead to unsuccessful premature attempts to identify with the object of those dependent longings and a continuing attempt at self-sufficiency and caring for others. Failure of these strivings leads to the development of thyrotoxicosis. It is this continued effort to mature and become self-sufficient which is the chronic emotional stimulus which mobilizes the thyroid for long-range efforts via corticothalamic pituitary pathways.

F. Alexander et al. (1961) started their experimental study from the premise, clinically derived, that hyperthyroidism is related to a well-defined and experimentally reproducible emotion, namely, fear concerning biological survival. They found these patients have a characteristic manner of dealing with such fear stimuli, the latter being inversely related to the intactness of the individual's capacity to use counterphobic denial and/or mastery as a major defensive response. Other manifestations included increased thyroid secretion, autonomous responses consistent with physiological manifestations of fear, and decompensation of certain ego functions.

Kaplan and Hetrick (1962) approach the problem of hyperthyroidism from what seem to be striking psychodynamic similarities between two disorders: thyrotoxicosis and traumatic neurosis. In both instances there are attempts to master fear that originally overwhelmed the ego. Onset of both can occur when there is an overwhelming influx of excitation from the environment. Other factors to be considered are the existing internal emotional conflicts, the meaning of the event for the individual, and his preparedness for stimulus influx. Kaplan and Hetrick note that, in the attempts to protect hyperthyroid patients from overstimulation, such individuals have been kept in a quiet, darkened room, anesthesia has been performed in the patient's own room to keep secret the time of the operation, and in certain instances "sneak surgery" has been done. In thyrotoxicosis, the organism appears to be metabolically (hyper) pitched to cope immediately with any external danger by absorbing the impact of trauma and proceeding with fight or flight patterns. Whether trauma will act as a "hair trigger" probably depends on the physiologic predisposition of the subject and the intactness of his thyroid regulatory mechanism.

CASE 29

CHIEF PRESENTING SYMPTOM	Jumpy nervousness
SENSORIMOTOR CONFIGURATIONS	Sensory configurations
	Interoceptive, temperature
	Linked with fluctuations in weight, strong dependency needs, concern about possible loss of important female figures, with concomitant hostility
	Motor configurations
	Activity
	Associated with attempts to defend against anxiety over physical integrity and sexual prowess, especially in comparison with father and older brother figures
SOMATIC IDENTIFICATION	Mother High blood pressure and heart disease with vertigo plus nervousness for the past 10 years (Direct)
	Older brother Heart murmur, nervousness (Direct)
	Wife Current pregnancy, poliomyelitis with shaky legs five years ago (Direct)
SENSITIZED ORGAN SYSTEM	Thyroid
STRESS (*surface meaning*)	Mother's illnesses, wife's illness and pregnancy, new job

VARIABLES

STRESS (*dynamic significance*)	Threatened loss of maternal figures' interest, and activated dependency needs, concern over ability to cope with responsibilities
DEFENSES	Overactivity Denial Projection Reaction formation

AFFECTS	*Intensity*	*Pathway of expression*
Anxiety	+++ (secondary)	Behavioral (motor), affective, ideational, somatization
Depression	++	Some ideational, somatization
Hostility	+++	Some affective and ideational, somatization

OTHER FACTORS	Very strong dependency needs Superego problems
HOMEOSTATIC SHIFT(S)	Regressive shift toward marked somatization as obsessional defenses become inadequate
DIAGNOSIS	Hyperthyroidism without evident goiter, treated, improved

case 30

Chills and Fever in a Markedly Neurotic Patient

CHIEF PRESENTING SYMPTOM

Chills and fever.

BASIC ANAMNESTIC EXCERPTS

The patient gives, without pause, the following associations: "Seven years ago when I came back from China, I broke out with the symptoms of malaria. Most of us had it over there. Once in a while we ate things we shouldn't and then got dysentery. I find that if I drink, it aggravates the condition which kicks up on me at unexpected times. Then I get hazy, blue, foggy. When I come out of it, I feel burned up; my face and lips feel parched, my throat is dry." These sensory clusters are collectively referred to as an attack, a state, a transient condition. "By the time they get me into the hospital, it would be mostly over. I've never had anything else wrong with me, outside of an eye injury which the doctors claim doesn't amount to anything. I imagine some of the cell tissues have been killed, and they left a spot on the eye.

"I have no family trouble, or anything to worry about. I've just completed three years of electrical school. I worked pretty hard, long hours at school and then an outside job; it tired me out. Now this time I felt something tight here—underneath the ribs; I imagine it's the spleen. But by the time I got here, it was practically normal. The whole thing has been a bad experience for me, because a man who has a wife and two children like I do shouldn't stop and have a drink, if it starts the chills and fever up. My wife figures it's the liquor, but it really isn't. I can go by 15 barrooms every single day, and all I have is just one drink, yet I'll come back sick. When I leave this hospital, I'm not going to drink again. A condition like this sometimes might affect the heart and bloodstream, like rheumatic fever.

"I want only to get back on my feet. My wife takes care of me; she's a registered nurse. I probably may not have another attack for nine

254

months. That's the way the cycle has been going. But my being sick takes my family's bread and butter away. If you slip on a few bills here and there, you're out. I have two kids, one that's four, and the other just a month. I had a baby girl a month ago. I didn't want to come into the hospital again, but everyone at home is trying to direct me. I live with relatives, in-laws. They say maybe the war made him neurotic or maybe he's got kidney trouble. I'm not neurotic, never had a nervous day in my life, even though I went through a lot. Working every day and then going to school—a nervous person couldn't do it, and my marks right along were up there. I'll be going back for another year now to finish. And I work around electricity. Now a nervous person has no right up there."

At this point the patient refers to having had a lot of family trouble: "That isn't healthy, because I believe that now when you get to a state where you might have an attack, it could be brought on if you get a little nerved up. I do sometimes, with my mother watching me. I have a home of my own, but I visit my mother frequently. When I go to see her, she is just always at me. I've got a mother-in-law that's the same way. I got a wife that's pretty lovely, calm and collected. That's about the only thing I've got at home I appreciate. My four brothers have their own ideas. Too many people interfere, and I'm too good a fellow to say, 'Well, mind your own damn business.' It only makes enemies."

References to past injuries follow: "Overseas we were teaching the natives how to operate the cement mixers. I was standing on the platform looking one over, and I stepped near the gears. They pulled my whole foot in. It chewed up the toes, and they had to cut part of the bone of each toe off and the skin away, but I came home and never asked for any pension. I'm not a griper. I try to be cooperative and considerate of the other fellow." There is a persistent denial of hostile feelings.

"Had chicken pox, measles, with a high temperature when I was a child. Mother was there, hovering over me. I did have an appendectomy when I was about 13. Nothing broke. I guess I ate too many grapes. It was in the summertime, and I would eat five or six bunches a day. Well, I did that for a month or two, and then all of a sudden, I started getting pains, cramps, so they took me to the hospital and operated on me right away. It was a small incision; you can hardly see the scar. People who have seen my operation say it was a wonderful job."

There are further associations about drinking: "My own father drank. When he had a few drinks, he was kind of boisterous, and he made things miserable, but he came out of it by himself, and we were very proud of him after that. I guess drinking can lead to a fever. Quinine controls it but doesn't kill it. I'd like to chop it off and get rid of it. When the fever is worst, I feel like somebody actually took a hot iron and put it up to my face. Some of the fellows with fever over there turned around and got gray hair overnight; others lost their teeth, and still others had their skin just shrivel up on them. The doctor told us, 'You fellows are going to have something when you leave here that you will either have the rest of your life or only a short time.' "

The patient talks further about himself and his family: "When I was a kid, I was the healthiest and heaviest in the family, the best eater. I have two older and two younger brothers. The oldest brother had rheumatic fever. The next one down had an operation, and his heart stopped right on the operating table. He's strong as a bull today, but he was awful sick then. One of the younger brothers was always a weak kid, never gained any weight. The youngest boy had asthma. They all had some little thing. I never had anything. The only thing I ever had was when I was eight. I was hit with a baseball in the left eye, knocking half the sight out. For a year I couldn't see anything out of it. When I was about 13, the doctors said that I had a permanent injury there."

The patient brings up his father's death: "He died of cancer six years ago. He was such a strong man, but he developed a cancer of the kidneys which took him in just three months. Somehow or other, I couldn't imagine he was dying. I had just come home from overseas. He was always complaining of pain, pain in both arms and his back. Then his right eye went blind. The cancer had gone up the spine and into the brain. He went down in weight, didn't eat any more, just went out. My mother is different; she's one of these women that's healthy as a dollar but always gets some kind of ailment."

PSYCHODYNAMIC IMPRESSIONS

The patient's volubility is impressive. Equally so is his defensiveness, need to deny tensions, and efforts to play down his drinking. At the same time, there is an overemphasis of the role of physical symptomatology. Secondary-gain aspects are involved in the pension he receives for injury to the foot. The original precipitating factors for his chronic state of tension and mild-to-moderate depression appear to have developed during the patient's combat experiences. Activating and reinforcing elements have been subsequently derived from tensions associated with his marriage and family responsibilities, his combined work and school program, and his uneasy contacts with his relatives.

There are long-standing dependent needs—his alcoholism being a more overt manifestation, and his infantile expectations of being looked after by his nurse–wife less obvious. Highly ambivalent attitudes toward maternal figures are further evident in his past and current reactions to

his own mother, whom he has to visit frequently, and yet whose interference in his affairs he resents. Other recollections from the past show
how the patient defensively compares himself with his brothers in physical
terms to cover up his own inferiority feelings.

His hostility frequently breaks through in affective outbursts with
subsequent guilt feelings, despite efforts to control angry impulses. There
is identification with the father—in terms of drinking and coming to a bad
end physically.

The symptom of fever is linked with associations having a symbolic
sexual significance as well as reflecting a narcissistic concern about body
integrity.

PHYSICAL HISTORY

The patient reentered the hospital for the second time because of
chills and fever beginning four days before admission. He had previously
been hospitalized six months ago because of a history of recurrent bouts
of fever and chills beginning about eight years before while the patient
was in the Orient. Each episode was described as beginning with sudden
chills, then fever and sweats, with headache, backache, and muscular soreness, followed by several days of weakness and disability. Studies at this
time failed to reveal any evidence of malaria, although the clinical history
was that of prolonged malaria. The patient reentered because of a recurrent
bout of feverishness four days before admission, headaches, generalized
malaise, nausea, and vomiting. Past history revealed an appendectomy performed at age 15, injury to right foot while in service, and in addition,
malaria, dysentery, and probably fungus infection of nose likewise contracted overseas.

PHYSICAL EXAMINATION

Temperature 98.6°F. Pulse 80. Blood pressure 130/84. Weight 155
pounds. Patient was a well-developed and well-nourished white male who
did not appear acutely or chronically ill. He seemed quite restless and rather
anxious. Head and neck normal. Fundoscopic examination revealed vascular irritation throughout the left retina. Ears, nose, and throat normal.
The remainder of the examination was within normal limits.

LABORATORY DATA

White count and differential, hemoglobin, urine, all normal. Serology:
negative. Stools: negative for occult blood. Alkaline phosphates 0.8. Van
den Bergh 0.1 direct, 0.9 indirect. Total protein 7.5. Formal gel negative.
Malaria smears: negative.

ROENTGENOGRAMS

Chest plate: negative. Kidney, ureter, and bladder: the spleen was not definitely visualized but did not seem to be enlarged.

HOSPITAL COURSE

Further information obtained after the patient was admitted and from his wife and brother indicated that since the patient had left military service, he has had periodic bouts of panic and depression. These had been further complicated by impulsive outbursts of anger. It was the consensus of the medical staff in consultation with the psychiatric service, that although the patient had had malaria in the past, his present difficulty was on an emotional basis with residuals of a traumatic war neurosis. The injury to his foot for which he receives a pension has secondary-gain aspects associated with it. The patient has had periodic alcoholic binges in an attempt to relieve his anxiety. Arrangements were made for the patient to get adjuvant psychiatric treatment on an outpatient basis.

DISCHARGE DIAGNOSES

1. Psychoneurosis, mixed type, severe, traumatic in origin.
2. Foot injury, old.

COMMENT

A complicated and chronic psychoneurotic condition is involved here. The patient obviously had malaria in the past. In terms of recurrence, no definite diagnosis of this illness has been established in the present. There is also an old foot injury which, however, has not increased the patient's incapacity in the last few years. He receives a pension from the government for the latter, but none for the former, yet it is to the former that he turns as an explanation for his physical symptoms, for his illness, and for his inability to do sustained work. At the same time, the patient would have it that he is basically not sick at all, and this defensiveness is apparent even as he is talking about his incapacity. Still further involved are his strong needs to drink and the attempted playing down of these needs. This rather uncontrollable manifestation of his dependency is covered over (or the attempt is made to cover it over) by the reference to what he calls his malarial attacks.

We thus see a neurosis which is persistent, secondary-gain aspects which are quite strong, and recurrent stress situations, all combined to give a clinical picture where the immediate focus tends to be on physical manifestations, yet these are secondary to the very severe psychological disturbances which are present.

The outlook is for a continuation of this patient's illness and chronic incapacity which will probably lead to further hospitalization, unless it will be possible to interrupt this trend by a consistent psychotherapeutic approach.

CASE 30

CHIEF PRESENTING SYMPTOM	Chills and fever
SENSORIMOTOR CONFIGURATIONS	Sensory configurations

Temperature, visual
Associated with drinking, early febrile illnesses, dependent expectations, and ambivalent relationships with maternal figures

Motor configurations

Chopping off, getting rid of
Linked with anxious and hostile competition, especially with brothers, and connected with castration fantasies and narcissistic concern over body integrity

SOMATIC IDENTIFICATION	*Brothers* Heart murmur, nervousness (Direct)
	Father Cancer of kidney with metastasis causing death six years ago; pain and blindness of right eye prior to this
SENSITIZED ORGAN SYSTEM	Not well defined
STRESS (*surface meaning*)	Combat experience during military service Current family responsibilities, pressures of work and school, and problems with relatives
STRESS (*dynamic significance*)	Increased feelings of inferiority and concern about bodily integrity
DEFENSES	Overcompensatory activity Denial Rationalizations Some addictive tendency

AFFECTS	Intensity	Pathway of expression
Anxiety	++	Some ideational, some affective, some somatic equivalents
Depression	++	Some ideational, some somatization
Hostility	++	Affective outbursts, some ideational, some somatization
OTHER FACTORS		Secondary gain Long-standing superego problems
HOMEOSTATIC SHIFT(S)		Somatization response secondary to very severe psychological disturbances
DIAGNOSES		a) Psychoneurosis, mixed type, severe, traumatic in origin; b) Foot injury, old

FOLLOW-UP DATA

INTERIM NOTE

In the next six years, the patient had repeated hospitalizations for recurrent episodes of severe anxiety. Interim psychotherapy had not been followed through. The psychophysical patterns already described tended to persist. Tensions associated with his marriage and family responsibilities (no additional children), his difficulties with relatives, and his attempts to maintain a job as electrician, all continued. There was some increase in his drinking. Toward the end of this period a new set of physical symptoms manifested themselves. The patient experienced alternating constipation and diarrhea, and was increasingly troubled with back pain. A hemorrhoidectomy was done because of painful defecation. This afforded relief for about a year. However, the symptom returned, and the back pain continued to worsen.

The patient was again hospitalized, some eight years after the admission already reported, with chief complaints of persistent painful defecation and back pain.

PHYSICAL EXAMINATION

Revealed a well-developed and well-nourished effeminate-appearing man. Vital signs normal. Right pupil slightly larger than left, but both react to light and accommodation. The remainder of the examination was negative except for a small external hemorrhoid at nine o'clock.

LABORATORY DATA

Hemogram, urinalysis, serology, sedimentation rate all within normal limits.

ROENTGENOGRAMS

Chest: negative. Lumbosacral spine: negative.

HOSPITAL COURSE

Several days after admission, anoscopy was done and revealed external and internal hemorrhoids at nine o'clock. A sigmoidoscopy was negative. Neuropsychiatric consultation confirmed the presence of a long-standing, seemingly intractable tendency toward anxiety reactions with intermingled depressive responses. Physical symptomatology rapidly abated and operative intervention for the hemorrhoids was not recommended. The patient refused referral to a mental hygiene clinic.

DISCHARGE DIAGNOSES

1. Anxiety reaction, chronic, severe, slightly improved.
2. Hemorrhoids, external and internal.

FURTHER COMMENT

The patient's traumatic experiences in combat precipitated an emotional illness which has cast long shadows over his life for some 16 years. This neurosis, with its infantile roots, has been reinforced and reactivated many times since the patient left military service. The stresses to which he has been exposed were not unusual ones and might well have been handled more adequately by a psychologically healthier person. Instead, they have contributed to the chronicity of his illness. The patient's physical symptomatology, derived largely from conversion reactions in different organ systems, appears most recently to have become localized in the anal region and in the back. In this connection there should be noted the references, many years before, to father's severe back pain (due to cancer of the kidney). At that time, while this symptom appeared in the patient's associations, it was not included as part of his own physical complaints. The patient's emotional illness had been recognized quite early, and psychotherapy had been prescribed then and on subsequent occasions. It is, however, one thing to recommend psychotherapy to a patient, but quite another matter for the patient to actually undertake such treatment or continue in it. In this case, the powerful psychological defense of denial, the tendency toward addictive use of alcohol, coupled with an entrenched secondary-gain factor, apparently have been able to nullify the motivating influence of any suffering experienced by the patient. Improvement thus has been minimal, and in any event not sustained.

case 31

Hazy Vision, Recurrent Stress, and Physical Crises

CHIEF PRESENTING SYMPTOM

Hazy vision.

BASIC ANAMNESTIC EXCERPTS

The patient begins with references to his eyes. "When I turn quickly or look to the side quickly, it would kind of haze over. I would just close my eyes, look again, and it would be all better. Usually it was when I turned to the left.

"I was getting severe headaches both in front and across the back of my head. Before all this began some six months ago, I had always been well, no serious illness, except mumps and measles as a child. When these headaches came on, and my eyes started acting up, I went to one doctor and he was feeding me several different types of pills. But I still didn't feel right, so I went to another doctor, and he immediately put me into the hospital. I was there for two months, then got a thirty-day leave. Now I'm back."

There are further references to his previous health: "I was a flight engineer on a big bomber. I weighed about two-twenty then, and, when I returned to civilian life, I had got up to two-sixty before I first took sick. I had a good life, eating all those fried foods, frappés, inbetween snacks. But then when I took over the gas station, I wouldn't eat regular, and guess I was eating the wrong things. I've always weighed over two hundred, since I was sixteen and in high school. When I was a kid, though, I wasn't oversized. My younger brother is as tall as I am and weighs as much. Now father was shorter but heavy. Mother, too, was stout.

"Father died of Bright's disease when I was ten years old. I can remember he was sick in bed for a long time; I could see him wasting away. It's one thing we were told always to be on the watch for. But with all the exams and checkups I've had, they never mentioned any trace of

262

it. I was told that Bright's disease has something to do with the kidneys, something wrong with the waterworks. Father was ill quite a long time, and toward the end, he had these terrible headaches and his eyes gave out on him. After he died, mother started working. When I entered high school, I was out working before and after school. My brother and I finished high school, but neither of us went to college. With mother away all the time, we depended on a very close neighbor to look after things in the house for us. She was very good to us and still is, for that matter."

Further and more detailed references to work follow: "After I left high school, I tried business school for a short while, but didn't like it. I started to work in a gas station then, driving an oil truck. Then I went into the service. When I came back, the fire chief had a job waiting for me. I couldn't stand that life—sitting and waiting—helped me put on the weight. It was then that I decided to go into business for myself. I bought one gas station, then I bought the oil trucks, and I finally got another station. Then I had to go and get sick. Once I got into that business, I couldn't call any time my own. Just when I was trying to relax, somebody would be looking for me. I got that second station only about six months before I took sick. Then I was busier than ever, between one and the other. I kept eating all the time. Mother was out working. But sometimes I'd have a good, home-cooked meal at night. I'm not married. I went into service, and my girl didn't wait for me. I don't have much of a social life. Play cards with the boys, sit around at the club, but they get me there, too. No matter where you were, you'd be expecting a call.

"I never had too much trouble sleeping until I got involved in that business. Now I can't get to sleep, can't breathe right when I lay down flat. A couple of years ago, I went through a heart clinic in town, and they told me I was overweight which I knew, but they didn't tell me anything about high pressure. They just mentioned the weight and said I should try and lose some. Carrying all that weight was no good; it shortened my breath. I lost about twenty-five pounds on the outside, by cutting down on sweets. When I came in here, they really chopped it off. They put me on a diet. They also told me here they didn't think I should go back to the gas business. Now I'll have to start all over again and find something without worry.

"I didn't think the business would worry me. I try to fit into whatever job I'm doing and not get too upset about things. I might get sore for a minute, but carrying on all day—no. Didn't fight as a kid—no real temper or anything. Our family gets along very well. My brother is married now. He lives in the same house with us, the upstairs apartment. I live downstairs. He's been married a couple of years now. We never did fight like a lot of brothers I know of. He has one son, ten months old. Anyway, they live their own life, and we—mother and I—live ours. Mother's never still, even when she's not at work. She's got to be doing something."

The patient's associations turn to his military experiences: "Now things over there were not exactly quiet. I flew about twelve hundred hours. Well, my hair started to turn gray. Once we made a touch-and-go practice landing, and the plane went over on her nose and caught fire. We just managed to escape. But then later I wouldn't get upset over it. Tried to see the brighter side of things."

Again there are references to the past in connection with his optimistic outlook: "I don't remember being in much trouble. Nothing went too wrong. Guess I got lectures if I was up too late. Should do this—shouldn't do that. But nothing very serious. Always took mother's advice. Sometimes resented it, but she was always right."

PSYCHODYNAMIC IMPRESSIONS

The anamnestic material indicates the patient's early and lasting dependence on his mother, as well as possible incestuous attachment to her. His orality is particularly prominent in reference to food intake and weight changes. Father appears as a devaluated, sickly figure during most of the patient's early life, and "water troubles"—Bright's disease—from which he died seem to have been a marked concern and preoccupation in the patient's fantasy life. The father's death, when the patient was 10 years old, left a long-lasting traumatic impression on him. At that time the family circumstances were considerably altered. The mother, and shortly thereafter the patient, began a life of constant activity and work, being hard-pressed financially. Later, the patient noted that he would become uneasy and anxious when it was not possible for him to maintain this overactivity. It appears to be a basic defense against opposite feelings of dependency and insecurity. While in military service the patient found separation from his mother to be very difficult for him. At that time his hair turned prematurely gray—as his mother's had when she had been his age. His tensions during military service were intensified when a plane in which he was a passenger cracked up and caught fire, although he actually sustained only slight injury.

On the patient's return to civilian life, he was "reunited" with his mother and settled down to live with her. His long-standing interest in fires, which appears to have been related to his early preoccupation with urethral fantasies, appears to have had some influence in his taking a job as fireman for several years. However, the frequent inactivity and accompanying uneasiness, led him to think of other work, interestingly, in the gasoline and fuel oil business. His ambitious aspirations were realized partly in a growing business of his own, but he then found himself in an ever increasing bind with no time practically that he could call his own. His emotional disturbance was not resolved. In fact, it was further complicated by the continuing close proximity to his mother, and now also to a married younger brother, an increasing trend toward avoiding women (except mother), and seeking the company almost exclusively of men. A masked depression appears to have been present for some time prior to the onset of his physical illness. It should be noted that he had always dealt with any strong feelings, particularly angry ones, by suppression, denial, rationalizations, and a turning inward of the emotion.

The eye symptoms, while overdetermined, appear in the anamnesis to have a particular psychological significance for the patient. The associative connections suggest that they represent a symbolic expression of the need to shut out (from awareness) his drift toward a homosexually oriented type of relationship with other men.

PHYSICAL HISTORY

The patient's first admission was five months before, lasting four months. At that time, he was found to have severe hypertensive cardiovascular disease with failure, eyeground changes, and some azotemia. He was treated conservatively with bed rest, salt-free diet, sedation, and antitensive drugs. On this regime he made an excellent recovery from the acute situation, and gradual improvement of all symptoms and signs occurred. Following discharge, the patient continued on this regime, maintained his weight around 180 pounds and worked only part-time. The only symptom has been occasional blurring of vision on far left lateral gaze. During this time repeated blood pressure readings have ranged from 140 to 150/95 to 105. He was readmitted for further evaluation.

PHYSICAL EXAMINATION

Temperature, pulse, and respirations normal. Initial blood pressure 180/120. Positive physical findings also included slight narrowing and tortuosity of fundal vessels, but no exudate and no papilledema. The heart was still slightly enlarged to the left, but apparently smaller than on admission previously. Liver was not palpable and there was no ankle edema.

LABORATORY DATA

Hemoglobin 12.2 g. Hematocrit 40 percent. White blood cell count 7,000. Serology: negative. Nonprotein nitrogen 26. CO_2, chlorides, sodium, and potassium were within normal limits. Urine: trace of albumin, negative sediment; on concentration test, a specific gravity of 1.016 was obtained. Phenolsulfophthalein test: 25 percent excretion in 15 minutes, 41 percent in 2 hours.

ROENTGENOGRAMS

Chest: Lung fields negative—no evidence of congestion; heart 1 cm smaller in transverse diameter as compared with previous examination; however, heart remains enlarged.

ELECTROCARDIOGRAM

Showed slight decrease in precordial voltage; otherwise no change in left axis deviation.

HOSPITAL COURSE

The patient was continued on a low-salt diet, antitensives and digitalis as before. Six AM and six PM blood pressures ranged from 120 to 160/ 84 to 120. In view of the progress the patient had made, sympathectomy for control of hypertension did not seem necessary at this time. In any case, the patient was opposed to surgery. He was to continue on the course as outlined and report to the outpatient clinic periodically.

DISCHARGE DIAGNOSES

1. Hypertensive cardiovascular disease with enlarged heart, compensated, treated, improved.
2. Possible arteriolar nephrosclerosis, untreated, unchanged.

COMMENT

The patient's reference to his first hospitalization is closely linked with the theme of loss and with specific associations to weight, water, food, and salt. Attempts to fill the emptiness he feels within himself are expressed in his craving for more and more food. But part of the weight increase is due to retention of fluid. While fluid shifts are phenomena resulting from a variety of complex disturbances in the physicochemical functions of the body, the psychological state of the individual in whom they are occurring usually tends to be overlooked. Of particular interest would be why, for instance, the symptoms and signs of congestion failure are occurring at a particular time. What has caused the decompensation to take place then and not at some other time? Is it the resultant of physiological changes alone which have finally reached a critical point resulting in the homeostatic shift? Or have psychological changes in the individual contributed to upsetting the physical homeostasis? In this patient a depressive trend and marked tension have been in existence and increasing during the past six months. Both emotional reactions appear to have been largely blocked from affective expression. Their impact on an already malfunctioning soma could well have triggered a further physical decompensation.

Chambers and Reiser (1953), in their study of 25 consecutive cases of congestive heart failure, found emotional precipitating factors in 23. In 19, or 76 percent, these factors were considered to be directly responsible for increasing work load beyond cardiac capacity. Though all patients suffered from severely diminished cardiac reserve from organic disease and had been living under chronic emotional strain, an additional factor of acute stress was considered to be the final precipitant of the acute episode of failure. The common stress was sudden rejection and loss of security. Deterioration of patient–physician relationship was noted in several of these instances. It was found surprisingly that the interviewing, even though it mobilized charged and sensitive topics, did not lead to further decompensation of an already embarrassed circulation but seemed to have a favorable effect. The confessional nature of the response seemed to result in a shifting of psychological defenses which had been mobilized against an overwhelming fear of death noted in the patients in acute distress. In addition, some of the patients with long-standing dependency needs who had experienced recent losses were reaching out for a supporting figure (the interviewer).

CASE 31

CHIEF PRESENTING SYMPTOM	Hazy vision
SENSORIMOTOR CONFIGURATIONS	Sensory configurations

Visual, pain, interoceptive
Associated with father's wasting illness, mother's absences, and attempted avoidance of dependent and possibly incestuous attachment to her

Motor configurations

Activity
Linked with inability to relax, to sleep, to breathe right, and serving as a defense against passive–feminine attitudes

SOMATIC IDENTIFICATION	*Father* Death due to Bright's disease with wasting and eye trouble when patient aged 10 (Direct, constitutional)
SENSITIZED ORGAN SYSTEM	Cardiovascular Renal Eyes

STRESS (*surface meaning*)	Separation from mother in military service—difficult No time he could call his own and other work tensions
STRESS (*dynamic significance*)	Increasing concern about adequacy, associated with activated dependency needs, followed by frustration and growing hostility
DEFENSES	Overcompensatory activity Denial Rationalizations

AFFECTS	*Intensity*	*Pathway of expression*
Anxiety	+++	Ideational, somatic equivalents
Depression	+++	Some ideational, somatization
Hostility	+++	Somatization

OTHER FACTORS	Orality prominent Latent homosexual tendencies and incestuous attachment to mother Trauma age 10, death of father Superego pathology
HOMEOSTATIC SHIFT(S)	Affect block and insufficiency of ideational systems cause shift, increasing impact of drive energies on soma
DIAGNOSES	a) Hypertensive cardiovascular disease with enlarged heart, compensated, treated, improved; b) Possible arteriolar nephrosclerosis, untreated, unchanged

FOLLOW-UP DATA

Following discharge from the hospitalization reported above, the patient returned to his work as gas station operator. He remained on a salt-free diet and antitensives. There were no disabling symptoms for about a year and a half, but the patient was not able to work regularly. He continued to feel under great strain when actively operating his gas stations. Then, on a routine checkup by his physician, the patient's urine was found to have both albumin and red cells in it. Hospitalization was recommended, but the patient deferred this for a month, until he had sudden onset of numb, tingling feelings in his right arm and leg which progressed to a point where he lost use of his right arm.

PHYSICAL EXAMINATION

Revealed an anxious-appearing 210-pound man looking older than his stated age. His speech was thick and slurred. Temperature 98.6°F. Pulse 100. Blood pressure 220/140. Examination of fundi: diffuse narrowing of arterioles and slight blurring of disc margins. Heart: enlarged to the left; A_2 greater than P_2. Neurological examination: slight right lower facial weakness; complete flaccid paralysis of entire right arm, colder than left, and with mottled cyanotic hue; general but slight weakness of right leg; diminished sensation, entire right side of body.

LABORATORY DATA

Hemogram: within normal limits. Serology: negative. Urinalysis: trace of albumin, no red cells on admission and repeat.

ELECTROCARDIOGRAM

Revealed left ventricular hypertrophy.

HOSPITAL COURSE

In the beginning the patient was put on 24-hour bed rest. Function of right arm and leg began to return and with the help of physiotherapy had been almost completely restored in these extremities at time of discharge. Blood pressure initially remained at high levels, but on a regime of 400 mg Apresoline daily, finally dropped to 180/110. Sympathectomy was considered to be necessary and the patient was advised to return in three months for this procedure.

DISCHARGE DIAGNOSES

1. Hypertensive cardiovascular disease with enlarged heart, compensated, treated, improved.
2. Thrombosis of left middle cerebral artery, treated, improved.

FURTHER HOSPITALIZATIONS

Three months later the patient was again hospitalized and had two operations. In the first operation, the right sympathetic chain from thoracic 4 to lumbar 4, and the splanchnic nerves were removed. Some 10 days later, a left dorsal sympathectomy was done. Following this the patient's blood pressure fell to 160/110. When seen in follow-up some three months later the readings were 156/110. The patient had been asymptomatic. He was then discharged with diagnoses of (1) essential vascular hypertension (2) hypertensive heart disease.

The patient was not hospitalized again until five years later, when he was admitted because of a troublesome left inguinal hernia of several month's duration. He had fallen accidentally against a piece of furniture at home, struck the left side of his abdomen sustaining a bruise, and had felt "something give" there. During the five-year period since his last hospitalization, the patient had led a quiet, seemingly well-stabilized life. He had sold his gas stations and taken a job as a toll collector on a super-highway. He had remained single and continued to live with his mother. No major events or issues had come up to disturb his life.

PHYSICAL EXAMINATION

Revealed a well-developed, well-nourished male with graying hair. Vital signs normal, blood pressure 130/80. Old sympathectomy scars. Fundi: minimal arteriolar narrowing. Heart: not enlarged. Abdomen: combined indirect and direct hernia, left. Neurological examination: slightly hyperactive reflexes, right upper extremity, otherwise negative.

LABORATORY DATA

Within normal limits.

ROENTGENOGRAMS

Chest: no cardiac enlargement or active pulmonary disease.

ELECTROCARDIOGRAM

Showed definite improvement over tracings of five years earlier when marked left ventricular hypertrophy had been noted.

HOSPITAL COURSE

Repair of hernia was done with uneventful postoperative course. Blood pressures remained well-controlled on rauwolfia.

DISCHARGE DIAGNOSES

1. Indirect and direct inguinal hernia, left, treated, improved.
2. Hypertensive cardiovascular heart disease.
3. Status postdorsal sympathectomy.

FURTHER COMMENT

The patient's way of life changed significantly about five years before this last hospitalization. He had been intensely involved in his business, hard-driving, constantly preoccupied with being a success. This overactivity served in the past to compensate for and to conceal deeply rooted dependent needs. At the same time other psychological defenses of denial and rationalization constituted a block against affective and ideational expression of his hostility. Then a deterioration in the patient's psychophysical state had set in and a further downhill course seemed likely, but this was interrupted by the sympathectomy. Shortly thereafter, the patient gave up an existence fraught with emotional tensions and constant overactivity for one of relative quietude and passivity. This was indeed a significant reversal, especially in terms of its psychophysical implications. It was a regression in a sense, but it made for the possibility of a stable equilibrium which has lasted for over five years. Thus it should be noted that it was not the sympathectomy alone that accounted for the change away from what might have been a serious outcome physically for the patient. The removal of stress, likewise, in itself was not the only favorable psychological determinant. The patient was also to give up certain basic overcompensatory defenses and settle into an essentially passive kind of life, working as a toll collector and living with his dominating, active mother. He was not invalided but had accepted, as it seems, the reverse of what he had earlier sought to achieve. It was not until the new psychophysical equilibrium had been in existence for some months that the blood pressure readings came down to the more normal levels. Thus a time lag may be noted between the subsidence of psychological tensions and modification or elimination of physical manifestations. An alternative explanation would be that the changes in the psychological state are themselves gradual, and consequently changes in physical symptomatology would also occur gradually.

CLINICAL MATERIAL FROM ANOTHER CASE

The following case is illustrative of a much larger number in which the presence of emotional crises preceding cardiac decompensation appears to be more than coincidental. A woman in her thirties, with long-standing rheumatic heart disease since early adolescence, involving particularly the mitral valve, had had frequently recurrent bouts of congestive failure since her marriage some 10 years before coming into psychotherapy. She held a responsible job as a junior executive. She was highly intelligent, capable, and worked very hard. The marriage was marred by frequent quarrels and a basic incompatibility. Her husband, somewhat older, was himself an intelligent person and a healthy one but with many feelings of inferiority, and he simply could not make a go of it in a number of jobs which he tried successively. The patient tended to be highly critical of her husband and he frequently threatened to leave her—something that was most upsetting to her, since she had never worked through the loss of her father after his sudden, fatal illness during her childhood. She had been an only child; her mother had remarried, and while the patient got along fairly well with her stepsiblings, her relations with stepfather were strained. Often a major blowup between patient and husband was followed by cardiac decompensation of varying degree, and on quite a number of occasions she had to be hospitalized. During psychotherapy the patient was able to recognize the intense hostility covered up by her ever-smiling and pleasing exterior; she also became more aware of her castrating tendencies, especially toward her husband. Finally, she was able to weep, something she had not really been able to do since childhood. The number of bouts of congestive failure during the three years she was in psychotherapy (once weekly) were considerably reduced, compared with previously.

However, as her behavior toward her husband began to change, with her becoming softer and less critical, he began to act out, drinking more heavily, and his last job took him away on the road more and more often. Changes in the internal organization of the store where she worked led to the replacement of a superior who had treated her with a most kindly paternalism. The new boss suggested that there might be changes in her job which the patient could not take. Then her husband announced he was definitely leaving her. Finally, the patient stopped her psychotherapy because she was moving to another city where a surgeon whom she had known since her illness was chief of cardiac surgery. She was studied there for the possibility of open heart surgery. These studies contraindicated surgical intervention. She decided to take a job in this city and shortly thereafter died rather suddenly in acute congestive failure which could not be reversed.

Chambers and Reiser (1953) in their series of congestive failure cases found that the doctor–patient relationship is of considerable therapeutic importance, especially in the long-term patients. The effect appeared to be related to relief of the patient's tension, some gratification of dependency needs, and opportunities for constructive emotional experiences.

case 32

Chest Pain Related to Psychological and Bacteriological Factors

CHIEF PRESENTING SYMPTOM

Pain in chest.

BASIC ANAMNESTIC EXCERPTS
PSYCHODYNAMICALLY INTERPRETED

The patient's physical discomfort made only a brief interview possible.

Pain is immediately located as being on the right side. It is associated with sleeping outside on a porch, being exposed to dampness during a rainy night. It is further linked with a persisting cold in the chest. The patient couldn't eat, couldn't take anything in, couldn't breath in because of the pain; the associations point toward limitation of motion and of intake. A persistent cough aggravated the pain and interfered with sleep. A doctor was called but didn't come. During this time the pain was also accompanied by a hot, flushed, feverish feeling and great thirst. Repetitive references to water appear: patient took a shower to cool off before coming to the hospital; drinking water helped to stop the cough for a while. There are also references to no intake of food, becoming very weak, and feeling faint when blood was taken out of him. The pain is like a pressure against something; at times it feels as if something snaps and hits against the side of the chest.

Further associations to pain lead to recollections of a severe injury involving the right hand—several fingers were lost while in military service. The patient was firing a bazooka gun, and something blew up in front of him, hitting him in the right arm, shoulder, neck, chin, and mouth. He was able to walk to a first-aid station with one finger hanging, spitting out his teeth. He was given an injection by a doctor. Later an operation (sympathectomy) in his back relieved a persistent burning pain in the fingers of the right hand. Still further associations to pain in the past lead to recall of childhood experiences, especially with an older, bigger, powerful

273

brother who often bullied him. Once he got the plug from the backlash of his brother's casting rod on the right side of his face. His face was torn, as was his ear, and there was much bleeding. Another recollection deals with pain in the left little finger, again while fishing, getting a hook caught in it and needing to have it operated on in a hospital. Still another memory deals with almost cutting a little toe (this time again on the right) while slipping in a shower. Such repeated references to injury, mutilation, and operation appear in the context of a marked concern about his masculinity and suggest the persistence of activated childhood castration fears.

Again the patient refers to his uneasy sleep, disturbed by cough. This leads to having to be laid up and being inactive, which produces uneasiness. He wants to be moving around, fishing, hunting, playing cards with the fellows. Once as a youngster he fell through ice into a pool, couldn't swim, was pulled out just in time, but did not get a cold. He was very active in those days, too, always on the go. Activity may thus be associated with narrow escape from disaster and as a defense against dependent needs.

Turning to another aspect of his childhood, after stating he had not been sick, he recalled that up to the age of seven he couldn't talk, that there was considerable attention paid to this by his mother who finally took him to a religious shrine, and thereafter he began to talk. He was laughed at a long time by the kids in school because of this speech defect. He remembers a companion who also couldn't talk, and who was then sent to a special school. The patient still has trouble pronouncing words. He was the fourth oldest of a very large family of 11 boys and 3 girls, the ones after him coming in rapid succession. He stood out, though, for seven years as the silent one in the family.

Mother was sick four months ago. She had a cold and pain in her right side also, and was laid up until shortly before the patient's admission. Her kidney was involved, and she had to drink lots of fluid. The patient lives at home with her and a number of younger siblings. The somatic identification with the mother is clearly evident. He is obviously closely attached to her, is rivalrous with the other siblings for her attentions still, and was very much ambivalently concerned about the seriousness of her illness and possible loss. He states he is going to be a single fellow to the end. If he married, he'd have to go to work for less than he gets now for his disability. He'd rather be with a bunch of fellows who hang around together, raise hell, although one of his best pals just "got caught" by a girl (engaged) a short time before the patient became ill.

The father has not been mentioned at all up to this point, and when the patient was asked about him, he briefly indicated that the father was a powerful, hard-working man who wasn't around much.

PHYSICAL HISTORY

This is the patient's second admission. He entered because of pain in the right side of four days' duration. He was previously hospitalized five years before for treatment of causalgia of the left wrist, resulting from trauma. He had a cervical sympathectomy done at this time. Four days prior to admission, the patient awakened with a feeling that he had caught cold. He noted vague malaise, a productive cough, and pain below the right costal margin which was accentuated by deep breathing or coughing. During the first two days of the illness, he had rather profuse diarrhea, dryness of the throat, weakness, sweating, right-sided headache, and five nosebleeds. Two days before entry, the patient noted an increase in anorexia and could eat almost nothing thereafter. The pain persisted until the time of admission, was pleuritic in character, but did not radiate to the back, groin, or shoulder.

PHYSICAL EXAMINATION

Temperature 101°F. Pulse 90. Blood pressure 140/80. Respirations 20. Weight 144 pounds. The patient was well-developed, somewhat thin, responding to questions slowly, but appearing oriented. Head and neck normal. There seemed to be a slight icterus of the sclerae; eyes otherwise normal. There was a large central perforation of the left eardrum. The nasal septum was deviated markedly to the right. There was complete edentia. Mucous membranes of the mouth appeared rather pale; pharynx was normal. The lungs were clear to percussion and auscultation. The heart was not enlarged; rate and rhythm were normal; there was a prominent third heart sound and a reduplicated first sound at the aortic area; peripheral pulses and vessels were normal. There was amputation of the second to the fourth left fingers and considerable muscular atrophy throughout. The remainder of the examination was not remarkable.

LABORATORY DATA

Admission white blood cell count 15,000 with 69 percent polymorphonuclear leukocytes; hemoglobin 9.4 g; hematocrit 32 percent; sedimentation rate 28 mm per hr. Subsequent white counts showed a progressive drop to within normal limits at the time of discharge. Repeated hematocrits remained within the range of 35 percent to 37 percent. Admission urine contained a trace of albumin; subsequent urinalyses were normal. Liver function studies: cephalin flocculation negative; prothrombin time 100 percent; Van den Bergh normal. Two hour urobilinogen 0.7 Ehrlich units. Cold agglutinins on two occasions were negative. Three stools tested negative for occult blood. Sputum culture on admission showed predominantly pneumococci. Blood culture: no growth. Five sputum examinations for tubercle bacilli were negative.

ROENTGENOGRAMS

Chest film on admission showed a density in the peripheral portion of the right upper lobe, presenting a ground glass appearance and associated with thickening of the minor fissure. It was interpreted as a resolving pneumonia. In addition, the film showed regeneration of a previously surgically resected posterior portion of the right third rib. The foreign bodies in the right hemithorax were again noted as unchanged from examination at previous admission five years before. A chest film one week after present admission showed there had been some resolution at the base of the lobe, near the fissure; however, a portion of the consolidation appeared to be somewhat increased above this point. A third film two weeks after admission showed no further change. Gastrointestinal series was normal. Gallbladder studies showed the gallbladder to have a normal appearance; a cluster of small calcifications were noted just to the left of the spine, slightly below the expected level of the pancreas. These could not be distinguished on the gastrointestinal series. Flat film of the abdomen showed no definite calculi in the region of the gallbladder and no other abnormal calcifications. Intravenous pyelogram normal.

HOSPITAL COURSE

At the time of admission, though evidence of a bacterial infection was not convincing, because of X-ray evidence of a pneumonia and his generally weakened condition, anemia, and possible liver disease, the patient was started on penicillin. The sputum was subsequently reported as showing predominantly pneumococci. Three days after institution of penicillin therapy, the patient developed a nonpruritic eruption of the face—thought to be a drug reaction; accordingly, penicillin was stopped at this point. The patient continued to run a low-grade fever, which reached 100°F during the first hospital week, then fell to normal, and remained normal thereafter.

Clinically, the patient continued to show improvement in his appetite and strength, and the pleuritic chest pain, although occasionally felt until the time of discharge, diminished steadily. Investigation to rule out the possibility of biliary or hepatic disease indicated no evidence of disease of these organs. No cause was found for the patient's mild anemia which improved rapidly. He was discharged with instructions to have a follow-up chest film in one month.

DISCHARGE DIAGNOSES

1. Pneumonia, right upper lobe, due to pneumococcus; treated, improved.

2. Traumatic amputation of second, third, and fourth left fingers; untreated, unchanged.

3. Foreign bodies, right hemithorax; untreated, unchanged.

COMMENT

The symptom of pain is connected with limitation of motion, of intake, and with a sensory cluster involving temperature gradients. There are recollective links to activities in childhood, some of which resulted in injury, others led to his being chilled, but most vivid of all was his speech inhibition associated with inspiratory–expiratory difficulties. This childhood problem, associated with feelings of being defective and disliked by other children, lasted until he was entering latency and is closely connected to his early, dependent relationship with his mother. He has remained closely and ambivalently attached to and identified with her.

The illness of the patient's mother stirred up an intense emotional reaction in him; he feared that she might die. Her recovery was slow and incomplete, tending to maintain the patient's concern that he might lose her after all. Concurrently, one of his best friends became engaged to be married and planned to leave the area. This served to reinforce the patient's sense of loss. Instead of depressive symptoms which one would have ordinarily expected, he showed little affective response. The patient's emotions had been blocked from expression and turned inward. Thus, it was in the presence of special psychological circumstances that there developed a physical dysfunction, possibly changes in local (respiratory tract) tissue susceptibility to microorganisms already present in the involved area.

Kaplan and Gottschalk (1958), having considered that "potentially pathogenic microorganisms can remain dormant and in balance with the host's tissues for many years and then suddenly proliferate, invade, and produce inflammation," set out to make an experimental determination of whether there was a relationship between one patient's psychodynamic state and the streptococcal population of her oropharynx. They cite studies in the literature that have related emotions to changes in pH, vascularity, and secretions in the nasooropharyngeal area. The mucosa thus could be considered a frequently changing culture media. Since there was no sign of inflammation, it appeared unlikely that the changes in bacterial flora of the patient's throat influenced her particular emotional state. A significant correlation, however, was demonstrated between the (antecedent) psychologic and bacteriologic variables. The authors felt that it was quite possible that emotional influences are of limited significance in the pathogenesis of infection, serving as contributory or precipitating factors, together with other as yet unknown causal factors.

CASE 32

CHIEF PRESENTING SYMPTOM	Pain in chest
SENSORIMOTOR CONFIGURATIONS	Sensory configurations

Pain, temperature, interoceptive

Linked with feelings of defect, close attachment to mother, rivalry with siblings for her affection, and current depressive reaction over losing her

Motor configurations

Motility

Associated with many activities and their inhibition—including that of speech during childhood, serving as means of bolstering masculinity, especially in relation to brother and father

SOMATIC IDENTIFICATION	*Mother* Right-sided pain due to kidney involvement four months ago (Direct)
SENSITIZED ORGAN SYSTEM	Respiratory
STRESS (*surface meaning*)	Mother's illness and "loss" of a friend who became engaged to be married
STRESS (*dynamic significance*)	Ambivalently concerned about seriousness of mother's illness with activation of oral-dependency
DEFENSES	Counterphobic and overcompensatory activity

AFFECTS	*Intensity*	*Pathway of expression*
Anxiety	++	Ideational
Depression	+++	Somatization
Hostility	+++	Somatization

OTHER FACTORS	Inability to talk up to age seven Orality and castration fears interwoven Sensitivity to loss situations Superego problems

HOMEOSTATIC SHIFT(S) Marked but brief somatization shift

DIAGNOSES
a) Pneumonia, right upper lobe, due to pneumococcus, treated, improved;
b) Traumatic amputation of 2-3-4 left fingers, untreated, unchanged;
c) Foreign bodies, right hemithorax, untreated, unchanged

Back Pain: Psychological Aspects

CHIEF PRESENTING SYMPTOM

Pain in the back.

BASIC ANAMNESTIC EXCERPTS

The patient often speaks irritably and complainingly: "I've been losing time from work and haven't got the funds to pay any more private doctors. The pain is hard to describe. It's like trying to describe a color. It wakes me up from sleep and keeps on increasing so that I finally have to get out of bed. After I've sat on a chair for a couple of hours, it will start decreasing. Then I'll sleep the rest of the night in a chair.

"If you were to ask me to describe a color, I couldn't do it. It's the same way with the pain. One doctor told me he thought it was pleurisy of the muscles—from pneumonia, that I had when I was 15 years old. Whatever it's from, I've tried everything. I can't afford to be here now. I should be working. I've got a family. I bought a house. Got to continue payments on it."

He recollects that he came close to dying of pneumonia at age 15: "My resistance got so low. Two physicians were keeping a check on me constantly during the critical period. After that I had pains in my lung for quite some time, sharp and piercing. This lasted for a year, and then it went away." The pain, now as then, is on the right side and sharp. "I've had it a couple of years, and it's getting worse. A couple of months ago it began increasing so that I don't get any sleep at all and have to take sleeping pills. I've had two accidents working on my machine at the shop. Too many sleeping tablets. I could have got hurt seriously."

The reference to onset two years ago is next changed to three years ago: "I overlooked it in the beginning—a lot of pains and aches coming and going. When it started to knock me out of work, I had to take it seriously. I work as a machine adjuster and have had this job just for the past three months. I'm really a commercial artist, sign painter, doing a little bit of this and a little bit of that. But I have a wife and kid and lots of bills, so I took a machinist job in addition to doing some retouching work at home. I originally went to commercial art school for three years. Then I got married four years ago, and I got pressed too hard, had to give up art. I have a son who has to stay with the folks because my wife has to work. With all these debts, someone has to work."

The pain is next considered as possibly starting from a fall some three years ago: "I tripped, fell, and landed on my back. It knocked the wind out of me. But I got up by myself. I continued on and didn't make much of it, even though I had a sore back. I've had plenty of falls in the past, from hockey, ice skating, and roller skating. I was very active when I was a teenager. I played in all different sports. My right knee often kicked out of joint. It was a trick knee, and I finally had an operation when I was 16. Then it stiffened up hard, and I couldn't do some sports afterwards."

Again there are references to breathing difficulties: "I smoke three cigars a day, used to smoke as many as seven. The respirations test kept me from becoming an officer in the air force. I had a broken nose for 10 years and didn't know it. In the tropics I had trouble breathing, and a physician looked at it and said it was broken. I guess I first hurt it when I was a youngster working on a tobacco farm. It was during summer school vacation, and it was to keep us out of mischief. It was from the sixth grade on. Father was earning only 15 dollars a week, with a family of five. I don't really know how I hurt my nose. Maybe I was poking it where it wasn't supposed to be (laughing).

"I was the second oldest. It was very hard for my family. We had a lot of stews. Mother used to go down to the welfare office to get a few things. When I was very small, I had trouble eating. I was skinny and couldn't seem to put any weight on. I used to be sleepy in the classroom, lack of nutrition. Every once in a while I would get a penny to buy some candy. Art was my pet subject. Didn't like the others, so I had siesta time. The teachers gave me heck and told my parents, but I used to do a lot of daydreaming, especially about good things to eat. The trouble at school lasted a long time. I was often sitting slouched in my chair, half asleep. Just didn't go for most of the subjects. Sort of hungry all the time. Guess I was puny in comparison to father and brothers. Finally, when I started to work, in my teens, I was able to eat better and get stronger."

The next associative connections refer to the health of his parents: "Father is pretty good, but mother has heart trouble. Her hands get very cold. When she touches you, it feels like an icicle at times. She turns white, has no color when she isn't feeling well. She's been told to slow down, but she keeps right on being active, overtaxing herself."

Further references to his own immediate family follow: "I told my wife that there's to be just one child. I dictate in the house. She accepts my verdict. I don't want any more, can't afford it. Each time we're to-

gether I worry that there'll be a slipup and she'll get pregnant. Takes the
pleasure out of it, having to interrupt. Anyway one's enough of a problem.
He's a problem eater, skinny like I used to be. Getting him to eat can be
mighty painful."

PSYCHODYNAMIC IMPRESSIONS

Childhood oral deprivation, accompanying malnutrition, and concern about small size were defended against during adolescence by marked
activity and taking chances in a counterphobic way with some resultant
accident proneness. Dependent needs and inferiority feelings have remained
rather consistently in the immediate background since then. Father is seen
as a devaluated object of identification. Mother is reacted to in an ambivalent way. Pain and loss are immediately interconnected. Rather open expressions of resentment about inadequacy of many different treatments
follow. There are also references to not getting enough to satisfy his
dependent needs. There are associations between pain and difficulty in
describing a color. It is only much later in the interview that color again
comes up, but in reference to his mother's illness and possible death. The
pain in this connection would appear to be a somatic expression of his
concern over the possible loss of his mother and the ambivalence involved,
expressed intermediately through visual and temperature sensory clusters.
In addition to mother's illness, a group of other disturbing situational
events appear to have accompanied the development and persistence of
the pain, namely, his marriage, birth of first child, need to limit the size
of his family, financial responsibilities, inability to work regularly, shift
from art work to machinist's job, and so on. Previously, the stresses of
separation from home and problems of readjustment to military service had
brought about a major decompensation with many gastrointestinal symptoms and evidence of an agitated depressive reaction. Return to civilian
life resulted in no marked improvement.

The reference early in the interview, about having to sit up in order
to sleep because of the back pain, is brought up later in the context of
childhood recollections about school. It was a milieu he disliked and one
from which he would retreat either by daydreaming or slouching sleepily
in his chair or actually falling asleep. The connecting link is avoidance of
a disagreeable situation: in the first instance, pain; in the second instance,
responsibility of school work. Thus, the unpleasantness of the current
stresses to which the patient is exposed may be symbolically represented in
his somatic pain.

PHYSICAL HISTORY

The patient was admitted with the chief complaint of pain in the neck of three years' duration. He gave a long and complicated history of multiple illnesses for 11 years, including choking sensations with difficulty in breathing, tightening feeling in the throat, operation for deviated nasal septum, and hemorrhoids. He was apparently hospitalized several times during his military service for nausea, severe anorexia, occasional vomiting, plus sour stomach and belching, with intolerance of spicy foods. This had recurred periodically with marked relationship to emotional upsets. He had been hospitalized in the service because of "belligerence, disgust, and depression" and was discharged because of "nerves." For a year following he lost 40 pounds. He attended several schools, had 8 or 10 jobs which he stated he had to quit because he felt he was "being pushed around." He also gave some history of accident proneness. He stated that about two years before admission, he began having nightly, sharp, steady pain over the right costovertebral angle region. This occurred only after being in the prone position a few hours and was relieved by sleeping upright. He also complained of severe, sharp pain over the lateral aspect of the right hip and over the right sacroiliac joint of about eight months' duration, associated with movement of the hip.

PHYSICAL EXAMINATION

Height 5 feet 8½ inches. Weight 174 pounds. Temperature 98.2°F. Pulse 76. Blood pressure 128/88. A well-developed and well-nourished white male appearing in no distress. There was considerable belching during the history taking. The entire physical examination, including neurological, was within normal limits.

LABORATORY DATA

Serology, urinalysis, hemoglobin, hematocrit, white count, and differential were within normal limits.

ROENTGENOGRAMS

Gastrointestinal and gallbladder series: no abnormalities noted except for a small diverticulum of the fundus of the gallbladder. Chest, right hip, sacroiliac plates showed no abnormalities.

HOSPITAL COURSE

On admission the patient was placed on a bland diet, sedation and aspirin as needed. The patient was seen in formal psychiatric consultation, and it was agreed that he represented a complicated neuropsychiatric problem. He continued to complain of back pain while in the hospital. He was discharged with a referral to a mental hygiene clinic.

DISCHARGE DIAGNOSIS

Psychoneurosis, severe. Untreated, unchanged.

COMMENT

The patient's symptom of pain appears to be a chronic conversion symptom. Actually he located this pain in a number of different areas when giving a history to the internist. Additionally, in the medical history, he described symptoms suggestive of globus hystericus, and references were made to trouble with hemorrhoids. The patient is one of the few who spoke rather directly about sexual difficulties, referring to coitus interruptus. These difficulties appear to play a considerable part in the "night troubles" that he has. All symptoms and their exacerbations are very closely and clearly related to stress situations, both chronic and acute, major and minor. The neurosis interferes significantly with his adjustment at work and at home. Potential for further development of depression or a more serious disruption of physical functioning, either in the gastrointestinal or respiratory tracts, appears to be present. Hopefully, psychotherapeutic intervention which was recommended will act in a preventive fashion against further severe regressive shifts, even if it does not significantly resolve the patient's basic conflicts.

This type of back pain for which there is no detectable organic basis is a commonly encountered physical symptom. The patient often gives a history dating the onset to some accident experienced in the recent past, just as in this case. It may well be that some actual trauma was sustained by the musculoskeletal structures in the body area, and that the patient actually did have symptoms as a result. Related altered sensory perceptions and motor disturbance may have occurred. However, after the condition had healed, the symptomatology either persisted, or after temporarily subsiding, returned without any physical precipitant. A psychological stress, if it is looked for, will be found, in each instance, to have become associated with the original physical trauma and related sensorimotor patterns that were then evoked. Such a somatic pathway may then be used as one among several discharge outlets for emotional tensions, or indeed may become a principal means for discharging excitations. It resembles the conditioned reflex type of response. Deconditioning or desensitization becomes progressively more difficult the longer the somatic discharge pathway is utilized, and especially in the presence of reinforcing secondary-gain factors.

CASE 33

CHIEF PRESENTING SYMPTOM	Pain in back
SENSORIMOTOR CONFIGURATIONS	Sensory configurations

Pain, temperature, visual, interoceptive

Linked with eating problems, malnourishment during childhood, resentment at inadequate treatment later, stressful situations, and ambivalent reaction to threat of losing nurturing figures

Motor configurations

Activity

Associated with falling, injuries and operations which interfere with this defense against feeling puny and unmanly

SOMATIC IDENTIFICATION	*Mother* Cold hands and pallor due to heart disease in recent years
SENSITIZED ORGAN SYSTEM	Musculoskeletal Respiratory Gastrointestinal
STRESS (*surface meaning*)	Mother's illness, work and financial problems, need to limit size of family Earlier—problems of readjustment to military service
STRESS (*dynamic significance*)	Increasing concern about adequacy, and potentiation of dependency trends
DEFENSES	Counterphobic and overcompensatory activity Projection

AFFECTS	*Intensity*	*Pathway of expression*
Anxiety	+++	Some ideational and affective, conversion
Depression	++	Ideational, some affective
Hostility	++	Some affective, some acted out

OTHER FACTORS	Orality marked Small size Some accident proneness Coitus interruptus Superego problems

HOMEOSTATIC SHIFT(S)   Hostile impulses directed inwardly with resultant depression; ideational and affective systems insufficient at times to deal with anxiety, resulting in conversion phenomena

DIAGNOSIS   Psychoneurosis, severe, untreated, unchanged

case 34

Constipation, Backache, and Somatic Identification

CHIEF PRESENTING SYMPTOM

Difficulty with bowels and sore back.

BASIC ANAMNESTIC EXCERPTS

The initial focus is on constipation: "I can't seem to pass a movement. I had an operation for adhesions 10 years ago. That took very good care of them. In fact, I was going regular. Still I get that sore back and wonder what's causing it. Last week I went to work and they sent me home. I had 102° fever. It was getting so that every day I went to work, they'd check my temperature and send me home. So I seen the doctor down there, and he told me that he thought it was internal hernias due to adhesions. They tell me since I've been here, I haven't had any high fever. When I'm working, maybe I work one up. Things are pretty hard. I have a family and I have to put in 48 hours at least to make any half decent living. I lost a child last year, and well, from one thing to another, last year was a bad year for us. We got kind of back on our bills but I've talked to people that I owe and told them my condition. They seemed to agree that it would be all right; I'll eventually be able to pay them. But I can't do it this way. The doctor tells me I'm pretty nervous. I admit that. I am nervous. But, before I got this constipated condition, I wasn't nervous.

"When I do have trouble with the bowels, it's the back. Right in the small of the back I get sharp pains. I can't understand what it is. Two years ago I went to the hospital for it. All the doctors could find was torn tissues—from forcing too much. But I didn't have any backache. The last time I came in and sat down on the hole, forcing it, there was a pounding like this in the back (bangs fist against palm) about 40 seconds. Now it isn't pounding that way, but I get that constant pain. I had Bright's disease when I was six years old. The doctor said I'd lick it as I go along, with proper care. I don't know if I did or not.

287 ·

"If I have a little adhesion—I mean—I would hate to get cut on. I guess every man does. But I'd just as soon see them out. That way we can settle that issue. I hate like hell to take too much time off. I'm a laborer in an armory. I get the work to the women. After they get done with it, I weigh it for them, because it's heavy. At the same time, I'm like a janitor. I clean up, sweep up. I'm expecting to be transferred to be an inspector. But I've lost so much time, lost a raise already, and maybe the job of inspector I'd like to get. I started there as a laborer with intentions of bettering myself. I thought I had a good chance until this happened."

The patient refers to his family's health: "My father was pretty sick when I was in high school, so I left and went to work. He had been up on a ladder, fixing up one of these steam boilers when he fell down on his back and broke four ribs. I put in close to 90 hours per week in a bakery, which is where I think I ruined myself. I got myself all tired out. We were working seven days a week. Father was out five to six months. He got that injury, and then he got . . . it started off with a cold, then it turned bad and the doctor told him to take an extra month. So he took an extra month, and he got up, and he was all right. Now he's out on his back again. He's not working any more. He got a slight shock a few days ago. His right leg is four inches shorter than his lef . . . I mean his left leg is four inches shorter than his right. Doctor claims the nerves are all shrunken. Father was a man who took a lot of bumps in his life. He worked hard on these steam boilers. It was a hot, tough job. That's the kind of life he had. He worked there 26 years. I'd like to see him have a few years to enjoy himself.

"Mother also was pretty sick. She weighed 152 pounds and went down to 87. I took her to a hospital where they took X-rays of her stomach. They could find nothing. It was something in through the throat that grows and kind of blocks. That year when she came out of the hospital, she was so thin and everything. I got a picture of her at home when she was so thin. She doesn't know I have it. If she knew, she's put up a fight. She wouldn't want anybody to see it. It's like day and night. Our family doctor gave her some pills and she finally gained back the weight she lost. She had Bright's disease, too, in the earlier part of her marriage, but I don't recall her having it after I was born. When I had Bright's disease, I was in bed with fever, chills, and a sore throat; it hurt to pass my water. I was on milk and water for quite a while, and I was very hungry in the course of it. Mother used to make a lot of pies. In them days they didn't buy pies, they made them themselves, and they used to smell awful good. I couldn't eat, so I told her to save me a pie (laughing).

"I remember at 13 I got the sickness again, and that's when I got constipated. They tried everything to make me go, but nothing worked until father gave me Epsom salts. I've had no trouble with it, until I grew up.

"I want to get to a point where I'm able to work and not have to come home a few hours later. That don't help me. If there's a little adhesions there, if the doctor thinks it's that—take them out. I was operated on 10 years ago. It just happened I was blocked like that then. I remember I had just gotten married about six months before. I was at the supper table. It was summertime and hot. My wife had just gotten pregnant. I felt some wicked cramps in my belly. The doctor told us—it looks like adhesions, and they operated the following morning. I got rid of my appendix when I was 16. 1 had wicked cramps then, too, so they took me right away to the hospital. Since these operations I had no trouble till about a month ago."

PSYCHODYNAMIC IMPRESSIONS

The patient is concerned with a variety of complaints, involving different body areas. The symptom of constipation is in marked contrast to his logorrhea. Preoccupation with lower gastrointestinal tract includes what he calls adhesions, the sequelae of an appendectomy, and these are currently blamed for "internal hernias" and soreness of the back. Another related symptom is that of feeling flushed and hot while at work, which is ascribed to the recurrence of a "temperature." There are associated references to sickness during childhood, in particular to Bright's disease, which apparently left him with much anxiety about his body and its integrity.

Somatic identifications are multiple and complicated. Father is pictured as formerly injured and now incapacitated again, by a shock, out on his back, with involvement of the left lower extremity which is described as shrinking and shriveling. Further sensory links with father are through references to temperature. Father worked in a very hot place and often was flushed and sweating. A particular recollection from puberty refers to the occurrence of "bowel trouble" and father's intervention, which finally enabled the patient to pass a stool, but this was followed by a bout of fever. Somatic identification with mother includes references to her having had Bright's disease, also, and to something being wrong with her insides, causing her to lose much weight. The collective identifications point in the direction of recurrent bodily defects.

The present symptoms are brought up against a background of situational difficulties: loss of a child, loss of good financial standing, his job advancement becoming jeopardized, and increasing family responsibilities. His work involves cleaning and sweeping up, and doing menial labor for other employees—mostly women. He pictures himself in a devaluated role, subordinate to his fellow workers, and in connection with work that has symbolic anal referents. Dependency needs were activated during childhood and puberty, when the patient was ill with what he calls "Bright's disease." Mother and wife appear as central figures who, when they frustrate such needs, evoke considerable hostility.

PHYSICAL HISTORY

This was the second admission of an armory worker who entered with the chief complaint of stomach trouble of one week's duration. The patient had previously been hospitalized two years ago for a similar complaint of sudden onset of constipation to obstipation, associated with low abdominal pain and slight nausea of six days' duration. There was also a history of rectal bleeding of one day's duration at that time. The patient was quickly relieved by enemata. No abnormalities by anoscopy and proctoscopy were revealed, and the patient was discharged on metamucil and increased water intake. He apparently had been doing well until approximately six days prior to the present admission, when he noted again the passage of scybalous stools followed by obstipation of three days' duration. He had associated low back pain.

PHYSICAL EXAMINATION

Essentially unchanged from previous admission. Temperature 98.2°F. Pulse 90. Blood pressure 110/70. The patient, as previously, showed a harried, unkempt demeanor. Throat was slightly injected. A small conjunctival hemorrhage was noted in the left lateral sclera. There was upper edentia compensated. Lower incisors remaining showed retraction of the gums and excess tartar formation. Heart and lungs were negative. Abdomen was soft: liver, spleen, could not be felt. There was right periumbilic tenderness, no rebound. There was a fusiform, nontender, lower left quadrant, nonfixed, soft mass. Peristalsis was normal. No other masses could be felt. The fingernails were short due to biting. The palms were sweaty. Examination of rectum revealed skin tags at five o'clock and a probable internal hemorrhoid at eight o'clock. The rectum was not packed with feces as it had been on the previous admission. Stool was 4+ guaiac. The prostate was slightly tender, 1+ enlarged, but of normal consistency.

LABORATORY DATA

Routine hematology, urinalysis, and serology were within normal limits. Repeat stool examinations reported guaiac 3+, 1+, and finally negative on the last two examinations; no ova or parasites were seen at any time.

ROENTGENOGRAMS

Chest plate showed a slight increase in the amount of interstitial tissue throughout both lung fields and some diffuse fibriotic change consistent with chronic bronchitis. A barium enema revealed no abnormalities. The terminal ileum was visualized and appeared normal. Both gastrointestinal and small bowel series were performed, and no abnormalities were found.

HOSPITAL COURSE

The patient was placed on a low residue, bland diet. A repeat proctoscopy was done. The scope was passed 4 inches to an area of spasm. The patient was given 75 mg of Demerol, and the scope was passed again to the area of spasm which relaxed adequately to continue passage to the complete 8 inches. A small area of granulated mucosa was seen at 4 inches on the posterior right lateral wall of the rectum. No other abnormalities were observed except a large dilated vein which appeared on the vertical wall at approximately 4 inches and ran to the sphincter without any evidence of bleeding or ulceration. No hemorrhoids were seen on anoscopy. Following the essentially negative gastrointestinal tract studies, the patient was again reassured. He professed some improvement in his condition, and was discharged.

DISCHARGE DIAGNOSIS

Psychophysiologic gastrointestinal reaction manifested by obstipation.

COMMENT

It has been known for a long time that gut reaction may be part of a general response to anxiety. A more dynamic relationship between bowel activity and psychological factors was advanced by Alexander (1950). Referring specifically to constipation, he noted the symbolic significance of intestinal content as a "valuable possession" in some cases, accompanied by an "anal-sadistic attitude, the inhibition of which contributes to the anal retention." There is a connection between the attitude of withholding something valuable and the inhibitory influence directed against elimination because of its symbolic hostile significance (soiling). The involved individual's highly ambivalent attitude toward excrement makes possible the shift from one attitude to the other. "Constipation, as rejection of the obligation to give, corresponds to the positive evaluation of the excreta as a valuable possession; whereas constipation as a result of inhibited aggressions corresponds to the negative attitude toward the intestinal content." Alexander felt that the gastrointestinal system had three major functions: intaking, retaining, and eliminating; it was thereby a particularly suitable pathway of expression for these basic tendencies if their natural expression through the voluntary motor system or sexual apparatus is blocked by internal emotional conflict. The upper end of the tract is associated with receptive or taking tendencies. The lower end is linked with giving, eliminating, and retentive tendencies. These tendencies may have variable sexual or destructive symbolic significance.

Somatic identification in this case was multiple and complicated, but seemed weighted in a more feminine, less manly direction. Such identification can be followed in much greater detail in the course of psychoanalytic treatment. In order to further illustrate this, clinical material from another patient will be introduced at the end of this case.

CASE 34

CHIEF PRESENTING SYMPTOM	Difficulty with bowels and sore back
SENSORIMOTOR CONFIGURATIONS	Sensory configurations
	Interoceptive, pain, temperature
	Connected with various losses, particularly of physical integrity in himself, father, and mother, and with anxiety about ability to meet stressful situations
	Motor configurations
	Forcing
	Associated with working too hard, ruining self, losing control (especially over-anger), and having to assume a passive–feminine role
SOMATIC IDENTIFICATION	Father Out on his back due to slight shock very recently
	Mother Weight loss, cause unknown; Bright's disease before patient's birth (Direct, organ constitutional—patient's childhood illness)
	Wife Pregnancy—10 years ago
SENSITIZED ORGAN SYSTEM	Gastrointestinal
STRESS (*surface meaning*)	Child's death, financial problems, job tensions, and increasing family responsibilities

STRESS (*dynamic significance*)	Increasing concern about adequacy, controlling, retaining, and rejecting tendencies
DEFENSES	Reaction formations Rationalizations Conversions

AFFECTS		*Intensity*	*Pathway of expression*
	Anxiety	+++	Some ideational and affective, conversion
	Depression	++	Some ideational and affective
	Hostility	++	Some ideational and affective

OTHER FACTORS	Marked body narcissism Loss—a recurrent factor Anal as well as oral referents Bisexual identification with feminine aspects preponderant
HOMEOSTATIC SHIFT(s)	Somatization shifts mild to moderate
DIAGNOSIS	Psychophysiologic gastrointestinal reaction manifested by obstipation

CLINICAL MATERIAL FROM ANOTHER CASE

A woman in her early thirties had entered analysis because of difficulties in getting along with women supervisors in her work and an inability to form a meaningful relationship with a man. A deeply dependent tie with her mother was defended against by using separation from home and career aspirations to emphasize her independence to herself and others. Sibling rivalry with an older sister was intense. Her father was remembered as an aloof person who was always away from home. Feelings were rigidly controlled, especially those associated with competitive strivings in relation to male colleagues at work. She had always been anxiously concerned about her physical condition. The patient gave an impression of being frail, although she had been in essentially good health for a long time.

After some months of treatment, a negatively weighted transference reaction developed. Most behavioral manifestations were in terms of her coming late, not paying her bill, not remembering what had gone on in the preceding analytic hour, and the like. The transference, however, was a split one, with more open and obvious reactions ideationally and affectively expressed toward parental figures in her work. At this time, the patient had had a viral infection, which left her very much underweight and weak. Her internist had put her on androgens to help her gain weight.

Shortly after this, the patient went to a farewell luncheon for the head of the personnel department where she worked. This man had been with the firm a long time, but had rather suddenly resigned to take another job. That morning before attending the luncheon, the patient had been preoccupied with thoughts about a summer cottage which she and a number of others—men and women—had rented for mutual use. She found herself quite irritated at how this was working out, thinking of herself as being overlooked and left out of the plans and activities of the group. She both resented and was envious of the rather "loose" sexual behavior of the people involved. One woman in particular was the focus of her bitterness; this was an older, sibling figure. That morning, the patient wore a tight-fitting sweater, ostensibly on account of her sensitivity to the air conditioning, but her colleague accused her of trying to overemphasize her charms. The patient felt a growing tension, uneasiness, and great anger as she set out for the luncheon.

Toward the end of the luncheon, the patient become aware of a sensation of tension in her left leg—as if someone were pulling at her stocking. The feeling of great pressure increased, and she thought her stocking was about to burst. As she got up from the table to leave, she noticed that her left leg was "enormously swollen." This had all occurred in the space of an hour and a half. The patient became very anxious and wondered if this was the first sign of a really serious illness. Her friends and colleagues commented on the swelling, some frightening her, some trying to reassure her. She returned to her office, and her panic grew as she looked at the swollen leg. Finally she called her internist whose secretary answered and at first refused to let her talk with the doctor. The patient's anger grew and grew, and for a while she "forgot" about the discomfort in her leg. She finally got through to her physician who felt that the swelling was due to an accumulation of fluid—but not due to the androgens she was taking. He suggested that it might be the result of the hot weather, and that perhaps her salt intake was too high. He recommended that she limit her salt intake and that she keep her leg elevated as much as possible. A male colleague came by and jokingly made some sexual references to her leg. She grew still angrier. Meanwhile the swelling had begun to subside and by that evening had mostly disappeared. Several days later, her internist examined her and noted only a slight swelling of the left calf. He could find no "reasonable organic explanation" for what had happened, suggesting that it was possibly a combination of heat and too tight stockings.

The patient further associated the following information: At the luncheon there seemed to be quite a commotion, with different people trying to dominate the conversation. The patient felt she was not getting any attention at all. Her thoughts about her boss who was leaving centered around his disinterest, particularly in regard to herself; he had seemed distant, aloof, even cold. She felt he never gave real answers, always seemed to hedge, and after each conference with him, she came away feeling nothing had been accomplished. In a previous disagreement with a colleague, her boss had not supported her. She had felt if he would only loosen up, be more friendly, act as if he really had an interest in her, then she might have learned to like him. It was quite clear that her boss represented both her father and the analyst. He appeared as a frustrating, nongiving, noninterested figure who was finally leaving her for two reasons: one, because she was not a boy and was therefore devaluated, and two, because he preferred another more attractive woman to her. The element of somatic identification finally appeared in a clear and unmistakable fashion. Her boss limped because of a crippled left leg, something she had not mentioned previously.

case 35

Itching, Nausea, and Generalized Malaise: New Symptoms (Readmission of Case 28)

CHIEF PRESENTING SYMPTOM

Itching, nausea, generalized aching.

BASIC ANAMNESTIC EXCERPTS PSYCHODYNAMICALLY INTERPRETED

The patient who had been seen two weeks earlier in a previous admission (Case 28) first describes an accident that occurred on his return to work as a laboratory assistant. The setting is one where he and his boss are emptying buckets. In the process, the patient hit his head against a bucket the other man was putting down. He sustained a small laceration and was given a tetanus shot. A week went by, and he developed an itch on his right arm where the tetanus shot had been given. He also threw up several times and felt a persistent aching in every part of his body. He told his wife, who was pregnant, that he didn't have any life in him. This all had been preceded by a rapid loss of appetite. He couldn't eat, couldn't keep anything down, and got the dry heaves. At this point in the interview there is an elaboration of sensory clusters involving temperature (hot, cold) and generalized pain, and a specific reference to the feeling of having a ball in his arm.

The patient next refers to the injection. They "shot him" with tetanus antitoxin. Sensory clusters concerned with hardness, softness, big, and little are introduced in connection with recollections about insect stings. He emphasizes how the itching area grew and grew. New associations dealing with contagion appear. The patient fears that he has caught poison ivy from his little girl. Visual percepts can now be noted. He tries to look elsewhere, distract himself from his preoccupation with the itching areas. However, he has to scratch. He then describes in very dramatic terms the need to

296

look at himself. Every part of his body is filled with lesions. He recalls
ordering his wife out of bed; when she looked at him she told him not to
come near her. He became very frightened and immediately thought he
had caught something serious from the laboratory. He was not reassured by
a doctor whom he called who ordered calamine. "I felt I would go crazy
scratching, and the more I scratched, the bigger I became; my stomach
swelled out and everything. I felt completely filled, all over my body, with
'it.'" (Again indirect references to pregnancy.) He warned his wife to
sterilize everything, and he was brought to the hospital in a taxi. There
the doctor told him he was having a tetanus reaction and wanted to give
him some pills and send him home. The patient resisted and referred to
his wife's "carrying" (pregnancy), her being unable to take care of him
like this (his infantile needs), and his being unable to sleep with her. The
doctor finally agreed to admit him. The patient continues in detailed dramatic fashion: "In the hospital they started shooting me with everything,
needles. I felt very sick, scratching and tearing at myself, and I had to be
in bed. When I started walking again, I got pains starting in my back and
going all the way down both legs, like a spasm."

The patient now elaborates on his present chief symptom, pain. "My
bottom is stuck so much it resembles a pin cushion. Pains are terrific."
He resisted the doctor's suggestion to try walking, protesting he was not a
cripple, not playing a part, but that the pain was too great. He tried to
convince the doctor about his spasms, taking his pants off, lying down,
having the doctor feel his thighs. He couldn't get a spasm because he was
lying down, but the moment he stood up he got one. "It felt like a
tourniquet had been tied there, and as though something is trying to get
through and can't. It's as if the thighs were being twisted in opposite
directions. It finally has become better, but it was a lulu of an experience.
I could be called Sad Sack—because everything happens to me." The patient
then refers to having had shots before, without any particular reaction. He
has never had blotches before. This leads to associations about freckles—
and further identification in terms of physical appearance (freckles, red
hair) with his little girl.

Again the patient returns to the pain. It seems to start in his rectum
and goes right through his legs like a current. "I've had shots in the
rectum (buttocks) and it hurts from sitting. Now it is like a prickly feeling,
numbness, like touching a light in the bathroom and it goes right through
you in a second. Walking helps and it isn't so bad. I sound like a chronic
old bastard, that's got everything from pregnancy down. It's terrible to
complain like this, but what's the use of keeping it inside?" The feminine
identifications are quite clear. The next associative patterns deal with the
patient's wife. She appears first as a kind of deceiving figure—in connection

with tricks she uses to get him up in time for work in the morning. He has no comeback. He likes to go to bed late and to get up late, preoccupied with looking at television. His wife may give birth early. The references to time now deal with her present and previous pregnancies. "The last time she was two weeks late and she was mad. This time she may be early because she is a very small girl and may have a large baby, even twins. She's against spending money for x-rays. The baby's not turning around either to come out on its head, or even by its feet. My wife is willing to wait. She is not a girl that lets go with her emotions; she's not a dreamer; she doesn't look for sympathy, and she doesn't sit down and worry about herself. She seems O.K." Narcissism is intensely expressed in the next associations. "If I were a woman and married to myself, I'd be bored (if I were her). I don't make much money and there's little to spend. But my wife doesn't complain. We bought a house with old stuff in it, and she didn't mind, but I fixed it up with new stuff, though she didn't ask for anything and asked why I did it because we can't afford all this new stuff." He then enacted the scene that followed in which he forced her to admit that she really wanted it. His aggression is diluted by references that she is very sensible and practical.

The patient now returns to the theme of his work. "It's nothing one would want to see first thing in the morning; not a nice smell; it stinks (laughter). The odor gets on one's body." The patient refers to his job as "distasteful—the part where I work in the morgue." He needed money, and there was nothing else open. He was told he would have to sew bodies. He then describes in dramatic detail his first day of work. Again there is an elaboration of olfactory sensory clusters followed by intense anxiety at the prospect of seeing knives used to cut bodies. He indicates he was given support and reassurance by an older man who was in charge of the work.

PHYSICAL HISTORY

The patient, who had been discharged several weeks before, returned to the hospital because of a generalized rash. He has had several admissions in the past, and on each occasion his gastrointestinal symptoms were considered to be due to functional disease. One week ago he accidentally cut his forehead, and was seen by a surgical resident here who administered tetanus antitoxin. Apparently, he was not sensitive on conjunctival test and was given 1,500 units, with no immediate reaction. On the night of admission, he suddenly felt warm all over, became nauseated, and vomited. Vomiting continued intermittently after this. He soon noted a generalized pruritic rash which spread over his body and trunk. He also noticed pain in all muscles and joints at onset, though soon afterward the pain was localized to the right deltoid, the left shoulder, and both supraclavicular areas. He denied receiving tetanus antitoxin in the past.

PHYSICAL EXAMINATION

Temperature 98.6°F. Pulse 90. Blood pressure 120/90. The patient appeared apprehensive and was lying uncomfortably in bed with diffuse tenderness in both supraclavicular areas. The chest was symmetrical. Heart, lungs, and abdomen were negative. The patient complained of some pain on extension of his left arm. There was a blotchy, erythematous, papular rash involving the trunk, face, scalp, and extremities. Each lesion was slightly raised and was flat with irregular borders. There were several small, non-tender, cervical and inguinal nodes.

LABORATORY DATA

Admission white blood cell count 11,000 with a normal differential. Hemoglobin 12.8 g. Hematocrit 42 percent. Sedimentation rate 12 mm per hr. Urinalysis and serology were negative. Repeat white blood cell count was 12,200 with a 219 eosinophile count.

ROENTGENOGRAMS

Chest plate: negative.

ELECTROCARDIOGRAM

Within normal limits.

HOSPITAL COURSE

Because of the time relations between the injection of tetanus anti-toxin and the patient's outbreak in a generalized rash, it was felt that this represented a case of serum sickness. Consequently, the patient was put on adrenalin in oil and pyribenzamine by mouth, resulting in the disappearance of the skin lesions within one day. The patient, however, complained of pain in the back of his thighs and legs, which he related to a stiffness which decreased gradually. He was discharged three days after admission.

DISCHARGE DIAGNOSES

1. Serum sickness. Treated, improved.
2. Somatization reaction with functional gastrointestinal complaint. Untreated, unchanged.

COMMENT

Despite the fact that preliminary physical tests showed no sensitivity to tetanus antitoxin, the patient developed serum sickness with gastrointestinal and skin symptoms. This occurred against a background of continuing stress. The patient was greatly concerned about his work in the laboratory and autopsy room. He was preoccupied with fantasies of being infected and infecting others. He wanted to leave his job and his responsibilities in general. He also maintained an ambivalent attitude toward his wife's pregnancy, with rather intense wishes that she be rid of it. More recently he had become unduly irritated over his daughter's catching poison ivy, and he worried about the condition of her skin. The patient's physical symptoms can be considered to be symbolic representations of his hostility and feminine identification. In reference to the latter, it should be noted that the process of identifying with emotionally significant objects is not purely psychological. It is more useful to think of identification in terms of its broader psychophysical aspects. Thus, an individual's reactions to objects may be expressed not only ideationally, behaviorally, and affectively, but also somatically.

Certain "specific" medication may mask or modify particular physical signs or symptoms, as in this case, the antihistamine effect of adrenalin and pyribenzamine administration was followed by rapid disappearance of skin lesions. This suggests that the underlying psychophysical disturbance has subsided, but this may not be so. If the intensity of the underlying psychological factors is sufficiently great, particular medication may serve to block emotional discharge through only one somatic pathway, with other sensitized physical pathways remaining or becoming available. It is also possible that a massive shift from predominantly physical to psychological channels of discharge may occur, following medication or surgery.

CASE 35

CHIEF PRESENTING SYMPTOM   Itching, nausea, generalized aching

SENSORIMOTOR CONFIGURATIONS   Sensory configurations

Interoceptive, pain, tactile, temperature, visual, olfactory

Derived from intensely narcissistic preoccupation with his body, linked with symbolic anal references to work and to concern about being infected and infectious, and also connected with further frustration of dependency needs by a deceiving maternal figure (wife)

Motor configurations

Emptying, being stuck

Linked with many associations of being in the passive–feminine role, including pregnancy fantasies and other sexualized references

SOMATIC IDENTIFICATION

Child Poison ivy dermatitis very recently (Direct)
Wife Pregnancy—current

SENSITIZED ORGAN SYSTEM

Skin
Gastrointestinal

STRESS (*surface meaning*)

Daughter's skin trouble; accident at work which he dislikes

STRESS (*dynamic significance*)

Activation of pregnancy fantasies, feminine identification, and fears of being infected and infectious—anal referents
Further activation of passive trends

DEFENSES

Rationalization
Projection
Denial

AFFECTS

	Intensity	*Pathway of expression*
Anxiety	+++	Ideational, affective, some somatic equivalents
Depression	++	Ideational, some affective
Hostility	++	Affective, ideational, some somatization

OTHER FACTORS

Marked narcissism

HOMEOSTATIC SHIFT(S)

Again a somatization response, mild to moderate, but involving primarily another organ system, influenced by an x-factor, tetanus antitoxin

DIAGNOSES

a) Serum sickness, treated, improved;
b) Somatization reaction with functional gastrointestinal complaint, untreated, unchanged

case 36

Pain in the Back, Multiple Stress, and the Effect of Certain Medical Procedures

CHIEF PRESENTING SYMPTOM

Pain in the back.

BASIC ANAMNESTIC EXCERPTS

"The last doctor suspected arthritis of the spine or possibly kidney trouble. I first went to another doctor who took a urine test and said there was a trace of blood. A week later another test showed that it had cleared up. But it made the doctor suspicious and he wanted X-rays. I have aches along the spine, all the way up into the neck. I also feel it in my legs and feet. I call it sciatic rheumatism. I'm a clerk. I use my arms a lot, working and using a rubber stamp; I get shooting pains down through my hand. A few days ago I got this other pain in the left back, very severe and stabbing; I was tender in this area.

"I had back pain about eight years ago on my first voyage going overseas. I got scared, being away from home, but the ship's doctor gave me a pill which put me to sleep, and the next morning I appeared to be alright. While I was over in the Pacific, I had some backaches but didn't pay much attention to them because I spent a lot of time lying on damp ground and in fog. I figured it was just from the conditions more than anything. I didn't bother to say much because what good would it have done? All they gave me was some sedatives.

"Now I'm bending over a desk most of the time. That would probably account for some of the aching in the back; dampness makes it worse. Had a little ache today because I was lying on the X-ray table which was cold and hard. When I do go to bed and rest and keep warm, it seems to help a lot. Of course, it doesn't satisfy me because I can't spend the rest of my life in bed.

302

"I feel more tired when I get up than when I went to bed. More dead, even. The tiredness is probably due to some anemic condition. I've been losing my pep and ambition, after having this feeling every morning for the past six months. When the aching started with it, I thought it was time to see the doctor. I attributed it to nerves. I belong to the National Guard. I'm an officer, and I've been trying for a promotion. Also I have an old house I'm trying to fix up. I figure my lack of ambition and pep are the result of worrying too much, working too much, the result of very little relaxation. But when I began to ache that way, I didn't think worrying was the cause of the ache, so I went to see the doctor."

The patient next recalled having had a lot of leg aches when he was a youngster: "I must have been eight, nine, or six. It happened mostly at night. I remember how my sister (nine years older) would rub my leg. She would spend an hour rubbing it. You see, my mother was dead. It happened when she worked in a candy factory and cut her finger on a corn husk. The first doctor said she needed a rest, that she'd been working too hard and was run down. Finally my father got another doctor who said it was tetanus. By that time it was too late. The only thing I myself remember about her sickness is that when she died, my father came in and told me about it, and I got a terrible pain in the stomach. I was only five or six then. Following mother's death, my sister quit school to take care of me and my two brothers. I was the youngest—the last."

From these recollections the patient continues with the theme of having many illnesses when he was a child: "I had pneumonia twice; chicken pox, scarlet fever, measles, mumps, whooping cough. I was quite sick quite often, you know. Lots of colds. I missed school a lot, especially because of an upset stomach. I was underweight at the time, and since. The aching in the legs continued until I was about 12. I've had leg aches since, but never like they were at that time. Pain to a child is different. The child will have pain and think it severe, whereas an adult will have the same pain and not think so. He'll pass it off, continue working with it, where the child will start crying for sympathy."

Being underweight is further elaborated in these terms: "One doctor thought I tended to be constipated, due to nervousness of the bowel, probably causing loss of weight. He recommended a diet. It wasn't for a working man; you only have half an hour for lunch, and you eat your lunch right where you work. I came from a poor family. I didn't get milk or other such things I should have had." Despite being underweight the patient tried to compensate for his smaller size by going around with bigger boys and trying to keep up with their many activities.

The combination of a taxing schedule of study and work while a junior in high school is related to his father's illnesses: "My father caught pneumonia two years in a row, almost died. He was advised by doctors not to attempt to go to work. I had to work to buy my own clothes and help out with expenses." The patient recalls that as a little child he also had pneumonia twice.

There are further references to the patient's current full schedule, described in terms of work, study, and worry all the time. Several matters are especially troublesome: "I have to prepare a class to give to the men in the Guard; if it isn't ready, I worry about it. Another thing is that I realize my wife has to have some recreation, and she doesn't get enough of it. Her mother lives across the street, and her sister-in-law lives nearby, so she can go and visit them. But she gets tired of seeing the same old faces.

"We've been married ten years and have one boy, nine years old. He's the only one because my wife hasn't been well. She had a suspension operation several years ago. She's had virus pneumonia, and now she has gallbladder trouble. She's been in lots of pain. Her mother and the doctor also advised her not to have any more. She was in labor a long, long time. When I came home from the service, we were living with her folks. We had one small room, and the three of us were in that small room. Naturally, we didn't have another baby there because there'd be no place to put it. Then we finally bought the house. But she began having trouble which led to the suspension operation, and she just about recovered from that, when she came down with virus pneumonia which left her weak and tired. She just about got over that, and she came down with gallbladder stones, and severe pain in her right side. It makes her very nervous and high-strung. She flies off the handle very easily. I'm nervous myself, but I don't fly off the handle. I probably take it out on myself. I don't argue with her. If she talks too much, I just put on my hat and coat and walk out the door."

PSYCHODYNAMIC IMPRESSIONS

The patient has obviously been preoccupied with intermittent pain over most of his life. In recent years, he has developed frames of physical reference, especially in diagnostic terms, to explain to himself the significance of the symptom. Pain is closely associated with movement and with work; in the beginning of the interview the dominant location of pain is left (symbolically feminine). Pain actually has many determinants; it is connected with separation, early from mother because of her death, later from older sister (mother substitute), and in military service overseas. It is associated with dampness and with unpleasant living conditions. Pain is relieved by situations in which the patient can indulge in a passive–dependent ritual; here warmth is a particular sensory percept that is stressed. However, while sleep permits temporary avoidance of painful realities and the somatic pain, it is an insufficient solution. Waking is associated with feelings of depletion, exhaustion, and lack of ambition, strongly suggestive of depressive equivalents. Again and again, current situational stresses, especially those involving his responsibilities as head of the home or head of the National Guard outfit, are brought into close association with the somatic symptomatology, which, although it has pain as a principal feature, includes other less emphasized physical referents.

The past is heavily and specifically represented in the associations. The leg pain follows the mother's death, and the features referable to her symptoms closely correlate with those the patient has related about himself in other connections. An older sister became a mother substitute, and the relationship with her is described in suggestively sexualized terms. Childhood is also pictured in terms of oral deprivations associated with gastrointestinal symptoms. Feelings of inferiority, particularly referable to body size and compensatory competitive efforts to overcome this through various physical activities, are evident. Further somatic identifications occurred late in the patient's adolescence and were concerned with the father's bouts of pneumonia which left him depleted and requiring long rests, again reminiscent of the patient's description of the sequelae following his own past pneumonia and recent symptomatology.

His marital situation appears to be another source of chronic stress. His wife has had one illness after another, and in this connection, the symptom of pain appeared prominently in the patient's associative recollections. The wife is very irritable and nervous. The patient describes himself in similar terms but indicates how he handles his own rage, particularly toward her; he uses avoidance, particularly physical separation, and conveys his hostility simply by absenting himself from the critical and nongiving wife and by forcing apologies from her. He obviously is deeply disappointed in his search for the loving parental figure. His identifications have bisexual elements, but are more strongly feminine.

Affect discharge is apparently converted to motor activity, and there is an awareness at least of the tendency to direct rage against himself. Thus, an affect block is not really present here. The references to dampness and wetness, suggestive of early enuretic experiences, become currently involved with the patient's fantasies about the possibility of kidney disease.

PHYSICAL HISTORY

The patient was admitted with the chief complaint of back pain, fatigue, and weakness. During the past four months, he has complained of dull, aching, constant pain located in the upper lumbar spine, occasionally radiating up the thoracic spine to the cervical area. The dull, nagging pain over this area has appeared to be worse in damp weather and when the patient is sitting bent over his desk. For the past seven years, he has suffered from low back pain with radiation down the back of the right thigh into the knee and leg, and occasionally the pain has radiated down the left thigh. Two months prior to admission, he developed a dull, aching pain in the costovertebral angle region bilaterally. He went to his physician who told him he had a trace of blood in his urine which later became clear. The aching pain lasted for two days and was treated with local heat. While in military service eight years ago, he had had a similar episode lasting for several days. No fever, chills, or urinary symptoms were noted with either attack. During the three months prior to admission, he had noted increasing fatigue and weakness. In childhood the patient had numerous attacks of tonsillitis, and seven years ago he had a tonsillectomy. Past history also reveals that he had scarlet fever at three years of age. System review was negative except that for the past 10 years he has had difficulty moving his bowels, moving at irregular intervals, and using laxatives in order to have adequate movements. He has also noted on numerous occasions a dull pain in the right lower quadrant. He had been told by several doctors that this was due to appendicitis, and by others, a nervous colon.

PHYSICAL EXAMINATION

Temperature 98.6°F. Pulse 84. Blood pressure 132/84. A well-developed, well-nourished white male in no acute distress. Head, eye, ears, nose, throat examination, heart, lungs, abdomen were negative. There was no costovertebral angle tenderness. The remainder of the physical examination was likewise within normal limits.

LABORATORY DATA

Hemoglobin 14 g. Hematocrit 40 percent. Sedimentation rate 0. White blood cell count 8,700 with 66 segmented cells, 11 band cells, 18 lymphocytes, 5 eosinophiles. Urinalysis: clear, acid, specific gravity 1.027, no albumin, no sugar, sediment 0 to 2 white cells per high power field, no red cells seen. Nonprotein nitrogen 35. Fasting blood sugar 102. Serology: negative.

ROENTGENOGRAMS

Chest plate: negative. Spine: no abnormalities noted. Gastrointestinal series: negative. Intravenous pyelogram: no abnormalities were noted in the urinary tract, except for extrinsic impression on the right lateral aspect of the bladder which was thought to be due to fecal content in the rectosigmoid region. Barium enema: there were no abnormalities of the colon. The terminal ilium was visualized and was normal in appearance.

HOSPITAL COURSE

The patient was afebrile and essentially asymptomatic during his hospital stay. Numerous urine examinations revealed no abnormalities. The patient was seen by the genitourinary consultant, who felt after reviewing the X-rays that cystoscopy was not necessary. A course of weekly prostatic massages, four to six in number, by a local physician was suggested by the consultant as being possibly beneficial.

DISCHARGE DIAGNOSIS

No disease found.

COMMENT

Chronic physical symptoms without organic basis may become closely linked with diagnostic terms and medical procedures and are frequently referred to in such terminology. This, of course, diverts the attention of the examiner away from the development of more meaningful psychological associations in the interview situation. In this case, the internist appears to have been distracted by such defensiveness on the patient's part, and thus missed the many psychological cues that could have been obtained.

The genitourinary consultant suggested prostate massages, but apparently only on the basis that "they might possibly be beneficial." These recommendations of doubtful value are not uncommon. Such procedures are often carried out with no awareness at all of the very considerable psychologic effect they can have on the patient and the possible trauma that may be caused. An old physical symptom may be reinforced; a new one may be started. Anxiety may be stirred up. These procedures frequently have symbolic psychological significance for the patient and should certainly not be recommended unless *both* the physical and emotional consequences are carefully considered. All too often, the patient becomes the object of unnecessary physicochemical manipulation. The danger is that such interventions may become so routine and mechanical that their possibly unfavorable impact on the patient's emotional state is ignored. It is the emotional, rather than the physical aspect that is more often overlooked or disregarded when, in fact, both should receive careful attention.

CASE 36

CHIEF PRESENTING SYMPTOM Pain in back

SENSORIMOTOR CONFIGURATIONS Sensory configurations

Pain, interoceptive, temperature

Linked with loss, especially mother's death, suggestive enuretic experiences and frequent illnesses in childhood, possibly sexualized in relation to older sister, later separation anxiety, and activated by current stresses, particularly wife's chronic illness

Motor configurations

Motility

Associated with work and feelings of inferiority, connected with defense against passivity, and with attempted control of affects

SOMATIC IDENTIFICATION *Mother* Death from tetanus infection, during patient's childhood

Father Pneumonia twice during patient's adolescence (Direct, organ constitutional—patient's two episodes of pneumonia, in childhood)

Wife Pain requiring suspension operation; also pneumonia and most recently gallbladder pain

SENSITIZED ORGAN SYSTEM Musculoskeletal system

STRESS (*surface meaning*) Marital problems; tensions in National Guard and regular work
Earlier—separation anxiety while overseas in military service

STRESS (*dynamic significance*) A continuing test of his manliness, increasing his concern about adequacy. Concomitant disappointment in search for loving parental figure

DEFENSES Overcompensatory physical activity and ambition
Avoidance
Rationalizations and some tendency to project

AFFECTS	Intensity	Pathway of expression
Anxiety	++	Ideational, conversion
Depression	++	Ideational, some somatization
Hostility	++	Acting out (motor), some somatization

OTHER FACTORS   Mother's death early in his childhood
Highly sexualized relationship to sister
Strong suggestion of early enuretic experiences

HOMEOSTATIC SHIFT(s)   Toward somatization when ideational and behavioral defensive alignments become insufficient

DIAGNOSIS   No disease found

case 37

Chest Pain in a Highly Narcissistic Patient

CHIEF PRESENTING SYMPTOM

Pain in chest.

BASIC ANAMNESTIC EXCERPTS

The symptom of pain is immediately described as burning, located in the chest, and associated with vomiting and a bitter taste in the mouth. Next, a cold is described; this resulted in pains in shoulders and joints that keep on aching. The patient tried to find out what was causing his pains: "My local doctor didn't give much help. Then I went to a clinic which put me through X-rays, electrocardiogram, and found nothing wrong. I had to go to the Soldiers' Home where they treated me for high blood pressure. It went up and down, up and down. Every time I'd do a little work, it would just pound back my head like a hammer so that I got dizzy and blacked out. I always had trouble with my chest and with my arms. Glands would swell up on me. At work I would look at my hands and the fingers would burn, clean down. Don't know what caused that. I was never injured there, though I did have head injuries when I was a child.

"I ain't working at my job regularly now for the past 13 months. This pain will go right through my shoulder blades, like a knife will stab me. When I use my arms, I have to quit. When I sit down and relax, the pain seems to go away; but when I start to work again, it comes right back. It's like an inflammation, a burning pain so that when I get up in the morning, I can't bend over. As the day progresses, it'll loosen up a little. I've had all kinds of jobs since I've come out of service, never could stick to one of them. I was sent to a clinic in Missouri where they put me on a strict diet. I began to lose weight, weaken. Every time I'd take a warm bath, I'd black out, pass out. My veins just pop on me in hot water. My high blood pressure goes up and down.

"I have a burning sensation in my rectum. The doctor told me I ought

310

to have them removed—hemorrhoids. Every time they come out, I've got to push them in again. There's itching and burning inside of me. There's pain inside my groin—sharp, stabbing. I forgot to tell the doctor who examined me here that I had venereal disease—gonorrhea—when I was in military service. I couldn't tell him that.

"Even in high school I was troubled with pain—stabbing me in back of the head, pains like this here in my arms and nipples. Don't know what brought this on. I don't smoke or drink. I've had aching pain in the joints, legs mostly. I've also had pain in the head, sinus trouble, in front like a knife. It just keeps adding up. Trouble is, I never look sick in my life, never do. Always have a red face, never pale. Every time I'd go to the doctor, he'd say: 'You don't look sick at all.' "

The patient returns to the theme of the accident he sustained as a child, age seven: "I remember, when I fell down those stairs and hit the bottom, a woman screamed 'O God, the boy killed himself.' I still remember those words. That's the first thing always on my mind. They put me on the table and my mother called the doctor, this and that. But it healed up pretty good. A cut in front, and a bruise on the fingers ... I was walking downstairs and I tripped. It was in the wintertime, and I was all bundled up. My mother had bundled me up. We lived upstairs and I wanted to go down in the yard and play. Then I fell. I just passed out. I can still envision (!) how it happened. If you get a knock like that, you remember it. My tongue was split and sort of grew on again (!). That was the real knock I got in my whole life."

Coming back to the present, the patient enlarges on the theme of money troubles due to his sickness: "I've spent the last dime I had trying to get well. Didn't do any good. While I worked for a while last year, I took insurance out which took care of a few bills. But the insurance expired after 13 weeks, and then I was on my own. Had to pay out of my own pockets. My father helped me quite a bit. Still I should be able to take care of myself at my age, don't you know? I can't depend on my father's help all the time. Pretty lucky how I'm living with him, otherwise I mean I'd be in a heck of a fix ... I haven't any income coming in. I'm in my folks' house together with my three brothers and three sisters; I'm the third oldest. I'm single. I used to go out with a girl. But there's no sense in going out with girls if you have no job and no money. I don't want my wife to support me ... I'm a working man. I like to work and it's up to the man to support his wife."

When asked about the health of his family, the patient shows irritation: "Mother's is—they're alright. No serious problems. I don't see any sense ... they have no trouble like I have ... I don't see how anything would be reflected on them ... sickness is a natural thing, but it's not unusual for them to be healthy and me to be this way here. . . . Look, I can take it; I keep on working. But when my pain hurts me so that I can't work, I've got to stop. I try to forget about pain and work as long as I can."

PSYCHODYNAMIC IMPRESSIONS

This patient is markedly preoccupied with his body, with various symptom clusters referable to different organ systems. A set of associative chains refers to warm baths, blackouts, veins popping out, blood pressure going up and down, burning sensation in rectum, hemorrhoids coming out and being pushed in again, and finally a confession about venereal disease. In turn there are further chains dealing with swellings in chest area again, stabbing in head and nipples. These are suggestive of a highly sexualized content, castration fears, and feminine identification. Pain, however, is the chief theme, and has many associative connections. Almost immediately it is related to several sensory configurations: temperature (burning), which is prominently repetitive, and taste. It is also related to motor referents: working, bending over, being pounded (a sadistic component). The patient not only thinks basically in terms of his body and physical symptomatology, but looks at himself a great deal. A long-standing problem in work adjustment is evident. Effort and activity lead to increased somatic preoccupation, except sports which are still experienced as pleasurable; passivity and being taken care of result in decreased concern about body sensations. Oral needs are directly expressed in terms of food and weight.

Despite his intense preoccupation with bodily ailments, the patient also has a need to deny these by exhibitionistically pointing out his healthy appearance. Similarly, his appetite is described as good.

He recalls a childhood accident associated with great anxiety and subsequent concern about his physical integrity. In the associations linked with it, the head and tongue appear as symbolic phallic representations, and the incident is recollected in terms of an intense castration experience linked with an activation of passive trends. There are associative chains which suggest that his present pain has similar castration referents.

In recent years the patient lives with his parents and siblings, and in effect is supported and taken care of by his father. Resentment is evident and openly expressed in content and affect when the patient refers to the health of his family and protests that it is not unnatural that he should be the only sick one. Actually, except for very brief references to these others, the content of his thinking is almost exclusively in reference to himself— an expression of intense narcissism. There is also very little direct reference to anything else but his health; any feelings of inadequacy or inferiority are expressed in somatic terms.

PHYSICAL HISTORY

This was the patient's first admission; his chief complaint was of joint pain, stomach and substernal pain of seven years' duration. The patient's history was extremely vague and quite jumbled in time relationships. He presents several clusters of symptoms: (1) For the past seven years he has had painful sensations in both shoulder joints and left hip, and sharp, stabbing sensations in the back of his legs. These attacks usually occurred in damp weather, and the patient's legs felt stiff and "creaked" when he walked. He often felt "wobbly on his feet." There had never been any redness or swelling with this. (2) He has also noted burning lower substernal pain radiating out to both sides, to the midback, and up the sternum. This was associated with a bitter taste and tenderness over the sternal area, usually worse several hours after meals, and relieved moderately by eating, but aggravated by fried, fatty, sweet food, and meat. It occurred as soon as he would awaken in the morning, except when it was sunny outside. Frequently he would vomit at that time with subsequent relief. The patient complained of a great deal of belching but no bloating sensations or jaundice. The vomitus usually consisted of yellow–green matter; his last episode was three months prior to admission. The patient had been constipated for two to three years, and usually took a laxative (cod liver oil). (3) The patient has been told he had hypertension four years before. He had supraorbital headaches with dizziness and occasional blackout spells when working or bending over, occasional palpitation, and flushed very readily. There was no orthopnea, cough, chest pain, edema, or cyanosis. (4) The patient claimed that he had been tired throughout the day, had slept poorly, and had lost about 14 pounds in the month previous to his admission. Appetite was good. Past history and family history were noncontributory.

PHYSICAL EXAMINATION

Temperature 98.6°F. Pulse 84. Blood pressure 138/102. The remainder of the physical examination was negative, except for a mild tenderness to palpation in the inguinal areas and slight left costovertebral angle tenderness. There were also a few spotty, discrete, nontender nodes in the axillary and inguinal areas.

LABORATORY DATA

Hemogram, sedimentation rate, urinalysis, nonprotein nitrogen, stool guaiacs, fasting blood sugar, blood calcium and phosphorus, serum amylase all within normal limits. Basal metabolism rate: −6.

ROENTGENOGRAMS

Chest plate, left hip and left shoulder, gastrointestinal series and gall-bladder series: all negative.

ELECTROCARDIOGRAM

Questionable left ventricular hypertrophy.

HOSPITAL COURSE

While in the hospital, the patient continued to have varied complaints, but with sedation felt somewhat more relaxed. His blood pressure tended to remain in the range of 130-136/90-94. He was referred to a mental hygiene clinic.

DISCHARGE DIAGNOSIS

Anxiety neurosis.

COMMENT

Here is a case where a traumatic event occurring in childhood had relatively minor physical sequelae but long-lasting psychological consequences. Among these, the somatic intensification of the patient's narcissism, i.e., preoccupation with body and bodily symptoms, is clearly manifested. Links with the past can be noted in the current symptoms and their associative elaborations, as expressed in the sensorimotor configurations already described. The patient has been settling into a pattern of semi-invalidism with strong secondary-gain factors acting to stabilize this regressed position. His psychological difficulties and their somatic reflections responded to sedation and reassurance only enough to produce slight diminution of symptoms, but in no way was there a real modification of the basic problems. Such a patient, who should have had psychiatric intervention long before, appears to be approaching a point where his incapacity may become relatively fixed. Even with more intensive psychotherapy, he still may encounter great difficulty in overcoming the compounded psychological problems. Nevertheless, a trial period of psychotherapy should be instituted, providing, of course, that the patient is or can be sufficiently motivated to undertake it.

CASE 37

CHIEF PRESENTING SYMPTOM	Pain in chest
SENSORIMOTOR CONFIGURATIONS	Sensory configurations

Pain, temperature, taste, visual

Linked with mother, childhood accident, and subsequent intense concern about many body areas; associations suggestive of oral needs, feminine identification, and castration anxiety

Motor configurations

Activity, passivity

Connected with working, resting, going up and down, coming in and out, pounding, swelling, loosening, suggestive of sexualized content, symbolic sadistic references, and expressive of difficulty in separating from family

SOMATIC IDENTIFICATION	None
SENSITIZED ORGAN SYSTEM	Circulatory Gastrointestinal Generalized body
STRESS (*surface meaning*)	Financial troubles and job problems
STRESS (*dynamic significance*)	Chronic concern over bodily integrity; intense narcissism maintained. Chronic passive–dependent position reinforced by unfavorable environmental factors
DEFENSES	Some projective tendencies Rationalization

AFFECTS	*Intensity*	*Pathway of expression*
Anxiety	+++	Ideational, some affective, somatic equivalents and conversion
Depression	+	Ideational
Hostility	++	Ideational, affective

OTHER FACTORS	Marked preoccupation with body Childhood accident and psychological trauma Secondary gain
HOMEOSTATIC SHIFT(S)	In direction of more fixed hypochondriacal position
DIAGNOSIS	Anxiety neurosis

Dyspnea, Somatic Identification, and Multiple Psychophysical Vicissitudes

CHIEF PRESENTING SYMPTOM

Difficulty in breathing.

BASIC ANAMNESTIC EXCERPTS PSYCHODYNAMICALLY INTERPRETED

Very hard breathing is associated with walking up a flight of stairs. The patient has to stop and catch his breath. He refers to his getting too fat, putting on too much weight, and his now being put on a 1200-calorie diet. There are further references to his "having water in his lung, catching cold awful easy, and throwing up a lot of blood."

Further elaboration of his breathing difficulty leads to associations of puffing "like a steam engine," when he has to exert himself. This has been going on for the last few weeks. His work doesn't require much walking; he is a draftsman who sits at a drawing board all day long. The next associations are about a baby. "It is almost two months old, and we (he, his wife, and the baby) have to stay upstairs in our apartment." The patient had an operation for mitral stenosis two years ago and then "had a baby." Actually his wife had the baby, but he makes a joke out of it, calling it a "mitral baby in reverse" (feminine identification).

References to the wife and conception of the baby continue. His wife is close to 40 years of age. She had a Caesarean section. She is a "very small girl," weighing only 92 pounds, and had been told beforehand she would have to have the baby by operation. His wife has suffered a lot, coming back and forth from work to the hospital in the past three years, visiting the patient during his repeated hospitalizations. She is anemic. "She never complains; if only she would once in a while, I'd feel better myself (guilt). During pregnancy my wife couldn't sleep; she was often up at night because the baby kicked every time she lay down. Finally when she came back from the hospital, she could sleep but the baby cried too much." They live in an eight-room single house with four rooms upstairs and four rooms downstairs. His wife and he have the upstairs and her parents live downstairs.

The patient next refers to his getting married four years ago. Three days later he suddenly had orders to go overseas on military assignment. The separation was a difficult one for him, and he began to feel ill while on duty overseas. He was depressed, felt like crying, but tried to carry on. He then noticed difficulty in breathing on exertion and started to throw up. He was hospitalized within two months and found to have a "rheumatic heart and double murmur." He was returned to this country where he spent many months in a hospital. He lost 50 pounds in 12 days. Again there is a reference to being unable to climb stairs. He denies having had a sick day, except that as a child he had had measles, followed by colds, and later a broken arm.

In further associations to his illness, the patient recalls that in the year preceding its onset a number of emotionally disturbing events occurred. His mother, who had been ill with tuberculosis and hospitalized off and on since the patient was 10, died early that year. He had been very close to her and couldn't leave her during her final illness. After she died, he hung around, feeling lost for about four months, and then was called up for military service. In the meantime, he met a girl and quickly got married. He returns to the subject of his mother: One of her lungs had to be collapsed, and ribs taken out on the right side; there were seven operations. He didn't have to take care of mother but wanted to of his own accord. An older brother was away in military service. The patient now recalls that very shortly after he himself had gone overseas, he learned that his father was also sick and had to be hospitalized; he had contracted tuberculosis from the mother. The patient reemphasizes that all these events occurred in the space of a year. The theme of losses is prominent.

He now turns to the past, and references appear about certain physical characteristics: He has always had weak eyes and has had to wear glasses since he was 10 years old. His teeth were soft and had to be pulled out when he was young and bridgework put in. He fell off a fence when he was a kid and broke an arm. However, he was a big baby, weighing almost 14 pounds when he was born. He has always been big and would always "get hell" for eating so much and would have to keep his weight under 175 pounds. Now he is on a salt-free diet. He began to work when he was 14 years old, even though he didn't have to, because he had a restless, active streak in him. Activity has been a defense against inferiority feelings.

The patient lights up a cigarette and refers to his smoking too much, a couple of packs a day. He has been warned to cut down on the number if he wanted to breathe better. He tried but has been unable to. Outside of his puffing, he feels good. Associations again turn toward the time he was overseas. He remembers that within a few weeks after learning about his father's illness, he himself started to cough; blood came up. He was hospitalized and was told he had pneumonia. He was put in an oxygen tent and has been sick ever since. (Somatic identification is recurrent.)

Though he has been sick for the past three years, he has been given a break at work where he is now a draftsman. He isn't paid "big money" but they understand the reason for his absences. He was a bartender and a machinist before he entered military service. His thoughts again turn to his mother and he remembers being called at work when his mother died. He further recalls that his mother was diabetic as well as tubercular. When she was able to be home, she complained mostly about her breathing. She also coughed a great deal. At one time she was a big person, until she got sick, and became awfully small. The patient looked after her when she was home. His wife wouldn't take care of the mother because her own father had died of tuberculosis; she was scared and kept her distance. The patient's mother had to go back to the hospital.

Finally the patient reverts to the theme of activity: He states his trouble is that he has been active all his life. Now with his condition he can't be. It's hard to adjust himself to it.

PHYSICAL HISTORY

This is the sixth admission of the patient, who complains of increasing fatigue and exertional dyspnea. His previous admissions have extended over the past three years for rheumatic heart disease with mitral stenosis, active rheumatic fever, rheumatic pericarditis, episodes of auricular fibrillation, pneumonitis, and pulmonary infarction. A valvuloplasty was done one and a half years ago. Since his last discharge about nine months ago, the patient had apparently been well, working as a draftsman, on a regime of 0.2 mg digitoxin daily, low-salt diet, and 280,000 units of penicillin by mouth prophylactically. However, for the past two weeks he has become easily tired and short of breath, and has noted some numbness and swelling of his right hand. He has had no chills, fever, or cough, no orthopnea or paroxysmal dyspnea. His weight has been increasing gradually.

PHYSICAL EXAMINATION

Temperature 98.6°F. Pulse 92. Blood pressure 132/90. The patient is a well-developed and well-nourished male in no acute distress. He has a lower denture and partial upper denture. Chest: well-healed, left-sided scar from sternum to back, just below the nipple line, tender anteromedially. Lungs: coarse rales at both bases. Heart: enlarged to percussion; point of maximal impulse in sixth interspace almost at anterior axillary line; no thrills; regular sinus rhythm; systolic murmur present at apex. Remainder of examination negative.

LABORATORY DATA

White blood cell count 8,200 with 53 segmented cells, 11 band cells, 36 lymphocytes. Hemoglobin 14.4 g; hematocrit 49 percent. Sedimentation rate 10 mm per hr. Nonprotein nitrogen 31. Urine negative. Serology negative. Venous pressure 175 to 180 mm of saline; circulation time 15 seconds—Decholin.

ROENTGENOGRAMS

Chest film: except for possible reduction in prominence of arch of pulmonary artery on the left border of the heart, there is no change since the last examination which revealed left ventricular hypertrophy.

HOSPITAL COURSE

The patient was given a 10-day leave of absence a week after his admission because of the death of his father. He returned having gained three pounds, but was relatively asymptomatic. He was seen in dental consultation and extraction of remaining upper teeth was recommended, done, and followed by continued treatment with penicillin. He was discharged a week later, to continue on a regimen of digitoxin 0.2 mg daily, low-salt diet, and prophylactic penicillin.

DISCHARGE DIAGNOSES

1. Rheumatic heart disease, mitral stenosis, enlarged heart, mild congestive failure; inactive, improved.
2. Status post valvuloplasty.

COMMENT

This patient has well-established organic heart disease and has already had a major surgical procedure for it. Retrospectively, and following the associative connections brought up by the patient, it is posssible to note both a series of situational factors of considerable significance for him, antedating the onset of his illness, and a current set which may be related to exacerbations of the disease process. The chief symptom is difficulty in breathing. Since the patient was 10, his mother has appeared as a person sick with pulmonary tuberculosis, whose breathing difficulties were a major symptom. There are indications of a very close attachment to her, a dependency defended against by a turn toward considerable activity and a feeling of being obligated to take care of her. Somatic identifications with her appear in the associative connections of size and respiratory symptoms.

References to his early past deal with both concern and denial of concern about his physical adequacy: eyes were weak and teeth were soft, but this is balanced by references to big size. The father and brother are represented as relatively distant figures.

During the year preceding his own illness, the patient lost his mother. Shortly thereafter he attempted to regain a substitute—an older woman who was small like his mother had become—by marrying a girl he knew. He "lost" her, however, when he was sent overseas three days later. Word came of his father's illness at a time when the patient was already having great difficulty in adjusting to overseas duty and was going through a depressed period, unable to cry. It was soon thereafter that he noted a cough, difficulty in breathing, and hemoptysis, and was hospitalized with what was at first called pneumonia. Later, a diagnosis of rheumatic fever and heart disease was made. A sharp psychophysical decompensation had occurred. Compounded losses had had a severe impact on the patient's emotional equilibrium. His tearless depression worsened. This was his psychological state before manifestations of organic disease appeared in what was already a sensitized cardiorespiratory system.

Oral needs now are expressed in the craving to smoke, even though this has been forbidden by his doctors and obviously increases the difficulties he has with his breathing. Turning to more recent exacerbations of his illness, his wife's pregnancy and the arrival of their first baby shortly after his valvuloplasty appear as related stresses. This is derived from the reference to walking upstairs, and its association to his wife and child, their living quarters being on the second floor, and its further connection with hard breathing. He has also had other manifestations of increased oral needs in his craving for food and resultant weight gain of considerable proportions. The baby is called a "mitral baby," his "baby in reverse," indicating a further aspect of his feminine identification. At the same time however, the baby is a rival for his wife's attention. During her pregnancy, his wife was sickly and could pay attention to him only with difficulty. The patient did not bring up any instance of hostile ideation and showed no evidence of any related affect during the entire interview. Although his father's condition had recently worsened, the patient did not bring this up during the interview. Nevertheless, the presence of depressive elements appears likely, and the development of mild congestive failure should be considered against his psychological background. The symptoms of pulmonary congestion and edema would then appear as activated physical manifestations of rheumatic heart disease in the presence of a tearless and masked depression.

Kaplan (1956) did a follow-up study of 18 patients who had undergone mitral commissurotomy. These subjects had had cardiac symptoms or knowledge of the disease for different periods of time; some only recently, others since childhood. The reaction to the illness varied from patient to patient, depending upon his life situations, premorbid personality, type of onset, duration of illness, and kind of relationship to family and physician caring for him. For some, the surgical procedure provided welcome relief, while for others the disease symptoms continued. The psychophysical equilibrium can be upset when remedial measures are taken. This of course can occur in any person who has had a significant illness of long duration, especially since childhood. There is a difference of response in persons sick for a short time; they find the illness often intolerable, unacceptable and strive for a return to premorbid patterns of adjustment following recovery. Others utilize illness for secondary-gain purpose and present difficult problems in rehabilitation. Poor reactions occurred so often in Kaplan's cases, that he urges psychological evaluation before the commissurotomy operation in order to help estimate postoperative reactions.

Meyer et al. (1961) also felt that the emotional state of candidates for mitral surgery deserves as important consideration as other factors in determining suitability for operation. They cite as reasons the proven susceptibility of the cardiorespiratory system to factors other than mechanical loads, the symbolization of the heart in psychological processes, and the lack of strict correlation between the anatomical changes brought about by surgery and their clinical consequences. They state: "The repair of the damaged heart may be out of consonance with the life pattern and the psychological defensive organization of the subject, a fact that may exert a significant influence upon the outcome of the procedure and lead to untoward postoperative organic and psychological sequelae."

CASE 38

CHIEF PRESENTING SYMPTOM   Difficulty in breathing

SENSORIMOTOR CONFIGURATIONS   Sensory configurations

Interoceptive, visual

Associated with overeating in childhood, early physical difficulties, many losses later—especially mother's death, physical breakdown in military service, and current guilt feelings over suffering, uncomplaining wife

Motor configurations

Activity

Modified considerably by illness, with increasing passive–feminine tendencies becoming manifest in the service of adaptation

SOMATIC IDENTIFICATION

Wife   Delivered by Caesarean section two months ago

Mother   Death due to tuberculosis with breathing and coughing difficulties involving many operations, four years ago (Direct)

Father   Hospitalized due to tuberculosis (Direct)

SENSITIZED ORGAN SYSTEM

Cardiorespiratory

STRESS (*surface meaning*)

Maladjustment to military service, patient's illness; more recently, wife's difficult pregnancy, baby problems.

STRESS (*dynamic significance*)

Intensification of dependency needs and loss of emotionally significant objects

DEFENSES

Overactive in past
Humor
Attempts at denial

AFFECTS

	Intensity	*Pathway of expression*
Anxiety	+	Some ideational, some somatic equivalents
Depression	+++	Some ideational, mostly somatization
Hostility	+	Somatization

OTHER FACTORS

Weak eyes and glasses since age 10
Extensive extraction of teeth in childhood
Compounded losses
Superego pathology

HOMEOSTATIC SHIFT(S)

Originally, when illness first began, a sharp decompensation occurred involving a marked somatization response
Subsequently, intensification of this response occurs with repeated environmental stress

DIAGNOSES

a) Rheumatic heart disease, mitral stenosis, enlarged heart, mild congestive failure; inactive, improved;
b) Status post valvuloplasty

case 39

Sore Throat in the Presence of Acute and Chronic Stress

CHIEF PRESENTING SYMPTOM

Sore throat.

BASIC ANAMNESTIC EXCERPTS

"I've been getting some pretty bad sore throats, so I went to see this nose and throat specialist. He told me that the thyroid gland was slightly enlarged and suggested that maybe I should have a metabolism test taken. The test proved that the thyroid was normal. I told the doctor that a couple of years ago an X-ray showed up an ulcer I had in my stomach. He seemed to think that was the cause of all my troubles. Due to the pain there, I wasn't eating normal and therefore was getting run down, getting sore throats and colds. So he suggested getting some treatment for it and some rest for it.

"I get pains in the stomach during the day, before eating, sometimes after eating. I don't think I have a vocabulary large enough to describe the pain. It's a dull pain. Guess I've had it two or three years. Lots of times my stomach hurts me when I'd be home or be working. If I can just lay down and take a nap, that helps the pain. But that's not possible at work. I've been a press operator for the past six years.

"Four years ago when I had stomach pain, I took a G.I. series, but the ulcer didn't show up. Anyway, in the last couple of months the pain's been worse and more frequent than ever before. I haven't felt like sitting down to a big meal. As a rule, I eat creamed soups and bread. Not too much nourishment in that. It's one of the reasons I get run down the way I am. I think my weight has something to do with these sicknesses I'm getting. I was never a great big eater, but liked most everything. There's just one thing I've never been able to drink—that's beer. It seems to me I'll never be able to stomach the stuff. I like the sight of beer. Sometimes you see people drinking it on television, and it seems like the nicest thing in the

323

world. It doesn't taste too badly, but I can't finish a glass because I'd throw up. I like onions—could eat them before, but it seems as though now they hit me harder and faster than anything else. It'll bring on pains in my stomach almost as soon as I eat them.

"My wife's a pretty good cook now, but she had her troubles when we first got married eight years ago. We have one daughter who'll be seven soon; we'll have another in three months. We had one born over a year ago, but she lived only a few months. One Sunday she got a cold. My wife called in a doctor who said the baby just had a cold—a virus—and would get over it. But the baby got worse, shaking in spasms, every two hours taking convulsions like. We rushed her to the hospital. What she died of I'm not too sure. Virus could mean most anything, a cold, pneumonia— or something like that."

The theme of pregnancy is now further elaborated: "Wife has no trouble. As a matter of fact, she usually has them rather fast. She used to get morning sickness until the doctor gave her these pills. She just couldn't eat anything for several hours after she got up. She's fine now; so's my little girl. She's gotten over her stomach trouble (pause), but I (laughing) haven't."

Turning to the past: "I was rugged, don't remember catching any of those normal childhood diseases like mumps and measles. Yet, I had two brothers, one year older and five years younger, and they seemed to catch everything that came along. They even had to have their tonsils out when they were kids, but I still got mine. I was the rugged one then (laughing), but they are the rugged ones today."

Returning to more recent times and continuing with the subject of parental health: "My father had some stomach trouble for years. A couple of years ago he had an operation for an ulcer; he had it removed. Since the operation he's a new man, better natured than he used to be. He's gained weight and is able to eat anything now. Now he can work without pain. He builds houses and fixes the plumbing and electrical work, the insides."

Again the patient refers to his own symptom of pain: "It would be something that would be real hard to trace back to my childhood, something like that. The only pain I've had before that was when I started having troubles with my shoulder. I must have dislocated it at least ten times. It started while I was on this training course in the service. All they did was reduce it, and the next day I was right back on duty. Ever since that first time, I had trouble with it. Every time they tried to reduce it and put it back in place it was quite a job. Gave me a lot of pain—so usually toward the end, they'd give me anesthesia. After the third time I dislocated it, they decided to have it operated on. It didn't work out too well, because after I got out of the hospital, I thought it was all set, put in an application to go to aviation cadets, passed and everything, was half-way through my training, when one day I happened to be doing calisthenics, chinning on the bar, and sure enough, dislocated it. Pretty sharp pain. When I got out of the service, it was still in that condition, and I continued to dislocate it. Finally I decided to do something about the shoulder, so they performed another operation here three years ago, and it hasn't been dislocated since."

PSYCHODYNAMIC FORMULATION

Initially the patient is greatly preoccupied with a variety of physical symptoms and the possible diseases causing them. However, as the patient continues to associate, pain in the stomach becomes the principal somatic complaint. It is linked with his work situation, though without elaboration. Its connections with food are more extensive and include the varied effect that eating has on it—increasing or decreasing the symptom. In this respect there is a comparison between himself and his wife. She had trouble eating in the early part of the most recent pregnancy but got over it, while he continues to have trouble with his stomach. Food has a strongly symbolic meaning for the patient as a source of emotional supplies. It is usually referred to in contexts of relatively recent occurrence. His mother is not directly mentioned, and childhood dependency is not directly brought up. He reacts to his wife as if she were a mother surrogate who fails him when he needs her most in that role. Her pregnancies represent for him a repeated interference with the fulfillment of his infantile oral needs. The babies appear as rivals for her attention and ministrations. Consequently, his reactions to her and them tend often to be highly ambivalent. However, his hostility is for the most part not directly expressed, and laughter tends to be used rather often as a cover-up.

Further associations to pain connect it with a shoulder dislocation sustained during a training period in military service. This condition made an already difficult adjustment more so, and has been blamed for slowness in his advancement both in military and later civilian life. However, there appears to be a long-standing concern with body integrity, recently much activated, though denied in recollections of childhood which portray him as having a rugged physique and being much healthier than his two brothers. The recent preoccupation with his physical health appears to have been reinforced by father's illness. He, too, has had severe stomach trouble, apparently for years, and two years ago had an operation, probably a subtotal gastrectomy. Thereafter the patient sees him as a new and more placid individual, suggestively less masculine. The patient's own feminine tendencies also seem to have been stirred up in reaction to his wife's current pregnancy. The references to pain in the stomach and enlargement of the thyroid have further associative links indicating a possible preoccupation with pregnancy fantasies.

Another event that occurred during the past year was the death of one of his children. This was doubtless a traumatic loss for the patient, but his feelings about it were not directly expressed.

PHYSICAL HISTORY

This was the patient's second admission. He was first seen three years before when a chronic dislocation of the right shoulder was repaired. Additional diagnoses at that time were enuresis, anxiety state, and postnasal discharge. About two years prior to the present admission, the patient first noted sharp, steady, nonradiating umbilical pain occurring before lunch and two to four hours after lunch or supper. This was relieved by most foods, but aggravated by fatty, spicy foods and recently by onions. It occurred almost every day and was accompanied by fatigue at the end of the day. He was seen by his physician at the onset of his difficulty, gastrointestinal series were done, revealing "ulcers." He was put on a bland diet, but no milk was given him, and Banthine 50 mg four times a day afforded but little relief. He denied weight loss, blood loss, or any precipitating psychic difficulties. Recently because of a sort throat, he had been told that he had enlarged tonsils and thyroid. However, the basal metabolism rate was normal, and he was told to seek hospitalization if possible.

PHYSICAL EXAMINATION

Vital signs: normal. A well-developed, moderately nourished male appearing well. There was a small amount of postnasal drip, and some reddening of the nasal mucosa. The remainder of the examination was entirely negative.

LABORATORY DATA

Serology, urine, hemoglobin, hematocrit, WBC, and differential were all within normal limits.

ROENTGENOGRAMS

Chest plate, gastrointestinal series, and gallbladder series: no abnormalities visualized.

HOSPITAL COURSE

On admission the patient was placed on a bland diet, Gelusil, interval milk, Banthine, and sedation. During his stay in the hospital, his symptoms continued but were of a minimal nature. He was reassured that no evidence of ulcer could be found and was discharged on a bland diet.

DISCHARGE DIAGNOSIS

Anxiety reaction, chronic, treated, improved.

COMMENT

The patient is under stress from two particular sources. One is his wife's pregnancy which activates considerable anxiety in him about his ability to deal with his increased responsibilities as head of the family. In turn there is a regressive pull which has two components. There is an activation of latent wishes to abandon the masculine position and identify with the woman (his pregnant wife), and infantile expectations of being cared for by his wife (mother surrogate) are also increased. Every child including the newly expected one is then seen as a rival from this standpoint. The other situation which has been stressful was the death of one of his children less than a year ago. His reaction to this loss also appears to have two parts. One is a reactivation of anxiety about his own bodily integrity, and the other is a grief reaction complicated by strong guilt feelings. The two major stresses have reinforced each other. The emotional reponses of anxiety and depression have been masked, but the former appears to be more intense. In any event, "laughing it off" appears as a psychological defense, but the main channel of tension discharge has been through physical dysfunction leading to physical symptoms, but without development of organic disease. The somatic manifestations represent both affect equivalents and symbolic expressions of the patient's pregnancy fantasies. If the current stresses have additional ones superimposed on them, the possibility of a further regressive shift in the patient's psychophysical equilibrium will be enhanced. What is unknown is the intensity and quality of affective response that may be evoked, and whether current defensive responses of somatization will be deepened and cause physical dysfunction to reach critical levels where the potential for organic disease may then be activated.

CASE 39

CHIEF PRESENTING SYMPTOM	Sore throat
SENSORIMOTOR CONFIGURATIONS	Sensory configurations

Pain, interoceptive, temperature, taste

Associated with multiple physical complaints, various foods symbolically representing emotional supplies, ambivalent emotional reactions to wife, and loss of child

Motor configurations

Activity, passivity

Related to work, aggravation and relief of symptoms, recent concern over body integrity, especially activated by father's illness and operation, seen as rendering him placid and less masculine

SOMATIC IDENTIFICATION	Baby	Upper respiratory infection with convulsions and death one year ago
	Wife	Morning sickness during pregnancy in recent years
	Father	Stomach ulcer with resection several years ago (Direct)

SENSITIZED ORGAN SYSTEM

Gastrointestinal
Musculoskeletal
Respiratory

STRESS (*surface meaning*)

Wife's pregnancy; and child's death less than a year before

STRESS (*dynamic significance*)

Wife unsatisfactory maternal surrogate, children seen as rivals for her attention; loss of one child activated masked affects

DEFENSES

Laughter
Rationalization

AFFECTS	*Intensity*	*Pathway of expression*
Anxiety	+++	Ideational, somatic equivalents, conversion
Depression	++	Little ideational, some somatization
Hostility	++	Little ideational, some somatization

OTHER FACTORS

Strong narcissistic focus
Orality

HOMEOSTATIC SHIFT(S)

Increasing somatization, with possibility of further regressive shift leading to organic disease

DIAGNOSIS

Anxiety reaction, chronic, treated, improved

case 40

Feverishness and Headache:
The Role of Environmental Factors

CHIEF PRESENTING SYMPTOM

Feverishness and headache.

BASIC ANAMNESTIC EXCERPTS PSYCHODYNAMICALLY INTERPRETED

Because of the patient's acute discomfort, the interview is brief. Feverishness is associated with sensory clusters relating to temperature and vision. There are multiple references to hot and chilly sensations and tiredness in focusing eyes because of severe headaches which interfere with clear vision. This leads to associations about his studies as a veterinary student in preparation for final examinations, straining his eyes, feeling fatigued because he also had to be up many nights due to the newborn infant's crying. His wife and he wanted to be sure they were providing the best care; they felt inexperienced and under a strain after the arrival of the baby. However, the patient next indicates that his own tension has been considerable for months before, during his wife's pregnancy, and he had been particularly concerned over the possibility of something going wrong, possibly a miscarriage. It was a great relief when the pregnancy came normally to term. His concern about the baby returned, however, soon after the birth.

The subject of pregnancy leads further to associations about a laboratory course he had been taking during the past six months. This was a course in veterinary obstetrics. He indicates a long-standing curiosity about conception and pregnancy since his childhood. He was the older of two siblings. His mother had had several miscarriages between his birth and that of his younger brother, and he recalls briefly her having to be away in the hospital at those times. He was left in the care of neighbors. He recollects that as he was growing up, he had a consuming desire to become a doctor. This could not be realized because his grades were not good enough, and he settled for being a veterinarian.

PHYSICAL HISTORY

The patient was in his usual state of excellent health until six days prior to admission, when he noted the onset of bilateral retro-ocular headache which persisted until the time of admission. Occasional aspirins afforded some relief. He was also tired and easily fatigued. Five days prior to admission he had a shaking chill, requiring three blankets. Since then he has experienced chilly feelings on several occasions, but no further fresh chills. He has been constantly febrile, his temperature being between 101° and 103°F. There has been anorexia and occasionally mild nausea. There has been no known exposure to live animals (work all in classrooms). No previous illnesses, no history of rheumatic fever, and no heart murmurs have ever been described. The only medication taken has been aspirin, and citrate of magnesia because of mild constipation. There was no known exposure to tuberculosis or other infectious diseases.

PHYSICAL EXAMINATION

A well-developed, robust male with a flushed face, who appeared ill. Temperature 102.2°F. Pulse 100. Blood pressure 120/80. Weight 195 pounds. There was questionable nystagmus on left horizontal gaze. The abdomen was soft, the spleen was felt easily three fingerbreadths below the left costal margin and was slightly tender. There was one node in the right axilla, measuring 1.5 cm in diameter. The remainder of the physical examination was negative.

LABORATORY DATA

Routine urinalysis was not remarkable; specific gravity was 1.032. Hemogram on admission revealed a white blood cell count of 5,700 with a normal differential; hemoglobin 14.2 g. Repeat hemogram essentially the same values except for slightly higher total white count. Serology negative. Heterophile agglutination was positive with a titer 1 to 7; negative 1 to 14. Agglutination tests for typhoid, paratyphoid, Proteus OX 19 were all within normal limits. Agglutination test for Brucella abortus was positive in a dilution of 1:1,280. Three weeks later it was partial at 1:2,560. Several routine blood cultures were sterile as well as several cultures for Brucella organisms. Tuberculin skin test negative, both first and second strength PPD.

ROENTGENOGRAMS

Chest film: no abnormalities. Film of abdomen revealed definite splenic enlargement.

HOSPITAL COURSE

Following the report of the positive Brucella agglutination at titer of 1:1,280, definitive therapy was instituted in the form of dihydrostreptomycin 0.5 g twice daily for a period of two weeks. At the same time, aureomycin 0.5 g four times daily for a total of three weeks was instituted. Within 72 hours after this, the patient became afebrile and remained so throughout the remainder of his hospital stay. On the first and second day following the start of this therapy, the patient sustained a frank, shaking chill. The spleen decreased progressively in size; by the time of discharge it was no longer palpable. It was learned that several months prior to his illness, the patient had taken a laboratory course in veterinary obstetrics which did give him contact with the bovine fetus. However, the school authorities stated that careful measures were taken to insure against securing such specimens from infected cattle; no other cases had been reported from the institution. The diagnosis could not be definitely established in the absence of positive blood cultures. The initial agglutination of 1:1,280 with a rise three weeks later to 1:2,560 made the diagnosis of acute brucellosis seem highly probable.

DISCHARGE DIAGNOSIS

Acute brucellosis due to *Brucella abortus*, treated, improved.

COMMENT

Because of limited interview material, comment necessarily has to be brief. The patient, however, was clearly under mounting tensions over a period of months, reaching a high point some weeks before he became ill, when a combination of stresses involving studies for final examinations, wife's pregnancy, and the arrival of their first baby occurred. It was against such a psychological background that the patient could have been exposed to brucella organisms in a laboratory course in veterinary obstetrics, when he handled an apparently infected bovine fetus. The necessarily fragmentary anamnestic material suggests remainders of intense infantile curiosity about sexuality, particularly pregnancy and conception. In addition, there appears to have been an activation of old sibling jealousy with the arrival of the new baby, with resultant mobilized hostility in the form of repressed death wishes against it. The activated dependency feelings were unsuccessfully defended against by intensification of study efforts. The intense aggression appears to have found no effective pathway for outward discharge and was internalized. The "accidental" introduction of the *Brucella* organism then took place against this psychophysical background. One could ask whether the "accident" was in part determined by emotional factors. This question is relevant not only for this case, but for many others where accidental factors are involved and their occurrence is understood only in terms of superficial determinants. An individual's carelessness or poor judgment may be the result of a strong but unconscious need to hurt himself.

CASE 40

CHIEF PRESENTING SYMPTOM	Feverishness and headache
SENSORIMOTOR CONFIGURATIONS	Sensory configurations

Temperature, visual

Linked with studies for final exams, especially in veterinary obstetrics, infantile curiosity about conception, recollections of mother's miscarriages, concern over wife's pregnancy, and ambivalence over birth of child

Motor configurations

Studying

Related to need to prove competence and ability to achieve satisfactory manly status

SOMATIC IDENTIFICATION	*Mother*	Miscarriages, in patient's childhood

SENSITIZED ORGAN SYSTEM	Spleen "Systemic"
STRESS (*surface meaning*)	School examinations; problems with newborn baby
STRESS (*dynamic significance*)	Concern about adequacy, activation of old sibling jealousy
DEFENSES	Intellectualization Intensification of study efforts

AFFECTS	*Intensity*	*Pathway of expression*
Anxiety	+++	Ideational, somatic equivalents
Depression	+++	Somatization
Hostility	+++	Somatization

OTHER FACTORS	Long-standing curiosity about conception and pregnancy Troublesome conscience
HOMEOSTATIC SHIFT(s)	Marked somatization
DIAGNOSIS	Acute brucellosis due to *Brucella abortus*, treated, improved

case 41

Abdominal and Back Pain: Influence of Somatic Identification

CHIEF PRESENTING SYMPTOM

Pain in the side.

BASIC ANAMNESTIC EXCERPTS

"I have pain in my side, sometimes both sides, when I'm driving my truck, and in my back. It's been like that for six months. Sometimes it doubles you right over. Sometimes it's sharp. I have to push in and hold it. The doctor said he examined me for appendix and everything and said I didn't have none. . . . That pain is like being stuck with a needle. I can't sit that long. It's the same at home. I lie on a couch. I can't sit on a straight chair. But my wife wanted me to go to the hospital and kept pushing me for the last two months."

The patient then reveals his dislike of hospitals: "I didn't want to go because I hate them. Seven years ago, while I was in the Army, I got an awful sore throat once; it felt like it was pneumonia. I kept telling them I was sick, and they laughed. Finally they sent me in. They kept sticking something down my throat, taking tests. If there's anything I hate, it's having something poked in my mouth and throat. A week after I was in the hospital, my legs started to get paralyzed, and I couldn't move them out of bed. After a few weeks, I sat up and walked. I used to get hell for it, but I couldn't stay in bed. Once before, I was in a hospital in Africa with venereal disease, a sore on the top part. They put sulfa drugs on it, gave me penicillin, and cured it. I got penicillin once before, when I had diphtheria. They also put antitoxin in my buttocks, and they gave me shots every three hours."

Prior to military service: "I started to work when I was just 14. There were 14 kids in the family, and the older ones had to go to work. I'm the fourth oldest. I remember first working in a woodworking shop for 11 cents an hour. They didn't have much at home, big family like we had. The kids

333

came pretty close in my family. My father had just bought a house, and we all helped out. . . ." Here the patient begins clearing his throat and continues to do so for a while. "Never was sick until a couple of times in the Army. I did get sore throats then, bad ones. I was in a military police outfit, directing traffic. As soon as the front line advanced, we moved. They'd switch us here and there, before I could get real medical attention. Quite a lot of change. More than I bargained for. I was only 19 when I joined up.

"I've been driving a gas and oil truck for five years, nothing else to do. I prefer to work outdoors. Otherwise, I feel cooped up. Outside you're practically your own boss. I drove a coal truck for a while, which I think is easier than gas and oil. Now I have a hundred feet of hose to pull out, delivering oil. It's a small town, and people are fussy. There are plenty of oil companies around. So if you don't satisfy the customer, they'll buy it from somebody else. You do it their way, not your way (pause). There's plenty you have to take—and hold it in."

The pain is linked up specifically with work: "The doctor claimed it was from riding the truck. It was knocking my kidneys up and down, bouncing me up and down. Yet I wouldn't like to quit and go back into the shop where I'd feel cooped up. The pain hasn't been so bad since I've been here. I feel better except for the things they've been giving me—castor oil last night, an enema this morning. They took X-rays. Pretty near killed me. I could have a pretty good physique from milk; I get the runs from pasteurized milk, so I used to drink raw milk." Further details about bowels are elicited: "They work good. Twice a day, every day. Have a regular schedule."

References to marriage follow: "I've been married seven years. No family. Don't know why. She's been down to see the doctor. I've been down to see the doctor. He gave me the treatment, poked his finger in there, and said, 'You're both all right, it takes time.' I know the wife wants babies badly, but what can you do? Anyway, my wife works every day. Meanwhile, got to have patience and time—but I might run out of time, get older." Here the patient becomes obviously reluctant to talk further in this direction.

There are further associations to injuries: "This finger here (middle finger, right hand), if I close my hands fast, it locks tight. I have to go to the doctor and he pulls it out. He says I must have injured it when I was young. The only thing I remember is when I was about eight or so, the doctor cut my finger open and drew out pus, after I hurt it playing baseball. He cut it and squeezed it and it hurt like a son of a gun. I remember him—an old doctor. He said it was something like a trick knee. When I was 14, I cut my back on a piece of slate; I was taking pears to my mother's house. I backed from a pear tree right up to a piece of slate sticking out from the roof of the porch in our house. It made a pretty good gash. My mother treated me for it. I have a pretty good scar. I was too poor to go to the doctor."

The family health is next referred to: "All the kids are alive. Mother is feeling good." (Pause.) The patient is asked about father: "He's been dead for about three years. He was a suicide. He hung himself." The patient becomes tearful, and then continues to cry for a while: "Mother found him, but it was too late. I don't like to talk about it." The patient falls silent for a few minutes. Then he resumes, fumbling for a cigarette: "My throat's too dry." Again a pause. "I was close to him. Father had worked for the same company, driving horses, then trucks. He had never seen a doctor and had always been healthy (pause)."

The patient returns to his concern about being in the hospital: "I want out, back to doing something. This job—I meet 70 different families a day. Women I hate to talk to. With men I can stand and talk all day. Women get on my nerves. Even my mother has at times."

PSYCHODYNAMIC IMPRESSIONS

Early in the interview the associative connection between pain and truckdriving is quite apparent. Late in the interview, recollections of father's suicide and his truckdriving job are also associatively connected and trigger off a marked emotional response in the patient. Another association links pain and his wife's pushing him. Thus, there is the connection between the pain of his father's death and the pain of his wife's pushing and their childless marriage. A sense of guilt is obvious in the patient's confession about contracting a venereal disease and is linked with many symbolic references to castration fears—cuts, paralysis, dysfunction of various extremities, and other phallic representations, and finally, a gash in the back, a feminine sexual representation. References to having things put down his throat and into his buttocks are also made in a highly sexualized context. The past is recalled in a mixed fashion: Mother rarely had time for any individual child, they came so quickly one after another. The patient felt overlooked by her. On the other hand, he started work, like his father, in the same place and doing the same things, thus identifying with and forming a close attachment to him. In this setting, the past is seen as one of health and activity. In the present, he attempts to continue to be active and work outdoors like his father, but it is clear that a depression has been hanging over the patient since his father's death. His own feelings of physical, and especially sexual, inferiority are poorly concealed. He tends to avoid social life. He finds it very difficult to get along with women; his hostility is easily aroused by them and by their criticism, and is rather openly expressed. His relationship to men is quite different and further indicative of the attachment to father. There are obvious tensions in connection with his work, especially the fussy customers who are female. His emphasis on the need for regularity in bowel schedule and his preoccupation with his sensitivity to pasteurized milk are suggestive of an early concern with the processes of eating and elimination. The patient's sore throat is also closely related not only to diphtheria but to his father's hanging himself by the throat, suggesting somatic identification in this body area.

PHYSICAL HISTORY

The patient was admitted with chief complaints of sore throat, right lower quadrant and back pain of six months' duration. He has had a constant sore throat described as a dry, scratching, tickling sensation. He has noted similar episodes in the preceding years, ever since having diphtheria seven years ago while in military service, but none of the episodes has lasted as long as this. He denied fever or chills, but stated that he does sweat easily, especially at night. He has also had a cough for the past six months, productive of a moderate amount of whitish phlegm. There has been no frank hemoptysis and no chest pain. For a similar length of time, the patient has noted attacks of right lower quadrant pain, which is usually associated with pain in the sacroiliac area. The pain is described as sharp, occurring in attacks which may last from 15 minutes up to the entire day. The attacks occur practically daily, but he may be free of them for weeks at a time. They occur mainly while he is at work driving a truck. Appetite has been poor for the past six months, with occasional nausea, but no vomiting, constipation, or diarrhea. Past history and system review were essentially noncontributory.

PHYSICAL EXAMINATION

Temperature 99.2°F. Pulse 70. Blood pressure 116/94. The patient is well-developed and well-nourished and in no acute distress. The entire physical examination was within normal limits.

LABORATORY DATA

Serology negative. Urine, specific gravity 1.030, negative examination. Hemoglobin 15.5 g. Hematocrit 51 percent. Sedimentation rate 2 mm per hr. White blood cell count 4,800 with 38 segmented cells, 16 band cells, 45 lymphocytes, 1 monocyte. Basal metabolism rate +12. Heterophile agglutinations 1:7. Stools negative for guaiac, ova, and parasites.

ROENTGENOGRAMS

Chest plate, lumbosacral spine, barium enema, gastrointestinal series, and gallbladder series all within normal limits.

HOSPITAL COURSE

The patient was afebrile while in the hospital. His symptoms were mild. He was seen in a formal psychiatric consultation, and his symptoms were felt to be an expression of chronic anxiety, although hospitalization was not considered necessary. The nature of the patient's complaints was explained to him, and he was reassured and informed that if he had further difficulties, he could apply to a mental hygiene clinic.

DISCHARGE DIAGNOSIS

Anxiety state, chronic, severe, untreated, unchanged.

COMMENT

Psychophysical reactions to a change in the physical condition, illness, or death of a relative are not necessarily limited to any one member of a particular family group. Such responses may occur in all family members and will, of course, vary considerably, depending on each individual's innate and developmental physical and psychological makeup, as well as his current psychophysical state. Among the psychological components involved, identification plays an important role. One of the simplest instances in which this mechanism is involved is when the patient has been envious of the incapacitated or deceased relative whose place he had long wanted to take. Guilt apparently influences the direction of the identification somatically, so that the patient then exhibits physical symptoms similar to those of the afflicted relative. Another variation of identification occurs when the relative represents a loved object for whose loss or threatened loss the patient attempts to compensate by this mechanism. Here again somatic identification with the relative may occur, but in a more complicated form when the relative is a person of the opposite sex.

CASE 41

CHIEF PRESENTING SYMPTOM	Pain in the side
SENSORIMOTOR CONFIGURATIONS	Sensory configurations

Pain, interoceptive

Connected with truckdriving, long-standing grief over father's suicide and search for a surrogate, resentment toward women, guilt over past venereal disease, and childless marriage

Motor configurations

Activity

Associated with being overlooked by mother, injuries and surgery in childhood; riding, bouncing, being stuck, having fingers poked in him—highly sexualized content, with special reference to castration fears

SOMATIC IDENTIFICATION	*Father* Death due to suicide by hanging three years ago
SENSITIZED ORGAN SYSTEM	Throat Gastrointestinal
STRESS (*surface meaning*)	Current work stress, marital difficulties; three years ago father's death by suicide; hospitalization in military service
STRESS (*dynamic significance*)	Increased feelings of physical and especially sexual inferiority; chronically persistent feelings of loss of significant object —father
DEFENSES	Overactivity Some projective tendencies

AFFECTS	*Intensity*	*Pathway of expression*
Anxiety	+++	Affective, ideational, somatic equivalents and conversion
Depression	+++	Affective, ideational
Hostility	+++	Affective, ideational

OTHER FACTORS	Pregenital—anal as well as oral components
HOMEOSTATIC SHIFT(S)	Mild to moderate somatization response
DIAGNOSIS	Anxiety state, chronic, severe, untreated, unchanged

CLINICAL MATERIAL FROM ANOTHER CASE

It was possible to study sibling reactions to the illness of a parent in one family unit made up of mother, two sons, and two daughters. A tendency toward being overanxious was present in all members, with varying degrees of phobic behavior manifested by each, except for the youngest daughter who had more hysterical elements in her makeup. All had recurrent, somatic manifestations, often without organic basis. The mother was troubled by migraine headaches and seasonal asthma. She was in her late sixties, and had developed mild hypertension and diabetes; she was mostly troubled by vertigo and attacks of paroxysmal auricular fibrillation. The oldest sibling, a son 47 years old, had for years been subject to seasonal hay fever and more recently experienced frequent bouts of vertigo and extrasystoles. The next oldest, a son 42 years old, had had migraine headaches, but recently had begun to drink somewhat more heavily than had been his wont, although this did not interfere with his work; he was also subject to spells of pathological emotionality in the form of rage reactions while under the influence of alcohol. The next oldest was a daughter, aged 39, who suffered from recurrent bouts of colitis and urticaria. The youngest daughter, aged 36, had mild seasonal hay fever.

The mother, who had been having some trouble with her hearing, began to complain increasingly to her children about this disability. A family conference was held and it was decided that the mother should have an expert checkup for this condition. An otologist diagnosed the deafness to be of the type found in elderly people and recommended a hearing aid. Further examination and fittings were done, despite the mother's resistance to the idea of wearing such a device. Each of the children except the younger son was involved in persuading her that it would be in her best interests to have a hearing aid. Several weeks later the oldest son developed troublesome itching of both ears. Examination revealed an otitis externa and a cortisone ointment was prescribed. The condition persisted in very mild form for six months and then became quiescent symptomwise. The youngest daughter at approximately the same time began to experience recurrent tinnitus; repeated examinations could establish no organic basis for the symptom, which lingered on for several months and then disappeared "spontaneously." This specific somatic identification, however, did not occur in the other two children. There was instead an increase in their habitual somatic responses, already described.

case 42

Biliary Symptoms, Syncope, and Psychological Stress

CHIEF PRESENTING SYMPTOM

Pain in ribs.

BASIC ANAMNESTIC EXCERPTS

"I came in for a gallbladder. I had an X-ray and it showed some small stones. I passed out a couple of times in the Army which I didn't like, and once a couple of months ago when mother got sick. That's what led me to have the X-ray for the gallbladder, to find out if there was any connection with the passing out. I fainted once in college before finals. When I was examined for military service they gave me one of those . . . that electro-encephalograph. They had one at the induction center. When I got out, I went to this doctor, and I got an EEG from him, and he said there wasn't anything he could see that was wrong. I came in here mainly with the idea I had some small stones. Now I did have some pain in here (right ribs). I had it so bad once—two years ago—that I went to a doctor. I was just bent over this way. The doctor saw me in pain and gave me a few things to chew up, but I might as well have chewed candy for all the good it did at the time. Just took a day or so to wear off." (Hostility is ill concealed by humor.)

"About two years ago I ran a temperature quite a number of days. I had iritis with it. The pain was pretty bad. I went to this doctor— this eye man—and he cured the iritis. He said it was some focal point of infection in the body. It cleared up so well, and I didn't have any more trouble, that I didn't do any more about it. I've had a sensitivity up here through my shoulders, a sort of dull but not a continuous pain, sir. Once I had jaundice with it."

Asked about other experiences involving pain when younger, the patient replied: "Always been pretty well. I did have my tonsils out, so I

340

did have an operation. I must have been about ten years old. Sister took second place then for a while."

He next refers to the health of his family: "We don't bury them unless they're over eighty. My own family—most of them—have been long-lived people. My grandmother lived into her eighties, and so did my grandfather on both sides of the family. My father is about sixty; mother is fifty-five. She's at the hospital now. She's had an operation. Quite serious in a way. What they call plantar warts. I don't know if it was through neglect partially, or just what it was she didn't do. I can't remember back. She's had them over a period of years. She evidently had X-ray treatments on them, and I think that was the wrong thing to do. Then she had to have them opened up for some reason or other last fall. She had a lot of pain over that. Anyway, she went into the hospital again about a week— maybe four weeks ago. Then they operated. They thought they would have to remove part of the foot. But instead, they decided to try plastic surgery. They had to graft skin. Can they sew the bottom of the foot, sir? They usually don't sew at the bottom, do they? And so they put her foot in a cast. The cast has been removed now. She's got to leave her foot up a month. I don't know how it's come out. But she's worked through that pretty well.

"Mother also had a gallbladder operation, and my father had his hernia operated on. She had had a lot of pain with it before, and I guess it wasn't in too good shape when she had it out. I don't know, but I guess she's getting along pretty well without it."

The patient next reveals why he is single: "I'm not married. I don't think it would work too well on a schoolteacher's pay. Couldn't afford it. But I haven't met anybody particularly, though some I've liked pretty well, but haven't done anything about it. I live with my parents and aunt. As I told you, my mother is in the hospital right now. Father can pretty well take care of himself. My aunt is 74 and still going strong."

The patient's reactions to a possible operation are further explored: "Well, there are things I'd rather do than that. I wouldn't relish having something cut out of me, but I would proceed (pause). When you're really younger, it's better to take care of those things than to wait."

Concern is expressed that he will be considered incoherent: "I hope you don't think I've been rambling. From now on I'll have more patience with my students when I find them incoherent (laughing)." The patient has taught high school for years. He has always wanted to be a teacher and has always liked history.

At this point the patient's face reflects anxiety: "I haven't had any nausea or throwing up. Is there such a thing that if you have the stones there is nothing that can be done about it outside of an operation? This dissolving business that you hear about once in a while is a lot of tommy-rot, isn't it? The doctor said to keep away from fatty foods and not to have an excess, but I trespass sometimes. When you eat out a lot, it is hard to get what you need. I eat out a lot because I live away—I mean I teach away from home. So it's difficult to watch your diet."

PSYCHODYNAMIC IMPRESSIONS

Initial associations are in terms of diagnosis and medical procedures. The patient then wonders if there is any connection between the symptom of gallbladder pain and his episodes of unconsciousness. Further associations about pain extend in a number of different directions. It is linked with hostility toward a physician whose advice afforded the patient no relief. The hostility is only thinly concealed by attempts at humor. Pain is also connected with eye trouble. Mother's illnesses, her own gallbladder condition and her plantar warts, have been characterized by frequent, severe pain. Somatic identification is chiefly with her.

For several months prior to his hospitalization, there has been considerable tension in the home where the patient, who is single, lives with father, mother, and an aunt. Mother's incapacity and finally her hospitalization have disrupted the previous, somewhat uneasy equilibrium in the home. The patient is obviously dissatisfied with the arrangements for getting his meals, but open expression of hostility is not evident. Strong oral components are manifested in his craving for food and his inability to keep from gaining excess weight. There is a long history of sibling rivalry and envy in relation to his sister who, he felt, was the preferred child. She is now married and lives in another state.

The patient rationalizes his being single on the basis of insufficient financial resources. Actually he is more concerned than he acknowledges about his manliness and physical adequacy. He regards the possibility of an operation with some apprehension; it appears to represent a symbolic castration, with further threat to his masculinity.

The epileptic seizures may be triggered off by stresses, particularly those in which the patient feels helpless and unable to cope with the situation by himself.

PHYSICAL HISTORY

The patient was admitted with the chief complaint of abdominal pain and blackout spells. In the past two years the patient has had two attacks of severe upper epigastric pain which was associated with jaundice, acholic stools, and dark urine. These attacks spontaneously subsided, and in the past year he has noticed vague epigastric distress which bears no relation to food intake. He avoids fatty, fried foods, although he does not know if these would precipitate attacks or not. He has occasional nausea, but no vomiting; there is no constipation, diarrhea, or melena. An X-ray several months ago was said to show small stones in the gallbladder.

Ten years ago the patient had a spell of unconsciousness lasting several minutes. Since then he has had eight similar attacks, usually occurring in the morning. There is no associated fecal or urinary incontinence, or convulsions. While in military service, he had five such attacks. He states that he has had several electroencephalograms which have been reported as normal. No visual disturbance, vertigo, or difficulty in walking. Past history and system review were essentially noncontributory.

PHYSICAL EXAMINATION

Temperature 99.6°F. Pulse 88. Blood pressure 122/80. The patient is well-developed, obese, and in no acute distress. The entire physical examination was with normal limits.

LABORATORY DATA

Serology negative. Hemoglobin 15.5 g. Hematocrit 48 mm percent. Sedimentation rate 2 mm per hr. White blood cell count 5,800 with 51 segmented cells, 32 lymphocytes, 17 band cells. Nonprotein nitrogen 31. Fasting blood sugar 97. Spinal fluid examination: entirely negative. Urinalysis: negative.

ROENTGENOGRAMS

Chest: negative. Skull: negative. The gallbladder concentrated the contrast material well, and a large, circumferentially calcified calculus was seen within the gallbladder; associated with this calcified stone were numerous translucent calculi. Gastrointestinal series was essentially negative.

ELECTROENCEPHALOGRAM

Revealed irregular activity in the alpha range in the occipital area and low voltage fast in the frontal. There were occasional bursts of high voltage and three to four per second irregular spike and wave formations predominantly in the anterior aspects.

HOSPITAL COURSE

The patient became afebrile and remained asymptomatic during his hospital stay. He was seen by the neurology service and transferred there for further study, with subsequent transfer to the surgical service for a cholecystectomy and choledochostomy as advised by the surgical consultant.

TRANSFER DIAGNOSES

1. Cholelithiasis.
2. Epilepsy, probable. To be further investigated.

ADDENDUM—NEUROLOGICAL SERVICE

On transfer to this service, patient appeared to be in no acute distress. Repeat neurological examination was again negative. The patient had sleep record and metrazol activation electroencephalograms, and in both there were noted seizure discharges, more predominant in the metrazol record, at which time it was also noted that the patient had clonic movement of the right arm while the metrazol was being injected. Pneumoencephalogram was done; ventricles filled well; there was no evidence of displacement or distortion. The patient was seen by the epilepsy consultant and started on phenobarbital ½ grain t.i.d. He was then transferred to the surgical service for gallbladder surgery with a transfer diagnosis of epilepsy, idiopathic, manifested probably by grand mal seizures.

ADDENDUM—SURGICAL SERVICE

An elective cholecystectomy and common duct exploration was done under endotrachial anesthesia. Numerous large and small stones were found in the gallbladder, but none were found in the common duct. The patient's postoperative course was relatively benign. The sutures were removed on the 11th postoperative day, and except for superficial stitch infections, the wound was well healed. The patient was discharged on a regular diet, to return to the follow-up clinic in one month.

FINAL COMMENT

Somatic identifications, predominantly with the mother, appear in connection with the patient's gallbladder symptoms, whereas none are evident in relation to the epileptic seizures. It seems, however, that the development of disease in his gallbladder, with formation of stones, proceeded for the most part "silently" until recently, as far as physical symptoms are concerned. However, there are indications that psychologically, the patient has been chronically tense and depressed for years, probably antedating his military service. More recently, stress has been related to tensions in his home and to mother's physical incapacities. Several episodes of marked physical dysfunction, brief in duration and involving the biliary system, occurred during this time. Within the past month, and concomitant with the mother's hospitalization and the very considerable disarray it introduced into the patient's life, a rather marked shift in his psychophysical equilibrium took place. The patient had an epileptic seizure for the first time in years and he became increasingly concerned about low-grade biliary symptoms.

For a number of years, the seizures had been effectively controlled while the patient was under specific medication. If the seizures were triggered by inwardly bound, aggressive-drive energies beyond those bound by his depression, then blocking this somatic outlet by medication meant that other pathways of discharge had to be found. The sensitized biliary tract could have served this purpose, apart from nonsomatic channels. With the recent, marked shift in psychophysical equilibrium, the patient's emotions rapidly escalated in intensity and could no longer be adequately dealt with by the existing psychological and somatic defenses. The protective effect of the antiepileptic medication was broken through. The result was a seizure, temporally coincident with the mother's entry into the hospital and reminiscent of earlier reactions under stress. It would seem that the patient's operation could be termed an elective one, since there were really no emergency indications for it. After removal of the gallbladder, one wonders what discharge pathways may be available to the patient in the future, should further unfavorable shifts in psychophysical equilibrium occur, with activated aggressive drives blocked from adequate discharge outwardly.

Dunbar (1954) refers to earlier observations by Langheinrich (1922) and by Wittkower (1928). The former found that with subjects under deep hypnosis and following the suggestion of fresh sweet butter ingestion, bile secretion is not only thick yellow liver bile but also dark brown bladder bile, and more copious than with the suggestion of bouillon or with just the introduction of a duodenal sound alone. Wittkower found that joy, sorrow and anxiety increased bile secretion two to six times, beginning almost immediately with the suggestion to the hypnotized subject, and subsiding equally sharply. Annoyance entirely or almost entirely inhibited bile secretion. The latter reaction is more probably due to spasm of the bile ducts than to decreased secretion. Wittkower felt that psychological processes may be a contributory factor in icterus as well as in gallstone formation. There are other references in Dunbar's bibliography to Schindler, Mohr, and Alkan, each of whom has written on the relationship between psychological factors and gallbladder disease. Schindler (1927) states that the history given by most gallbladder patients is typical: "The first serious colic comes after a violent conscious annoyance. Similarly, the second and third, but then the attacks come without annoyance, and finally especially after errors in diet." Mohr (1925) likewise considers that emotional factors play an important role in the development and elimination of gallstone colic. Alkan (1930) refers to emotional disturbance as significant in the acute flare-ups of chronic cholecystitis and stone formation. Further quotation from Dunbar: "Every abdominal surgeon has had those annoying cases where a stone expected with certainty was not found, and not even a kink or an adhesion which could explain the colic: where, as if laughing one to scorn, the gallbladder lies there in the body of the narcotized patient without any sign of spasm. In these cases the surgeon, according to his temperament, leaves the organ in the body or resects it." Even in the case of infected gallbladders, "resolution of the spasm by elimination of the central factor (neurosis, and the associated fear component) will be curative."

Medication and its affects must be considered from a number of different viewpoints. The agent used may have a specific pharmacological effect with direct or indirect influence on physicochemical processes in the body. Symptoms against which the treatment is directed may then be eliminated, modified, lessened, masked, or sometimes exacerbated or replaced by other symptoms. The medication may also have a symbolic significance for the patient and at times exert a "placebo effect," influencing the symptom manifestations as well as the general psychological state of the individual. However, physical pathways and symptoms at times and to a variable extent do provide discharge outlets for emotional tensions. An evaluation of the total effect of medication should take into consideration what happens to these energies when somatic outlets are blocked or eliminated. If the emotional conflicts remain essentially unchanged, other avenues of discharge will be involved either ideationally, affectively, behaviorally, or somatically. These possible aftereffects of medication, and the usefulness of psychotherapy as an adjunct in preventing undesirable sequelae, need further investigation.

CASE 42

CHIEF PRESENTING SYMPTOM   Pain in ribs

SENSORIMOTOR CONFIGURATIONS   Sensory configurations

Pain, interoceptive

Associated with syncope, hostility toward unhelpful physician, eye trouble, operations undergone by parents, old unresolved sibling rivalry, and recent upset in his dependent relationships at home

Motor configurations

Passing out

Linked with stressful situations in which he feels helpless, and with intensified hostility which cannot be sufficiently discharged through other pathways

SOMATIC IDENTIFICATION

Mother   Painful plantar warts operated on very recently; gallbladder pain and operation nine years ago (Direct, organ constitutional)

Father   Hernia operation in recent years

SENSITIZED ORGAN SYSTEM

Brain
Gastrointestinal—gallbladder

STRESS (*surface meaning*)

Mother's illnesses, military experiences

STRESS (*dynamic significance*)

Activation of passive dependency needs, fears about manliness, and associated frustration and hostility

DEFENSES

Humor
Rationalizations

AFFECTS

	Intensity	*Pathway of expression*
Anxiety	++	Ideational, some affective
Depression	+++	Some ideational, some affective, somatization
Hostility	+++	Some ideational, somatization

OTHER FACTORS

Fantasy fear of anal attack
Oral components
Long history of sibling rivalry
Superego problems

HOMEOSTATIC SHIFT(S)

Seizures blocked by medication, and impact of aggressive potential shifted to sensitized biliary tract, but then with further activation again focused on brain as target organ

DIAGNOSES

a) Cholelithiasis and cholecystitis, treated by cholecystectomy, improved;
b) Epilepsy, idiopathic, treated, improved

case 43

Episodes of Weakness in a Patient with Severe Neurosis

CHIEF PRESENTING SYMPTOM

Spells of weakness.

BASIC ANAMNESTIC EXCERPTS

The patient describes spells he has been having for almost eight years: "Spells seem to run generally like this: They start off with a very strong feeling of nervousness, apprehensiveness. Immediately, within a second or two, maybe ten or fifteen seconds, I get very nervous, and I have this tingling sensation in my fingers and my hands, and then the heart starts to race and pound from blood rushing into my head. I come very close to losing consciousness. One time, when I had a second spell like that, seven years ago, I did lose consciousness for about forty-five minutes. Recently, spells began to come so frequently without apparent reason or cause, that they interfered with my business. You see I practice law for myself, and of course there is a certain amount of nervous tension attached to that. Two years ago, there was a big automobile-train accident near my home; men and women were killed and lying in the roadway. I had one of those spells then.

"The spell I had this year, I was just sitting in church. Of course, I never liked to go to church. I always associate church with death, and I have an extremely morbid fear of death and dying. I've had it for quite a long time. I was desperately ill with empyema for fourteen months when I was in the Army. They sent my mother a telegram that she'd better come because my hours were numbered.

"When I have one of these spells, one of the first things that pops into my mind is that I'm going to die from it. But it irritates my mother something awful sometimes, you know, because she thinks I'm making life hard for myself because we all have to go sometime, and worrying about it every time you have the slightest thing wrong with you isn't going to do the slightest bit of good. I don't have to have anything wrong with me to give me that feeling. Having the doctor examine me, especially my heart and blood pressure, he has to go through a ritual, and then he says, 'That's all.' When I walk out, I have ten thousand kinds of fears that there is something desperately wrong with me that he won't tell me about. My imagination—just give it a few minutes and it'll do a good job."

Associations to specific symptoms are then elicited: "There's tingling. Like shutting off the circulation, and then the blood starts to run in again —that needle-like feeling, not strong but something like that. I have some white pills. I know they're nothing more than a sedative. Whether it actually helps me or whether it's the psychological effect, I don't know. But they do seem to help. Like the spell I had when I was in church. I couldn't see. Like a flashbulb in a camera if you looked into it. Blinded for a minute. In one of my spells, I was visiting my girlfriend. When we got to the doctor's, my heartbeat then was way over a hundred twenty.

"The longer my heart beats and pounds, the more light-headed and weak I get. If somebody put an egg in my hand, I don't think I could crush the shell. Once when I passed out, it was after I went to the movies with mother. The theater was very crowded. I had that sensation of heat that passes over my body. The next thing I knew I woke up in the bedroom with the doctor there. Some people had carried me upstairs. I have an apartment; just my mother and I. My father is dead. He died eighteen years ago last—when I was about twelve—last month—in May (pause)."

The patient now associates further to his father's death: "He had a heart attack. He was forty-nine. I would have been twelve in June, and he died in May. As far as we know, he had never had any heart attacks or any spells, but there is heart disease in my father's family (sighing). I've got an aunt that is suffering from heart trouble now. Father'd been working out of town. He'd been traveling back and forth over the weekends. He was around the house all that day. He was reading the paper. My mother asked him what he would like for supper. He told her, and my mother turned around to go to the cupboard. She heard the papers go on the floor. By the time she got there, fifteen feet farther along, he was dead. I can remember practically everything that was said or done, almost verbatim. My aunt arrived in the meantime. She says, 'You had better go outside and sit down for a while.' So I went out and sat on the front steps of the house for a while. After a while, she came out and said to me, 'You'll have to be a brave boy now. You're all mother's got left now. Your Daddy's gone.'

"After my father died, I didn't want to go into the house. I said I could always see my father there.

"Of course, I don't like funerals. I don't suppose anybody does. I really dread them. This was the first funeral I ever went to. Of course, my father and I were very close. He was very proud of me because I was the only child. He'd been living away from home for over eight months before he died; except on weekends."

Further details about "spells" are elicited next: "I can't understand why all the time I was at Dartmouth I never got a spell. I really enjoyed it up there. Then I came home, commuted for three years to Boston, law school there, and had spells. Had spells visiting my girlfriend. I was waiting to get married, but feel I owe something to mother. Mother doesn't approve of marriage. It's just foolishness, she says, in my financial condition to go out and get married. Don't know if that's the real reason, or whether she doesn't want to let me go.

"My girl's mother died of angina last January; she had had hypertension for several years. One morning she got up, said she didn't feel good. Doctor said, 'Better get her into the hospital.' So they got her into the hospital, and at 2:20 she was dead. We decided to set the date for the marriage. We set September as the date. There is a possibility that I might work for the Department of Agriculture in Washington, and we might move down there."

PSYCHODYNAMIC IMPRESSIONS

The main theme of this patient's detailed and lengthy associations centers around the spells which constitute his chief physical complaints. It is clear that they are anxiety equivalents. Symptoms of tingling, cold perspiration, heart pounding, blood rushing, indicate that the cardiovascular system is the target organ. Syncopal or near-syncopal tendencies are also involved. The increasing frequency of the spells within recent months is clearly related to an accumulation of situational stresses within that period: the responsibilities of a new law practice and the setting of a date for his marriage despite his mother's marked opposition.

The spells are physical expressions of a sense of impending doom— especially a fear of death, of dissolution. This particular anxiety has many associative connections. It is linked with visual, auditory proprioceptive, and temperature sensory clusters in recollections about his father's death, his own severe illness and brush with death, other people being killed, sudden and violent death in general. There are also connections with being together with mother or his girlfriend or other girls in situations described as hot, uncomfortably crowded, with sexual overtones.

The patient is an only child whose relationship with parents was one in which there were particularly intense emotional elements. There are indications of a close but ambivalent attachment to a father remembered as being rugged but who tended to be often away. After the father's death, the ambivalent relationship with the mother also appears to have intensified. She, too, was away then quite often, working. It would seem likely that the patient's emotional problems center around an oedipal triangle in which ambivalence is involved—but the more marked negative elements are directed toward the mother. Physical well-being and absence of spells are associated with being in the presence and company of men, and the opposite with being close to women. Somatic identification with the father and also a substitute mother figure are in terms of heart, blood pressure, and chest troubles.

PHYSICAL HISTORY

This patient entered the hospital because of attacks of weakness and jitteriness beginning about eight years ago. At that time, while in military service, noncombat, the patient had a "spell" which has been repeated in all details on numerous occasions since. Each episode begins with a feeling of extreme apprehension, followed by light-headedness, fullness of the chest and face, tingling in the hands and occasionally the feet, tachycardia, and the sensation of extreme jitteriness. During the episodes there is blanching of the face, mottling of the fingers, and extreme weakness. The attacks, as far as the patient can recall, have usually occurred two to three hours following his last meal. He has never had an attack in the morning before breakfast. On one occasion the patient was unconscious for a period of 45 minutes, during which time he vomited, but had no incontinence, convulsions, or tongue biting. He was seen by a physician during this episode, and was told that no physical basis could be found for his being unconscious. During the attacks the patient has the uncontrollable fear that he is dying. The attacks have occurred at widely varying intervals, approximately two times yearly. They have occurred in a barber shop, while walking on the street, while in church, with no known precipitating event. The patient described three of these episodes during the past few months and due to the increase in their number recently, he sought hospitalization.

Past history reveals that nine years ago, while in military service, the patient developed pneumonia accompanied by empyema. In an attempt to drain the empyema and close the subsequent cavity, the patient had four operations on the right chest. As a result of this, he has noted reduced exercise tolerance and occasional twinges of pain in the right side. In addition, he has noted occasional numbness of the fourth and fifth right fingers, which he relates to the surgery. Five years ago the patient was treated for what was called pyloric spasm, which was characterized by morning nausea and vomiting.

PHYSICAL EXAMINATION

Temperature 98.6°F. Pulse 100. Blood pressure 120/80. Weight 208 pounds. In no apparent distress, oriented and cooperative. Examination of the chest and lungs revealed multiple old surgical scars over the posterior right chest; there was dullness and diminished breath sounds over the lower two thirds of the right chest; left lung and diaphragm were normal. There was a pronounced mitral first sound with a very questionable pre-systolic rumble; P_2 was greater than A_2 and there was a Grade I pulmonic systolic murmur; no cardiac enlargement was demonstrated. Peripheral pulses and vessels were normal. Genitalia: there was a small left varicocele, otherwise normal.

LABORATORY DATA

White blood cell count 6,100 with 68 percent polymorphonuclear leukocytes, 31 percent lymphocytes, 1 percent eosinophiles. Hemoglobin 14.4 g, hematocrit 48 mm percent, sedimentation rate: normal: Urinalysis: normal. Serology: negative. A five-hour oral glucose tolerance test revealed a fasting blood sugar of 89; ½ hour: 165; 1 hour: 142; 2 hours: 107; 3 hours: 70; 3¾ hours: 52. At the 3¾ hour level, the patient had an episode such as that described at the time of admission. Accordingly, the glucose tolerance test was ended at this point, and the patient was fed. A subsequent 5-hour oral glucose tolerance test showed a 3-hour level of 84 and a 4½ hour level of 78. At 3 hours, the patient again had a spell of anxiety, weakness, and trembling, and at this time the blood sugar was normal.

ROENTGENOGRAMS

Chest plate revealed resection of the third through the eighth ribs on the right, leaving margins of the ribs posteriorly. The upper rib resected areas have partially regenerated. The major amount of compression of the lungs is from the seventh to the tenth rib. No abnormalities of the underlying lung were noted. The left lung appeared normal. Spine: moderate scoliosis, middorsal region, with convexity toward the right. The cardiac silhouette was shifted toward the left hemithorax due to the scoliosis. KUB normal.

ELECTROCARDIOGRAM

Normal.

ELECTROENCEPHALOGRAM

Normal.

HOSPITAL COURSE

During his hospital stay, the patient had two episodes similar to those described in the history. Both of these occurred during the time he was having an oral glucose tolerance test. However, no change in the blood sugars was noted at that time, and accordingly, it was felt that hypoglycemia was not a cause of these episodes. He was seen by a member of the consulting staff who felt that pheochromocytoma was extremely unlikely in view of the history of unconsciousness of 45 minutes, which suggested a possible emotional factor. The patient was seen in consultation by a staff psychiatrist to whom he related an episode in which he regained consciousness during one of the chest operations and had the feeling he had died. He gave a history of chronic anxiety, however, for years preceding this episode. In view of the patient's anxiety and its possible exacerbation due to chest surgery, it was recommended that he should receive psychiatric treatment, which he elected to take on an outpatient basis.

DISCHARGE DIAGNOSES

1. Acute and chronic anxiety neurosis, untreated, unchanged.
2. Thoracoplasty, right chest; untreated, unchanged.

COMMENT

In this case, a relatively early and highly traumatic event has remained as a chronic psychological irritant to the patient for many years. The event, of course, was the father's death, and there were many recollective sensory links to it, which form the nidus of the later "spells" and determine to a large extent the kind of perceptual clusters that accompany them. In addition, the motor referents similarly derive from this original episode, and are connected with the current symptoms. This psychophysical gestalt has been activated by recurrent stresses, major and minor, with manifestations that are more or less severe, but are basically expressed as they have habitually been for a long time.

This patient has had severe, recurrent anxiety reactions with florid somatic equivalents for many years. During this time, however, no more than passing attention was paid to the psychological factors in his case. Whatever medical surveys were done focused chiefly on the physical symptoms and the ruling out of organic disease. Severe anxiety with its somatic manifestations can be as incapacitating and distressing in its own way as severe physical illness.

CASE 43

CHIEF PRESENTING SYMPTOM	Spells of weakness
SENSORIMOTOR CONFIGURATIONS	Sensory configurations

Tactile, temperature, visual, auditory

Associated with "spells" which represent fears of dissolution, and linked in turn with recollections of father's death, his own severe illness and brush with death, and other people being killed

Motor configurations

Losing consciousness

Connected with activation of intense anxiety, especially in situations which have sexual overtones

SOMATIC IDENTIFICATION	*Father*	Sudden death due to heart disease, patient then age 12
	Aunt	Heart trouble
SENSITIZED ORGAN SYSTEM	Cardiovascular system	

STRESS (*surface meaning*)   Job tension, marriage date set, problems with mother; earlier severe chest illness while in military service

STRESS (*dynamic significance*)   Conflict heightened between need to prove himself a man and activated infantile dependency with ambivalent attachment to mother

DEFENSES   Rationalization

AFFECTS	*Intensity*	*Pathway of expression*
Anxiety	+++	Some ideational and affective, somatic equivalents
Depression	+	Some somatization
Hostility	++	Some ideational, some somatization

OTHER FACTORS   An only child; particularly intense ambivalent relationships with parents. Early traumatic event, father's death

HOMEOSTATIC SHIFT(S)   Mild to moderate somatization response

DIAGNOSES   a) Acute and chronic anxiety neurosis, untreated, unchanged;
b) Thoracoplasty, right chest; untreated, unchanged

case 44

Throat and Stomach Symptoms as Symbolic Expressions of Emotional Tension

CHIEF PRESENTING SYMPTOM

Trouble with throat and stomach.

BASIC ANAMNESTIC EXCERPTS

As the patient begins to talk, he interrupts with coughing and clearing his throat. He first refers to trouble in swallowing and breathing: "It seems as if something is stuck in there." His throat is very irritated all the time. Again the patient pauses and clears his throat. Again he repeats it is like something "stuck in there." He thought it was tonsils, but it wasn't (more throat clearing). There is difficulty with breathing, too; he has to breathe three or four times before he can get a full breath. While he has been aware of nervousness for seven to eight years, his throat has been troubling him only about a year or so.

Shortness of breath is also brought into associative connection with nervousness. He has noticed this particularly when he has been walking alone. Again there is reference to a hurting sensation in the throat; it feels as if he is "gagging all the time" (more throat clearing). A doctor prescribed pills and recommended that he come to the hospital. His stomach has also been giving him trouble; almost every morning he seems to throw up whatever he had for breakfast; this has been going on for the past six months. Nothing seems to help.

The patient's nervousness is linked to loss of sleep in overseas duty in jungle areas. He had only five to six hours' sleep in a month because of day and night air raids. He drank black coffee to keep awake at night so that watch could be kept at all times. He recalls some trouble in breathing at that time, but it became much worse a year ago. Liquids are not difficult to swallow, but solid food is. However, there is always a pain in the

355

throat. He recalls having had malaria with bouts of chills and fever, sweating, and aching bones when he was overseas, but he was not hospitalized then. This is his first hospitalization, and he would rather be home.

The patient elaborates on his home life: "My wife and baby are there (throat clearing). I've been married about a year and a half. The baby is a girl, but she eats enough." Another is not being planned; it costs too much money. This association leads to the subject of the patient's work. He works in a cemetery, runs a machine which digs the graves. It would take a man four to five hours to dig one manually, but the machine does it in 10 to 15 minutes. Formerly he cut grass and took general care of the place. He has been there five years. He used to work for a beef company, delivering meats; before that he worked on auto body sales. "I changed to the cemetery job because it was steady for one thing; I could always show a week's pay, and it was like being my own boss without being bothered by anybody; there is a foreman but he's never around; the rest—they're all dead. I would have liked to have my own business—landscaping, but didn't have enough money to buy equipment."

He has never had money because he had to support his mother and father; he is the only one in the family. His father wasn't working, and the patient turned in all the money to the family. There are two sisters in Europe. "My father died several years ago; he had trouble passing his water, and one day he jumped out of the window, he was suffering so much. He had been suffering for over a year. The doctor sent him to the hospital so that they could watch him, but he jumped out anyway from the second floor; he died right away. It happened two years ago this month." At that time the patient had been living with his parents, but afterwards— several months later—when the patient married, his mother went to live with him. She has never been sick, and has never been one day in the hospital.

The patient continues: "My wife was sick when she had the baby; it was an instrument baby, and they had to pull it out—it was stuck. She was having a hard time, and they told her they would have to use instruments (almost continuous clearing of throat)." Following this difficult birth, the patient decided that there should not be any more children for a couple of years at least.

Drinking doesn't help the congested feeling in his throat. He drinks only a little beer now and then or a little homemade wine for dinner. There is a noticeable smell of liquor on his breath, and he is asked if he had anything to drink before the interview. He indicated that he had a shot of brandy—usually does in the morning.

PHYSICAL HISTORY

The patient entered with chief complaints of dryness of the throat and epigastric distress. For the past year he has noted a chronic dryness of the throat with a feeling that food stuck in a region just above the larynx. However, he denies any difficulty in swallowing, even of solid objects, but still the sensation is present as if something were stuck there. For two years he has noticed a dull, nagging sensation in the epigastric area, usually in the morning, before breakfast. The sensation is associated with gagging and retching after breakfast, and he frequently vomits about 20 minutes after eating. His appetite has been fair to poor during this time. No hematemesis, constipation, diarrhea, blood, or melena. In addition, he complains of transient momentary pain in the chest, over the pericardium; the pain is described as a knife-like sensation, lasting a second or two, and not related to exertion. He complains also of difficulty in breathing, appearing to coincide with the sensation that something is sticking in his throat. Past history and system review were noncontributory.

PHYSICAL EXAMINATION

Temperature 98.6°F. Pulse 96. Blood pressure 160/100. A well-developed, well-nourished male in no acute distress, but extremely apprehensive and rather vague in giving his history. There was a marked gross tremor of the outstretched hands. The remainder of the physical examination was within normal limits.

LABORATORY DATA

Hemogram, serology, sedimentation rate, urinalysis, nonprotein nitrogen, and fasting blood sugar within normal limits.

ROENTGENOGRAMS

Gastrointestinal series: no abnormalities were visualized. Esophagus: study of the hypopharynx and esophagus failed to reveal the presence of any intrinsic or organic pathology. The mechanism of swallowing was normal, except for the fact that the patient did swallow a considerable amount of air following the swallowing of the barium water mixture. There was a suggestion of two small lateral pouches arising in the region of the origin of both pyriform sinuses.

HOSPITAL COURSE

The patient was afebrile during his hospital stay. Further studies including repeat blood pressures were completely normal, and it was the feeling of the service that this patient's symptoms were of a psychological nature. He was given reassurance, the nature of his condition was explained to him, and he was discharged.

DISCHARGE DIAGNOSIS

Anxiety state, chronic, untreated, unchanged.

COMMENT

This interview is characterized both by frequent pauses and by repeated throat clearing on the part of the patient. He often appears to be unable to verbalize, and he acts as if he were trying to dislodge something from his throat. Symbolically, the patient may be trying to rid himself of unpleasant situations. There are associations to traumatic combat exposure in which it was necessary for him to be constantly on the alert to danger from air raids. More recently he was concerned about his wife's difficult pregnancy; the baby was "stuck." Furthermore, having children is seen as a financial responsibility for which the patient does not feel himself ready. The new baby is also seen as a competitor for his wife's attentions. The patient would also like to avoid responsibilities involved in starting a business of his own. His work in a cemetery as a grave-digger is rationalized as acceptable because it's steady work and he is left pretty much to himself, without having to account for what he is doing. He indicated that he felt depleted because he had had to support his parents for many years—a duty he resented. He was, however, very disturbed by his father's painful illness, his inability to urinate, and his death. The patient is now, in effect, "stuck" with his mother and caring for her.

The patient's physical symptoms thus appear as highly symbolized representations of various emotional irritants. They are expressions of a "body organ language" and are multidetermined.

Rubin et al. (1962) undertook a study of the relationship between emotional states and esophageal motor function. It involved recording esophageal motility, using transducer techniques during unstructured psychiatric interviews. A significant relationship between affectively charged material and nonpropulsive activity in the esophagus was consistently found in two of five subjects and during some interviews in other subjects.

Emotional states may influence esophageal motility in two ways: first, anxiety may induce an *overall* tendency toward nonpropulsive activity; second, particular affective states might organize such activity selectively. In one interview subject there was a high level of anxiety, and 67 percent of the total activity was nonpropulsive; *depressed* affects also seemed strongly related to individual periods of such activity.

CASE 44

CHIEF PRESENTING SYMPTOM	Trouble with throat and stomach
SENSORIMOTOR CONFIGURATIONS	Sensory configurations

Pain, interoceptive

Associated with concern about ability to handle adult responsibilities, and with hostile feelings of being drained by others, especially his parents

Motor configurations

Being stuck, dislodging

Related symbolically to stress, past and present, particularly wife's recent difficult pregnancy, and need to provide for his mother

SOMATIC IDENTIFICATION

Father Trouble passing water, jumped from window to death two years ago

Wife Difficult delivery with instruments (Direct)

SENSITIZED ORGAN SYSTEM
Throat
Gastrointestinal tract

STRESS (*surface meaning*)
Earlier, related to combat duty overseas
Several years ago, father's death by suicide
Recently, financial problems and need to limit size of family

STRESS (*dynamic significance*)
Activation of concern about adequacy as a man and frustration of passive-dependent needs, especially after birth of child

DEFENSES
Rationalization
Attempts to be the "supplier"

AFFECTS	*Intensity*	*Pathway of expression*
Anxiety	+++	Some ideational and affective, somatic equivalents
Depression	++	Ideational, some affective, some somatization
Hostility	++	Some ideational, affective, and somatization

OTHER FACTORS Long-standing concern about manliness with underlying passive-feminine tendencies

HOMEOSTATIC SHIFT(S) Utilization of multiple pathways of psychophysical discharge: ideationally, affectively, behaviorally, and somatically

DIAGNOSIS Anxiety state, chronic, untreated, unchanged

case 45

Back Pain in an Accident-prone Patient

CHIEF PRESENTING SYMPTOM

Pain in the back.

BASIC ANAMNESTIC EXCERPTS

The patient begins by recounting an episode occurring six weeks before admission: "I picked up this bucket of concrete, and when I threw it on my shoulder, something gave in here. The pain shot down into my toes. Then it went away, but started coming back in about two weeks. I went to see this mill doctor, and he said it's probably a sore muscle. Went to clinic and they sent me here. The doctor said it's a disc that's painful all the time. The doctor told me I'll be transferred to orthopedics and they'll put a cast on it or something. You feel as if you're not stepping on solid ground. It's pins and needles. You're not sure of where you step." (Pause)

The patient briefly describes his work and then refers to other accidents: "I've always done heavy labor. I got this here wrist (right) crushed by a steel freight car. There was a big piece of slag on top of it. We grabbed the slag, but the other fellow lost his grip on it, so it rolled over, pinned me against the side of the car. Didn't bother me. Six years ago I was crushed between a freight car and trailer truck. I was hospitalized a year. There were no aftereffects, not a pain or ache. It was my biggest accident. Before that there was another in the service. Refueling a B-29. There was a big explosion that knocked me off my feet; jarred me up.

"I got a broken arm when I was nine. Then when I was fourteen, I was carrying this case, and I dropped it on the same arm (right). Broke it right at the elbow, while playing piggyback. The fellow I was on ran toward a tree, lost his balance. It seemed like the bones were cracking. I was crying, screaming awful. This muscle here was way out. Police surgeon came along in an ambulance. He grabbed the arm, pushed the muscle down. Then a cast was put on. Afterwards the arm seemed OK. At home they were kind of mad about it. Mother was crying—I remember. That's about the only serious accident I ever had as a kid. . . . A few years later a case dropped on me. This guy gave me 2 dollars to load his truck. I was thirteen. I slipped in oil. This big case hit me square. The muscle was sore for a long time afterwards.

"I didn't have to work. My father worked for the railroad. But there wasn't much money there. My father's a big man. Mother's quite large, too. She is heavyset, 5 feet, 9 inches, always healthy. Father's retired. He used to be 6 feet, 2 inches—now he's 5 feet, 10 inches. I don't know why. Unless he's growing older and starting to stoop over a bit. I'm the one that gets sick or in trouble the most, I guess; I mean injured. I live now with father and mother and two brothers. My sister got married six years ago. So I turned around and got engaged two months ago. It's about time, isn't it? I had been going out with the girl two years, so I had to decide about settling down." (Lack of enthusiasm and depressed look.)

"I'd rather do a day's work than sit around in the hospital. But there are some people who have ailments and keep putting them off, and all the time things get more aggravated. Just like people I know. They doctor the toothache with all kinds of junk. If you've got a bad tooth, there's one solution—pull it out. I had one. Had it pulled out (noise). The reason I don't care about my teeth is that when I got hit in the chest by the freight train, it loosened every tooth in my head. This doctor who was setting my jaw wired all my teeth together. The day the dentist took the wires off, he wore rubber gloves. All of a sudden he said, 'Let go of my finger.' I didn't know it, but I had a bite on his finger."

The patient describes his attitude toward all the accidents he has been involved in: "Might as well smile, it's no good to take them any other way. I'm very cautious now. But the saying goes that cautious people get injured. The careful drivers get into more accidents than the normal drivers would. It doesn't pay to be too cautious, just careful. Then there are others that take crazy chances."

PSYCHODYNAMIC IMPRESSIONS

Mobility or immobility are frequently referred to in one form or another in the associative connections. There are also references to being off balance for a while. A situational stress exists involving a recent decision to become engaged, but with much misgiving on the patient's part. Again this is linked with a reference to not being sure of his step, not being on solid ground. Pain is linked with a number of accidents in which the patient has been involved, a very serious one occurring six years ago. Accident-prone tendencies can be noted in the recollections of his early life.

There appears to be a defensive protest about his current enforced passivity, and in particular about people who delay finding out about their ailments. Secretly, he is worried about the significance of his symptoms, although he tries to give the impression that his attitude toward accidents and their sequelae is a fatalistic one. However, there are also indications that he is becoming more cautious in his activities. This indicates a shift away from what seems to have been a counterphobic position which had served to deny a long-standing, underlying timidity and passivity.

PHYSICAL HISTORY

The patient was admitted because of pain in the right leg and hip lasting five weeks. Six weeks ago patient had acute onset of severe sharp pain in the right hip, radiating down the back of the leg to the inside of the foot and big toe. The pain occurred while he was lifting a pail of concrete. The pain subsided in about 15 minutes, and one week later a similar aching pain set in and has been constantly present since. The pain was aggravated by walking, standing, and coughing; some paresthesias and numbness have been present. Past history negative, except for severe crushing injury six years ago, causing multiple fractures and ruptured diaphragm, with full recovery. System review negative except for chronic hoarseness since childhood; the symptom has been investigated numerous times, without any etiology being established.

PHYSICAL EXAMINATION

Vital signs: normal. There was a systolic murmur at the aortic and pulmonic areas, soft Grade I changing in intensity with respiration and shifting position, considered to be functional. Spine: no bony tenderness. Extremities: straight leg raising test: right 30°, left 85°. Neurological examination reveals hypesthesia of right lateral thigh and lower leg. Otherwise, remainder of physical examination within normal limits.

LABORATORY DATA

Hemograms: normal. Urinalysis: negative. Serology: negative.

ROENTGENOGRAMS

Chest: negative except for some calcifications in the left coracoclavicular ligament. Lumbosacral spine: normal.

HOSPITAL COURSE

The patient had been on bed boards and was seen by the orthopedic consultants who concurred in the diagnosis of ruptured nucleus pulposus and asked that he be transferred to their service. On transfer, the patient showed limitation of flexion of the spine and limitation of straight leg raising on the right; there was also definite hypesthesia over right lateral thigh and lower extremity. A myelogram disclosed a filling defect at L-4 and L-5 on the right. Pain and spasm gradually subsided. The patient was fitted for a chair-type back brace, instructed in a program of back exercises, and discharged.

DISCHARGE DIAGNOSIS

Herniation, lumbar intervertebral discs, L-4, 5, treated, improved.

COMMENT

In this case, counterphobic tendencies, together with superego pressures which produce considerable guilt and an associated need to hurt himself, force the patient to act in such a way that he becomes involved in accidents which he might otherwise have avoided. The musculoskeletal system has been the principal target organ. His most recent accident, which led to the ruptured discs, occurred shortly after the patient decided to get married, a prospect which he faced with considerable ambivalence and which activated doubts about his masculinity.

CASE 45

CHIEF PRESENTING SYMPTOM	Pain the back
SENSORIMOTOR CONFIGURATIONS	Sensory configurations

Pain

Related to many accidents, and associated with a secret concern over the significance of his symptoms and possible loss of stature, as happened to his father

Motor configurations

Mobility

Expressed in terms of not being sure of his step, especially in connection with recent decision to become engaged, and also in associations of biting and teeth pulling which have symbolic hostile implications

SOMATIC IDENTIFICATION	Father Stooping over, back bent (Direct)
SENSITIZED ORGAN SYSTEM	Musculoskeletal system: lower extremity

STRESS (*surface meaning*)	Accidental injury; setting of engagement date
STRESS (*dynamic significance*)	Approaching test of manliness
DEFENSES	Fatalistic outlook Counterphobic tendencies

AFFECTS	Intensity	Pathway of expression
Anxiety	+	Some ideational
Depression	++	Some ideational, somatization
Hostility	+++	Behavioral (accident-prone), some ideational, somatization

OTHER FACTORS	Accident-prone tendencies Oral aspect emphasized
HOMEOSTATIC SHIFT(S)	Internalized aggression leading to increasing somatization response
DIAGNOSIS	Herniation lumbar intervertebral discs L-4, 5, treated, improved

CLINICAL EXCERPTS FROM ANOTHER CASE

Another patient in his forties, morally strict, who was really a very angry person, but presented generally a pleasant facade, had symptoms from an intervertebral disc. These also followed an accident and persisted over many years with occasional exacerbations. Except for these episodes, the patient's physical condition was relatively stabilized. Following the death of his father, toward whom he had long felt competitively hostile, the patient developed gastrointestinal symptoms, and the diagnosis of ulcer was confirmed shortly thereafter. On a conservative medical regimen, the ulcer symptoms subsided, but then his back and leg symptoms became unbearably severe because of too much golf, which he had been told to avoid. Operative intervention was advised, and a fusion operation was done. Recovery was slow and was complicated by persisting painful muscle spasms. The father had been ill with a wasting carcinoma of the stomach. In the course of his illness, he had developed confusional episodes and required hospitalization in a mental institution; while there, he had fallen out of bed, sustaining severe back injuries. The patient's somatic identification with his father was quite clear. His depression, complicated by much guilt and ambivalence, was masked as far as emotional manifestations were concerned. The activation of physical dysfunction and slowness of recovery appeared to be related to this psychological state.

case 46

Abdominal Cramps Associated with Marital Crisis

CHIEF PRESENTING SYMPTOM

Cramps.

BASIC ANAMNESTIC EXCERPTS

"On Tuesday night I started to get these cramps. Every time I'd go to sleep, I'd wake up and have to go to the bathroom. It started to get worse. Thursday night I called the doctor. He said it might be appendix, and said I should go to a hospital. Now my stomach feels bloated all the time. The place that's normally hollow—my chest—is bigger than my stomach. When I stand up, the swelling seems to drop down.

"It's a gnawing kind of pain most of the time. Then all of a sudden it would get sharp. I had a sharp pain right down to my left testicle. Right now it's not sharp, just a little gnawing."

References to cramps in the past are next elicited: "I've had heat cramps, when I was working in submarines, if I didn't take salt pills. Your stomach seems to contract. You drink a lot of water. But this was a different sort of thing. It doubles you right up. I had diarrhea from ptomaine poisoning when I was in military service. They traced it back to spaghetti in a pot. I was in the infirmary with the grippe; there was an epidemic of it. We ate the spaghetti from that pot, and the whole ward came down with it—ptomaine poisoning. I had greenish movements which smelled awful, and I ran a fever (pause).

"I've had pain in my abdomen on and off. They start at the belly button and work down. The right testicle feels under a strain, it's awful painful. It's been happening maybe once a week, maybe twice—for about six months. But my appetite has been tremendous. I've been working in a hotel and eating all the time. I'm a waiter there.

"Actually, carpentry is my trade. I quit as a waiter before I went on vacation because I wanted to get back to carpentry. Before that I was in

366

California, working as a riveter. Then I've been in New London doing submarine work—as an electrician. There isn't anything I haven't tried. I don't stay in one place too long.

"I've had my fill of hospitals, have had four operations—fascia from my leg to my shoulder because of an injury 11 years ago. I was playing football on a muddy field, when this fellow kicked me on the shoulder and dislocated my collarbone. So they sent me to the hospital and wired it with ordinary shoulder wire. Then they sent me back to duty. I fell out of the back of a truck. It had suddenly started up, and I was sweeping out the back. I again landed on my shoulder. This time they took fascia out of my leg and put it there. Then the muscles of the leg didn't grow back right, so they had to open that up and stitch it. That didn't do any good. When I came back from overseas, I went into the hospital again, so they took fascia out of this leg and grafted it on the other one. It isn't too bad now. Now it gets weak only once in a while when I run or climb a ladder or something."

The patient now turns to his past health: "I had asthma from age 12 until 16, when I went to a work camp. I didn't seem to have much trouble with it until I hit Africa, and then I couldn't breathe because of the dry heat. That's why they sent me back to the States. I couldn't breathe. I had this glass atomizer for eight years. When I was going on vacation I was rinsing it out, and this glass part broke off. Since I get a pension on the asthma, I wondered if I could buy a new one at a deduction. The pension is also for this leg and shoulder. When I went to the work camp, I got pneumonia, and again later when I first entered the service. Outside of these things, I would consider myself healthy today if the pains would only stay away. I would like to go back to the Cape. I start sunning myself on the beaches early in April; I go to this place which is partitioned off. They allow only men there and they can lie around naked, except for a fig leaf. I can't see why this should attack me all of a sudden."

The patient next brings up his marital troubles: "Work got scarce, and I came down to this area. My wife wouldn't come with me. She wouldn't leave her mother. But work was scarce in Boston, so I went out to California. I sent for my wife out there, but she wouldn't come. If she's that involved with her family, she doesn't mean anything to me. So the next thing I get is a letter that she's going to start divorce proceedings. We had one child when we were first married, but it lived only five days and then it died. We tried eight years to have another—no soap. They examined her and found nothing wrong with her. I was never examined, so I don't know if it was me. There was only one child like I told you. It was a premature baby, seven months old. It had an obstruction of the throat. Since then my wife hasn't been pregnant. I wanted to get examined, but I couldn't get up enough courage to go. I wanted to adopt some children but she didn't. She wanted her own. She has another man. I knew even when I'd been living with her that there was somebody she liked better than me. My mother-in-law was always in my house, no matter what time of day I came home, no matter what job I had. She was always wanting to know all our business. Anyway, I'm going with a very nice girl myself now. I met her three months ago. She was married and divorced. She's got a little baby girl, and we get along fine. I'll get married as soon as the divorce comes through."

Further details about the patient's own family are elicited: "I'm an only child. My mother is dead. I told the other doctor that my father was dead, but actually he left my mother when I was five years old. Did I tell you mother was dead? I'm sorry. She isn't. She's 63 and she's a nurse. After her divorce from my father, she didn't remarry, but I didn't live with her. I lived with an aunt because mother had to go out to work. My father never contributed to my support. My aunt had a son of her own. He died of appendicitis when he was 21. He had complications—peritonitis, you know. He was already dead when I came to live with my aunt. I occasionally see my father every once in a while—just a friendly visit. Mother is a very strong person. When she first came to this country, she had a goiter taken out of her neck. When I was sixteen years old, they took out an eight-pound tumor together with all her ovaries. She also had an accident once. She fell while she was in my house, broke her kneecap which split, and it had to be wired together. Once she broke both her wrists slipping on ice, and also split her head open. She's 63 years old now and as healthy as can be. I remember when they took out all her organs, the night of the big hurricane. I went to the work camp the next day after her operation. Father has no toes. He had gangrene there. He has to go to the hospital and get some dead bone scraped off every so often."

Returning to his current symptoms: "A good laxative would wash everything out. I remember my mother used to do that to me, but today you're appendix-conscious and afraid to take a laxative for fear it's the wrong thing to do."

PSYCHODYNAMIC IMPRESSIONS

The patient is an only child. His parents were always quarreling, and the father left the family when the patient was five years old. Shortly thereafter, his mother went to work, leaving the patient in the care of an elderly aunt. As a child he felt lonely, isolated, had no stable masculine figure to identify with, and deeply resented having been abandoned. Early in his life there were frequent respiratory difficulties, often aggravated by heat. He was subject to frequent cramps and had trouble with his bowels;

there have been numerous hospitalizations and at least four operations, so that a generalized concern about body integrity has become well established in him. This, in turn, is connected with feelings of inferiority and pre-occupation with lack of virility. He has noted an intermittent restlessness which is associated with looking for "something" he can't seem to find (parental love). His considerable roaming and travelling has also repre-sented a reaction to being cooped up—a defense against repressed passive longings which threaten to immobilize him.

His image of his mother is that of a strong-willed, selfish person who survives illnesses, operations, and accidents. There are, however, associative connections which suggest the patient has strong somatic identification with the physical defects in her as well as in his father, without reassurance of eventual full recovery.

The patient has had severe problems in his own marital adjustment. Recently, he has been exposed to acute stress in this regard. His wife prefers another man, and is suing the patient for divorce. His mother-in-law is pictured as aiding and abetting his wife. The patient's hostility toward both has mounted unbearably. He has attempted to restore some measure of self-confidence and has looked for a supportive figure in a divorcée who already has a child and is apparently not interested in having more, thus being relatively nonthreatening to the patient's shaky estimation of his masculinity.

In the present emotional crisis, the sensitized gastrointestinal system has been a target organ as the patient reacts to the overhanging threat of separation and loss, but he is already trying a relationship with a sub-stitute object.

PHYSICAL HISTORY

The patient was admitted because of severe nausea, vomiting, and diarrhea of three days' duration. He had felt well until the evening three days prior to admission when he developed a sudden urge to defecate, associated with lower abdominal cramping pain. Thereafter, he had con-tinued to have watery diarrhea, with six to seven movements daily, con-taining no blood or pus, cramping lower abdominal pains which waxed and waned, leaving a dull ache between the acute periods, and nausea with occasional vomiting. After the onset, he was able to take only some liquids by mouth. He had no chills, fever, or jaundice. He had been at a beach resort with friends two days before the onset of his symptoms and ate only the foods eaten by his friends. No one else had similar symptoms. For some months the patient has had occasional bouts of stomach upset with nausea, vomiting, and occasional heartburn.

PHYSICAL EXAMINATION

Temperature 100°F. Pulse 110. Blood pressure 124/80. Patient is a well-developed, well-nourished male who complained occasionally of abdominal pain and appeared moderately ill. He was oriented and cooperative. There was a serous nasal discharge and deviation of the septum to the left. Heart and lungs were negative. He complained of some tenderness on percussion over the left flank and on palpation in both lower quadrants. There was no spasm or rebound tenderness. Peristalsis was diminished but of normal character. The patient complained of severe tenderness of the anus which prevented adequate examination of the rectum on admission. Multiple operative scars of the left shoulder and both thighs were observed.

LABORATORY DATA

Hemoglobin 15.5 g. White blood cell count 22,700 with 35 segmented cells, 48 band cells, 10 lymphocytes, 1 basophile and 6 monocytes; normal platelets. Hematocrit 49 percent. Urine: rare white blood cells per high power field. Stool guaiacs: negative. Serology: negative. Repeat white blood cell count on the day prior to discharge 10,350.

ROENTGENOGRAMS

Chest: some mild accentuation of trunk markings in the lower portions of both lung fields, considered to be within normal limits for the patient; no evidence of emphysema.

HOSPITAL COURSE

The patient was placed on bed rest with bathroom privileges, liquid diet as tolerated, and given atropine grain 1/150 on admission, every 4 hours, p.r.n. for abdominal pains, and an intravenous injection of 1,000 ml of 5 percent glucose in saline, followed by 1,000 ml of normal saline. On the second hospital day, he was put on a soft diet as tolerated. He felt better following the intravenous feedings, and no antibiotics were started. He was soon asymptomatic and was discharged five days after admission.

DISCHARGE DIAGNOSIS

Acute gastroenteritis, cause unknown, improved.

COMMENT

The patient's physical illness occurred against a background of increasing environmental stress. For some months before the onset of the acute symptoms, there had already been evidence that the gastrointestinal tract was reflecting the patient's growing tensions, with manifestations of increasing dysfunction. What then followed in that physical system might have been considerably influenced by a further sharp increase in stress due to a divorce-and-remarriage crisis which confronted the patient. The resultant escalating dysfunction in the target organ (gastrointestinal) could then have led to local tissue changes favorable to an invasion and proliferation of microorganisms, whether bacteria or viruses already present or introduced by exposure from outside contacts.

CASE 46

CHIEF PRESENTING SYMPTOM	Cramps
SENSORIMOTOR CONFIGURATIONS	Sensory configurations

Pain, interoceptive
Associated with childhood loneliness; no stable masculine figure for identification; hostility at being abandoned by parents and, more recently, by wife; frequent respiratory and gastrointestinal illness, and various operations

Motor configurations

Roaming
Linked with search for loving parental figure, as well as with reaction against passive and homosexual trends

SOMATIC IDENTIFICATION	Mother	Goiter operation, many years ago; abdominal tumor and ovaries removed, 15 years ago (Direct—Constitutional)
	Cousin	Death due to appendicitis and peritonitis many years ago (Direct)
SENSITIZED ORGAN SYSTEM		Gastrointestinal system
STRESS (*surface meaning*)		Chronic and recently acute exacerbation of marital difficulties
STRESS (*dynamic significance*)		Concern about virility, competitive with other males; marked hostility to deserting and castrating parental figures
DEFENSES		Roaming, travelling

AFFECTS	Intensity	Pathway of expression
Anxiety	++	Some ideational and affective
Depression	++	Somatization
Hostility	++	Some ideational and affective, somatization
OTHER FACTORS		Barely masked homosexuality with exhibitionistic and voyeuristic tendencies Abandoned by father at early age and then neglected by mother Only child
HOMEOSTATIC SHIFT(s)		Acutely mobilized hostility insufficiently contained by nonsomatic defenses, with resultant sharp impact on target organ
DIAGNOSIS		Acute gastroenteritis, cause unknown, treated, improved

CLINICAL MATERIAL FROM ANOTHER CASE

Another patient, a salesman aged 35, had an episode of what was diagnosed as mild coronary insufficiency after a period of cumulative external stress. During this interval, he had been experiencing annoying but not severe chest pain, usually in the precordial region. Because of sexual dissatisfaction with his wife whom he considered to be frigid, he had become increasingly preoccupied with sexual fantasies of a sadomasochistic nature, in which he enacted the role of a rapist. He was greatly concerned that he would lose control of his impulses, and became anxious and unable to work as effectively as before. This inefficiency, in turn, led the patient's employer to question whether he should continue at his particular job. This enraged the patient, but he "kept the lid" on his feelings. Then he had the episode of severe precordial pain, with the physical diagnosis noted above. Subsequently, he was carefully checked over a period of six months and considered to be fully recovered from his physical illness, but the symptom of chest pain, now less severe, more diffuse, and shifting in location, continued. He was advised to seek psychotherapeutic help. He began treatment, and it soon became apparent that the pain was more related at this time to spasm of chest musculature than to coronary disease. There was a general stiffness in his posture, and the particular muscle spasms appeared to be connected with a strong need for control over unacceptable sexual and aggressive impulses.

The patient was an only child, and his father and mother had often quarreled. There were many violent scenes that he remembered from childhood, and he early got the impression that this was somehow connected with his parents' sexual life. When the patient was 15, his father died suddenly following one of his "fits of passion." According to the patient, death was due to a heart attack.

As the psychotherapy continued and the patient was able to express his feelings to some extent, the chief physical symptom of chest pain lessened in intensity and became minimal. At this point certain reality factors made it necessary for the treatment to be interrupted. A period of six months elapsed before the patient was next heard from again. He had moved to another city, was free of physical symptoms, but had developed a distressing phobic reaction. He found it difficult to leave familiar surroundings and especially to be out driving on the road because of the fear that something unexpected and terrible might happen to him then; he would be overwhelmed with anxiety, lose control of his faculties, and be unable to function. The basic emotional problems which had first been defended against by a somatization process were now eliciting a new and different defensive response—that of a developing phobic reaction.

PART THREE

Discussion

Results

The preceding 46 cases have been presented in the order in which they were originally admitted. The 46 admissions include one readmission, thus comprising 45 different patients, of whom one was mute with no psy-

TABLE 1

PHYSICAL ILLNESS	NONPHYSICAL ILLNESS	MIXED
Case Number	Case Number	Case Number
2	1	3
5	12	4
8	13	6
9	17	7
10	19	27
11	22	35 †
14	24	
15	28	
16	30	
18	33	
20	34	
21	36	
23	37	
25	39	
26	41	
29	43	
31	44	
32		
38		
40		
42		
45		
46		
TOTAL = 23 *	TOTAL = 17	TOTAL = 6

* Actually 22, since insufficient data were available in one case. No. 15.
† No. 35 is readmission of No. 28.

chological data available. Each presentation has included a comment on clinical and theoretical psychodynamic points relevant to the particular illness under consideration, with pertinent references to the work of others. A more systematic, detailed, and comprehensive consideration of the influence of psychological factors on physical dysfunction will now be undertaken, using the psychological data from all the cases. Although a wide variety of sicknesses is involved, the cases have been divided into two principal categories: those with a diagnosis of physical disease, and those with a diagnosis of psychological illness. A third and smaller group is made up of cases in which both kinds of diagnoses have been established (see Table 1). The raw psychological data in every case have been explored for the following variables: (1) overt and more subtle indicators of psychological stress, (2) shifts in psychological equilibrium; (3) affective responses; (4) psychological mechanisms of defense; (5) processes of somatic identification and related psychological sensitization or conditioning of organ systems; (6) recurrent sensorimotor patterns; (7) other factors. The general findings for each variable are given in the text, and tables follow, listing the results specifically for each case. There is a further discussion of each variable singly, and then a consideration of what combinations of these variables might be associated with the physical symptoms of organic disease as compared with those found in emotional illness. Next, there is an examination of what possible combinations of these variables might be used as predictive factors and in further psychological or psychophysical research on organic disease, with emphasis on their role in the development, exacerbation, and remission of such illness. Finally, the usefulness of these variables for application in clinical practice is discussed. References to the literature are included wherever pertinent.

STRESS

In this study, when the data were examined from the superficial and descriptive standpoint, multiple stresses were found in 30 of the 45 cases (67 percent) and single stresses in the other 15 (33 percent), so that stress factors were present in all the cases. Work problems had the highest incidence, 22 cases (49 percent); illness or death of a relative were present in 20 cases (44 percent); financial difficulties in 10 (22 percent); in smaller percentages were marital difficulties (including sexual incompatibility, prospective marriage, problems with relatives or in-laws, and recent or expected births), school maladjustment, disturbed children, injury, robbery, and previous military adjustment. In every case, the development of physical symptoms and of physical or mental disease was also a stressful situation of varying degree. Thus secondary stress factors inevitably appeared and added to the already existing tension. Each patient reacted to this complex of stresses in a highly individualized way.

Only one type of stress, when examined further, but still from a superficial standpoint, showed a 100 percent correlation with the occurrence of organic disease. This was sickness or death of the patient's mother, an event which occurred in 7 cases.

Psychological stress becomes more meaningful when its dynamic significance can be established (see Table 2). In every case in this series, the patient had sustained some loss or was faced with threat of such a loss. Most often this involved a person (object) who had always been emotionally important to the patient, or one who had taken the place of the originally significant figure. However, there was also loss of money, prestige, reputation, or other external factors which had served to maintain the individual's self-esteem. These also included alcohol and various drugs, or obsessive hobbies—"sources of supply"—which had become unavailable for one reason or another. Loss of part of the body through injury, mutilation, or operation, and loss of normal physical functions through illness were other forms of this basic stress. In the latter instance, the stress could at times be designated as secondary.

SHIFTS IN PSYCHOLOGICAL EQUILIBRIUM

Homeostatic shifts occurred in all cases in this series (see Table 3). A large number were in one basic direction; others went in several directions or included reversals. Of 22 cases of physical illness, 14 (64 percent) had markedly insufficient psychological defenses of the more differentiated kind, with subsequent regressive shift to physical-systems involvement and marked somatization response. Eight (36 percent) had moderately insufficient secondary-process defenses, with subsequent shift to moderate somatization reaction. In the 17 cases of nonphysical illness, the more differentiated defenses were moderately insufficient in only 2 patients (12 percent), and only slightly insufficient in 15 patients (88 percent). The regressive shift in all 17 cases included a conversion reaction. In two cases of physical sickness (Case 6 and Case 27), as the disease manifestations lessened, there was a shift to severe mental illness, but after several weeks a reverse shift occurred, with recovery from the psychotic episode, while the physical condition continued to improve. In one instance (Case 8), both secondary-process defenses and conversion reaction proved insufficient to maintain equilibrium under stress; this was followed by involvement of the respiratory tract in a somatization response. In another case (Case 25), the somatization response was modified by surgical intervention. In Case 42, medication blocked seizures, but with stress there was a shift in somatization site to the biliary system. In Case 3, coping responses in the form of

TABLE 2. STRESS (DYNAMIC SIGNIFICANCE)

+ = increase
− = decrease

PHYSICAL ILLNESS	NONPHYSICAL ILLNESS	MIXED
Case Number	Case Number	Case Number
2 + dependency; + competitive and sexualized father relationship	1 + dependency; + castration fear	3 anticipated loss of mother
5 critical object losses; + dependency	12 + competition with father figure; + castration fear	4 + dependency; less + castration fear
8 + insecurity; + castration fear	13 + castration fear	6 + dependency; threat to body integrity
9 + dependency; + helpless feelings	17 anticipated loss; + dependency	7 + dependency; + inferiority feelings
10 critical losses; + dependency	19 + inadequacy feelings; less + dependency	27 + feelings of being dominated; + inferiority feelings
11 + dependency; + competition with authority	22 + inferiority feelings	* 35 + passive trends; + feminine identifications
14 + dependency; + competition with parental figures	24 + dependency; + addictive tendency	
16 threat of critical loss; + dependency	28 + passive–feminine tendencies; threat of loss of attention	
18 threat of critical loss; + dependency	30 + inferiority feelings	
20 + dependency; + inadequacy feelings	33 + inadequacy feelings; + dependency	
21 + dependency; threat to security; + competition with parental figure	34 + inadequacy feelings	
23 + helplessness; + concern about manliness	36 + inadequacy feelings	
25 + dependency; + inadequacy feelings	37 + concern over body integrity; + passivity	
26 threat of critical loss; + dependency	39 + passive–feminine tendency	
29 threat of critical loss; + dependency; + inferiority feelings	41 + inferiority feelings; + recurrent feelings of loss	
31 + dependency; + inadequacy feelings	43 + inferiority feelings; + dependency	
32 threat of critical loss	44 + inadequacy feelings; + dependency	
38 + dependency		
40 + dependency (sibling rivalry), + inadequacy feelings		
42 passive–dependency		
45 + inadequacy feelings		
46 concern about manliness; + competitiveness; + dependency		

* Readmission of No. 28.

TABLE 3. HOMEOSTATIC SHIFTS

R = Regression
SD = More Differentiated Psychological Defenses
S = Somatization Response
C = Conversion Response

+ Mild
++ Moderate } Intensity
+++ Marked

PHYSICAL ILLNESS

Case Number

2 SD: +++ insufficient; R → +++ S
5 SD: +++ insufficient; R → +++ S
8 SD & C (gastrointestinal) : ++ insufficient; R → +++ (respiratory)
9 SD: +++ insufficient; R → +++ S
10 SD: ++ insufficient; R → ++ S
11 SD: +++ insufficient; R → +++ S
14 SD: +++ insufficient; R → +++ S
16 SD: ++ insufficient; R → ++ S
18 SD: +++ insufficient; R → +++ S
20 SD: ++ insufficient; R → ++ S
21 SD: ++ insufficient; R → ++ S → SD
23 SD: +++ insufficient; R → +++ S (fixed)
25 SD: +++ insufficient; R → +++ S → + S (aftersurgery)
26 SD: ++ insufficient; R → +++ S → R → psychosis → ++ S → R → psychosis → ++ S
29 SD: +++ insufficient; R → +++ S
31 SD: +++ insufficient; R → +++ S
32 SD: ++ insufficient; R → +++ S → + S
38 SD: +++ insufficient; R → +++ S
40 SD: +++ insufficient; R → +++ S
42 SD: ++ insufficient; R → +++ S (brain) → +++ (biliary system)
45 SD: ++ insufficient; R → ++ S
46 SD: ++ insufficient; R → ++ S

TOTAL = 22

NONPHYSICAL ILLNESS

Case Number

1 SD: + insufficient; R → + C
12 SD: + insufficient; R → + C (multiple areas)
13 SD: + insufficient; R → ++ C
17 SD: + insufficient; R → ++ C
19 SD: + insufficient; R → ++ C
22 SD: ++ insufficient; R → ++ C
24 SD: ++ insufficient; R → ++ C
28 SD: ++ insufficient; R → ++ C
30 SD: ++ insufficient; R → ++ C
33 SD: ++ insufficient; R → ++ C
34 SD: ++ insufficient; R → ++ C
36 SD: ++ insufficient; R → ++ C → + C
37 SD: ++ insufficient; R → ++ C
39 SD: ++ insufficient; R → ++ C
41 SD: + insufficient; R → ++ C
43 SD: + insufficient; R → ++ C
44 SD: + insufficient; R → ++ C

TOTAL = 17

MIXED

Case Number

3 SD: + insufficient; R → + C (anus) and ++ S (mouth)
4 SD: ++ insufficient; R → ++ S
6 SD: +++ insufficient; R → +++ S → R → Psychosis → ++ S
7 SD: + insufficient; R → + S
27 SD: +++ insufficient; R → +++ S → Psychosis → ++ S
*35 SD: ++ insufficient; R → ++ S (another organ system)

TOTAL = 6

* Readmission of No. 28.

381

conversion symptoms (anus) were insufficient and in the presence of a nutritional deficiency, another target area, the mouth, became involved in a somatization reaction. In Case 35 (readmission of Case 28), a further shift under stress, away from psychological systems, involved the immunologic equilibrium and the skin.

AFFECTIVE RESPONSES

In this study, the affects of anxiety, depression, and hostility were considered. They were graded in three categories of intensity: mild (+), moderate (++), and marked (+++). Their pathways of expression were listed as affective, ideational, behavioral, and somatic. It should be noted that the anamnestic material was examined for the relevant data as manifested in patterns, which were considered to exist prior to the onset or exacerbation of the physical symptoms which led to hospitalization. As far as possible, affective reactions to the illness itself were separated out as secondary responses and not included in the tabulation. Marked anxiety was found to have preexisted in 11 out of 17 (65 percent) cases of non-physical illness and in only 4 out of 22 (18 percent) cases having a diagnosis of organic disease. Marked hostility appeared to preexist in 19 out of 22 (86 percent) cases of physical disease, but in only 1 out of 17 (6 percent) of nonphysical illness. Severe depressive trends were noted as preexisting in 14 out of 22 (64 percent) cases of physical disease, but in only 1 out of 17 (6 percent) of nonphysical illness (see Tables 4, 5, 6).

TABLE 4. ANXIETY +++

PHYSICAL ILLNESS Case Number	NONPHYSICAL ILLNESS Case Number	MIXED Case Number
26	1	4
29	12	6
31	13	7
40	22	27
	33	* 35
	34	
	37	
	39	
	41	
	43	
	44	
TOTAL = 4/22	TOTAL = 11/17	TOTAL = 5/6

* Readmission of No. 28.

TABLE 5. HOSTILITY +++

PHYSICAL ILLNESS	NONPHYSICAL ILLNESS	MIXED
Case Number	Case Number	Case Number
2	41	4
5		6
8		27
9		
11		
14		
16		
18		
20		
21		
23		
25		
26		
31		
32		
38		
40		
42		
45		
TOTAL = 19/22	TOTAL = 1/17	TOTAL = 3/6

TABLE 6. DEPRESSION +++

PHYSICAL ILLNESS	NONPHYSICAL ILLNESS	MIXED
Case Number	Case Number	Case Number
2	41	4
5		6
11		27
14		
16		
18		
20		
21		
26		
31		
32		
38		
40		
42		
TOTAL = 14/22	TOTAL = 1/17	TOTAL = 3/6

The pathways of expression for the affects are designated as affective, behavioral, ideational, or somatic. It has been suggested (Fenichel, 1945) that all affects can be replaced at times by equivalents of somatic sensation. Classically, such affect equivalents have been noted usually only in reference to anxiety. In the text below, the term "somatic representations" refers to physical expressions of anxiety, hostility, and depression, directly linked to symptoms and sensorimotor configurations in the associative anamnesis, but without the individual's being aware of their affective significance. An inferred somatic pathway is designated when its presence is only indirectly indicated by the anamnestic material.

TABLE 7. ANXIETY—PATHWAY OF EXPRESSION

A = Affective
B = Behavioral
I = Ideational
S = Somatic

PHYSICAL ILLNESS		NONPHYSICAL ILLNESS		MIXED	
Case Number		Case Number		Case Number	
2	I	1	S, I, A	3	S, I, A
5	I, B	12	S, I	4	I > A, S
8	I, A	13	S, I, A	6	S
9	I > S, A	17	S, I	7	S, A
10	S, I	19	S, I, A	27	I
11	I, A	22	S, I, A	* 35	I, A > S
14	S, I	24	I > S, A		
16	I	28	I, A > S		
18	S, I	30	S, I, A		
20	S, I	33	S, I, A		
21	S, I	34	S, I, A		
23	I, S, A	36	S, I		
25	I, A	37	S, I, A		
26	I, A > S	39	S, I		
29	S, I, BA	41	S, I, A		
31	S, I	43	S, I, A		
31	I	44	S, I, A		
38	S, I				
40	I, A				
42	I, A				
45	I				
46	I, A				

TOTAL = 22	TOTAL = 17	TOTAL = 6
Total S with others = 11	Total S with others = 17	Total S with others = 5
Total A, B, I	Total A, B, I	Total A, B, I
without S = 11	without S = 0	without others = 1

* Readmission of No. 28.

TABLE 8. HOSTILITY—PATHWAY OF EXPRESSION

A = Affective
B = Behavioral
I = Ideational
S = Somatic
(S) = Somatic pathway inferred

PHYSICAL ILLNESS	NONPHYSICAL ILLNESS	MIXED
Case Number	Case Number	Case Number
2 S > I	1 A, I, S	3 I
5 (S) > I	12 S > I	4 S > I, A
8 S > A	13 S	6 I > A
9 S > I, A	17 I, A > S	7 I, A
10 S > I	19 I, A	27 I, B
11 (S) > I, A	22 I, A	† 35 A, I
14 S > I	24 B, A	
16 S, I	28 I, A > S	
18 (S), I	30 A > I	
20 S, I, A	33 A, B	
21 (S), I, A	34 I, A	
23 S, I, A	36 B > S	
25 (S), I	37 I, A	
26 (S), I	39 I, (S)	
29 S, A, I	41 A, I	
31 (S)	43 I	
32 (S)	44 I	
38 (S) > I		
40 (S), I		
42 S, I		
45 B > S		
46 S, I, A		
TOTAL = 22	TOTAL = 17	TOTAL = 6
S = 12⎱*	S = 6⎱*	S = 1
(S) = 10⎰	(S) = 1⎰	
	A, B, I without S = 10	A, B, I without S = 5

* In combination with A, B, or I.
† Readmission of No. 28.

Pathways of expression for anxiety were divided as follows: In 22 cases of physical illness, somatic representations alone were found in none; somatic representations in combination with other pathways, 11 (50 percent); and other pathways (affective, behavioral, and ideational) without somatic representations in 11 (50 percent). In 17 cases of nonphysical illness, somatic representations alone were found in none; somatic representations in combination with other pathways, 17 (100 percent). For hostility, the figures were: In 22 cases of physical illness, somatic representations

TABLE 9. DEPRESSION—PATHWAY OF EXPRESSION

A = Affective
B = Behavioral
I = Ideational
S = Somatic
(S) = Somatic pathway inferred

PHYSICAL ILLNESS	NONPHYSICAL ILLNESS	MIXED
Case Number	Case Number	Case Number
2 I	1 I	3 I
5 I	12 I	4 S I
8 I	13 I (masked)	6 I
9 I A	17 I, A S	7 I, A
10 S, I	19 I S, A	27 I, A
11 I, B, A	22 I, A	* 35 I, A
14 S, I, A	24 I, A, B (masked)	
16 S I	28 I A	
18 (S), I	30 I	
20 (S), I	33 I, A	
21 (S), I	34 I, A	
23 I, A	36 I S	
25 (S), I	37 I	
26 (S), A	39 (S), I	
29 S, I	41 I, A	
31 (S), I	43 S, I	
32 (S), I	44 S, I, A	
38 S I		
40 (S), B		
42 S, I, A		
45 I		
46 S, I		
TOTAL = 22	TOTAL = 17	TOTAL = 6
Total S = 7	Total S = 5	Total S = 1
Total (S) = 8	Total (S) = 1	
Total A, B,	Total A, B,	Total A, B,
I without	I without	I without
S or (S) = 7	S or (S) = 11	S or (S) = 5

* Readmission of No. 28.

alone were found in none; somatic representations in combination with other pathways, 12 (54 percent), inferred somatic pathways in combination with other pathways, 10 (46 percent). In 17 cases of nonphysical illness, somatic pathways alone were found in none; somatic representations in combination with other pathways, 6 (35 percent); and other pathways without somatic representations in 10 (60 percent); there was one inferred somatic pathway. For depression: In 22 cases of organic disease, somatic representations alone were found in none; somatic representations in combination with other pathways, 7 (32 percent); inferred somatic pathways in combination with other pathways, 8 (36 percent); and other pathways without somatic representations, 7 (32 percent). In 17 cases of nonphysical illness, somatic pathways alone were found in none; somatic representations in combination with other pathways, 5 (39 percent); and other pathways without somatic representations, 11 (65 percent); there was one inferred somatic pathway (see Tables 7, 8, 9).

PSYCHOLOGICAL MECHANISMS OF DEFENSE

In this series of cases, representing principally the lower socioeconomic groups, the most prevalent mechanism which served the purpose of psychological defense was compensatory overactivity. This was exhibited in various sorts of work, skilled and unskilled (including manual labor), and sports of all kinds, especially during the patients' earlier years. The defense was directed particularly toward maintaining repression of passive–dependent tendencies and coping with anxiety about adequate masculinity. Some manifestation of overactivity was present in 16 out of 22 patients (74 percent) with physical disease and 7 out of 17 (41 percent) with nonphysical illness. It appeared in 24 of the total cases (55 percent) (see Table 10). Another psychological defense structure appearing prominently was denial,

TABLE 10. DEFENSE—OVERACTIVITY

PHYSICAL ILLNESS	NONPHYSICAL ILLNESS	MIXED
Case Number	Case Number	Case Number
2	1	3
5	13	
6	17	
8	30	
9	33	
10	36	
11	41	
14		
18		
21		
23		
27		
29		
31		
32		
38		
TOTAL = 16/22	TOTAL = 7/17	TOTAL = 1/6

in 13 of 22 (59 percent) physically ill patients; in those with nonphysical illness the rate was 7 out of 17 cases (41 percent). The defense of rationalization was noted in 9 out of 22 (41 percent), cases of physical sickness, but in cases of nonphysical illness, the ratio was 10 out of 17 (59 percent). There were 14 cases (31 percent of the total) in which the mechanism of projection was found. Of these only 2 were organic illnesses (9 percent) and 8 were nonphysical illnesses (47 percent). Thus, the latter two defense structures were much more prominent in the psychological disorders. All these defenses were considered to have been present before the patient's illness began.

SOMATIC IDENTIFICATION

This variable refers to similarities between the patient and those figures emotionally significant for him, expressed directly in terms of the patient's physical sensations, symptoms, or illness itself, or in terms of other references to malfunctioning body areas, organs, or physical systems. The factor of somatic identification appeared in all but one of the cases reported in this series, principally in three different forms: (1) direct, with constitutional elements, if the same body area is organically involved in the patient as in the important object; (2) direct, if the same body part is physically involved in the object but only symptomatically referred to as being present in the patient; (3) indirect, if there is no direct link, expressed in physical terms, between the involved organ system in the patient and the significant object, but there are suggestive, though often disguised, associative connections pointing to this in the patient's verbal responses.

Of the 22 patients with organic disease, 19 (90 percent) had direct somatic identification elements of one kind or another as compared with 12 out of 17 (70 percent) of patients with nonphysical illness. However, when the same body area, organ, or organ system was affected by physical disease in both subject and significant object, an hereditary factor was considered to be involved. Such constitutional elements appeared in 11 of 22 (50 percent) organic cases, in contrast to only 2 of 17 (12 percent) cases of nonphysical illness (see Table 11).

SENSORIMOTOR PATTERNS

A tabulation of the chief presenting symptom in each case revealed that pain was by far the largest single category of symptoms, being noted in 21 out of 46 patients (44 percent). It occurred in approximately 50 percent of patients with physical illness and those with nonphysical illness. In contrast, only one patient presented nervousness and/or tension as the basic complaint. Approximately 20 percent (10 patients out of 45) localized the chief symptom in the stomach, whereas 33 percent (15 patients)

TABLE 11. SOMATIC IDENTIFICATION *

I = Indirect (subject, object)
D = Direct (subject, object)
C = Constitutional Elements
R = Reverse (object, subject)

PHYSICAL ILLNESS		NONPHYSICAL ILLNESS		MIXED	
Case Number		Case Number		Case Number	
2	D, D, I, I, I	1	D, I	3	I, I, D
5	DC, I	12	D, I	4	D, D, D, I, I
8	DC, RC, I, I	13	DC, DC	6	DC ?
9	I	17	D	7	DC, I
10	I, I, I	19	I, D?C, I	27	D
11	DC	22	I, D, I, D	† 35	D, I
14	DC, I, I	24	I, D, I, I		
16	DC, I	28	I, I		
18	DC, DC	30	D, I		
20	DC	33	I		
21	D	34	D, I		
23	I, I	36	I, D		
25	I, D, I	37	none		
26	I, DC	39	I, I, D		
29	D, D, D	41	I		
31	DC	43	I, I		
32	D	44	I, D		
38	I, D, D				
40	D				
42	DC, I				
45	D				
46	DC, D				
TOTAL = 22		TOTAL = 17		TOTAL = 6	
DC = 11		DC = 2		DC = 1	
				and 1 (?)	
D = 9		D = 10		D = 4	
I = 12		I = 14		I = 4	

* Some aspect of somatic identification was elicited in all cases.
† Readmission of No. 28.

localized it somewhere in the gastrointestinal tract, the most frequently involved organ system. References to interoceptive sensations in general occurred in 12 out of 22 (54 percent) of patients with organic disease and in 12 out of 17 (70 percent) of patients with nonphysical illness. The distribution for temperature sensations was 8 out of 22 (36 percent) in organic disease and 8 out of 17 (47 percent) in emotional illness. Other sensory percepts occurred less frequently in both groups of patients.

TABLE 12. SENSORIMOTOR CONFIGURATIONS

PHYSICAL ILLNESS	NONPHYSICAL ILLNESS	MIXED
Case Number	Case Number	Case Number
2 Temperature, motor	1 Interoceptive; activity	3 Visual-tactile; inserting-itching
5 Pain-tactile-proprioceptive; activity	12 Pain-interoceptive; activity-being attacked	4 Pain; walking
8 Auditory-temperature-tactile; hyperactivity, getting rid of	13 Pain; working	6 Interoceptive-pain; fainting-being operated on
9 Visual-tactile-temperature-proprioceptive-pain; chewing-gnawing	17 Pain; activity	7 Pain-visual-tactile; walking-postural changes
10 Tactile-visual-auditory; cutting-scratching	19 Visual-interoceptive-taste; losing	27 Visual-interoceptive; looking-getting away
11 Pain; activity	22 Temperature-interoceptive-visual working-resting	* 35 Interoceptive-pain-tactile-temperature-visual-olfactory; emptying-being stuck
14 Pain-temperature-interoceptive; gnawing-tearing out	24 Pain-tactile-visual-interoceptive; activity	TOTAL = 6
16 Pain; operative interventions	28 Temperature-interoceptive-taste; going down-coming up-working	
18 Pain-tactile-temperature-interoceptive; motor	30 Temperature-visual; chopping-getting rid of	
20 Pain-interoceptive-auditory; tightening-ejecting	33 Visual-interoceptive-pain-temperature; activity	
21 Interoceptive; activity	34 Interoceptive-temperature-pain; forcing	
23 Pain; activity	36 Pain-interoceptive-temperature; motility	
25 Pain-interoceptive; activity	37 Pain-temperature-taste-visual; activity-passivity	
26 Interoceptive; ejection	39 Pain-interoceptive-temperature-taste; activity-passivity	
29 Temperature-interoceptive; activity	41 Pain-interoceptive; activity	
31 Visual-pain-interoceptive; activity	43 Tactile-temperature-visual-auditory; losing consciousness	
32 Pain-temperature-interoceptive; motility	44 Interoceptive-pain; being stuck-dislodging	
38 Interoceptive-visual; activity	TOTAL = 17	
40 Temperature-visual; studying	* Readmission of No. 28.	
42 Pain-interoceptive; passing out		
45 Pain; mobility		
46 Pain-interoceptive; roaming		
TOTAL = 22		

General references to activity or motility were noted in about half of the cases of both physical and nonphysical illness. More specific references to motor activity also occurred in both groups—in the cases of physical illness: getting rid of, chewing, gnawing, scratching, tearing out, ejecting, passing out, roaming; in the cases of nonphysical illness: being attacked, losing, working, getting rid of, forcing, losing consciousness, dislodging. The references in the cases of physical sickness generally appeared to reflect a more primitive type of motor activity.

In order to study the psychodynamic aspects of physical symptoms more effectively, it is necessary to elicit as many associative connections to them as is possible. Among these associations there will generally be found a variety of sensorimotor patterns which, in the past, have tended to be regarded as insignificant byproducts. Actually, they are important sources of information as links between the patient's physical symptoms and bodily functions, his affective responses, behavior, and reactions to significant figures and events in the past and present.

A wide variety of sensorimotor combinations was found to be present in the anamnestic material from patients with both physical illness and nonphysical illness in this series. From this standpoint no significant correlations were elicited that served to distinguish one from the other of these two categories. Any specificity that emerged appeared more related to repetition in the individual case. Each patient seemed to have sensorimotor patterns of reactivity to stress which tended to persist within a certain range of combination and alteration specific for the individual (see Table 12).

SUPEREGO-EGO TENSIONS

These were present in all cases but with some variations in intensity. The patients with physical illness, for the most part, were estimated to have severe superego-ego tensions. The frequency of these tensions was somewhat less in the nonphysical illnesses, and there was somewhat greater fluctuation in intensity in this group (see Table 13).

FURTHER CONSIDERATIONS

The factor of psychological stress has generally been acknowledged to play a greater or lesser role in man's illnesses. Unfortunately, however, it has too often been made to appear the sole or basic cause of disease, or has been mentioned only briefly, or described superficially. It has also become associated with the state of being only noxious. Such concepts have vitiated the meaning and distorted the role of psychological stress, and have rendered difficult the further development of knowledge about it. What is

TABLE 13. SUPEREGO–EGO TENSIONS

+ Mild
++ Moderate
+++ Severe

PHYSICAL ILLNESS		NONPHYSICAL ILLNESS		MIXED	
Case Number		Case Number		Case Number	
2	+++	1	+++	3	+++
5	+++	12	+	4	?
8	+++	13	+	6	+++
9	+++	17	+++	7	+++
10	+++	19	?	27	+++
11	+++	22	++	* 35	+++
14	+++	24	+++		
16	?	28	+++		
18	+++	30	+++		
20	+++	33	+++		
21	?	34	+++		
23	+++	36	++		
25	+++	37	+		
26	+++	39	++		
29	+++	41	?		
31	+++	43	++		
32	+++	44	++		
38	+++				
40	+++				
42	+++				
45	++				
46	++				

* Readmission of No. 28.

essential to understand about such stress is that it derives particularly from the individual's interaction with his fellow human beings and from his reactions to the social, economic, and cultural settings in which he finds himself. It is a force or process which has origins either inside the individual, outside him, or both. By increasing stimulus influx, it exerts a disturbing influence on the existing organismic equilibrium, evoking various coping responses which first involve psychological systems and then may affect the biological and physiological systems positively or negatively. This definition corresponds rather closely to Engel's (1962). Since psychological stress and the individual's response to it are highly complicated phenomena, their more accurate evaluation requires consideration of many different aspects. In addition to intensity, frequency, and duration of the stress, it is especially important to know its meaning (often symbolic and outside awareness) for the particular individual, and to determine on what psychophysical equilibrium the stress is exerting its impact.

Stress of utmost intensity—catastrophic events—will produce reactions in any individual, though the nature, duration, and relative severity of response will vary. In those whose capacity for mastering the disturbing stimuli is impaired or limited, less overwhelming stress may produce traumatic reactions; in others, the ability to bind the same excitation is sufficient to prevent untoward aftereffects. It should be noted that if motor release is possible at the time of acute stress, some relief may be afforded in this way from the full impact of the potentially traumatic event. The more unexpected the stress, the greater the excitatory effect. The common manifestations of traumatic neurosis include: (1) impairment of ego functions, with blocking of many perceptions and marshalling of energies to master the intrusive excitation; (2) emotional eruptions of rage, crying, anxiety, which are partially nonspecific; (3) insomnia and repetitive nightmares as well as repetitive daydreams; and (4) secondary psychoneurotic elaborations. However, there may also be a wide variety of somatic responses to traumatic events. Many of these are physical symptoms which represent affect equivalents. Others may herald the beginning of a more serious physical dysfunction. However, sudden, massive stress is not the only cause of disturbing and painful psychophysical responses; accumulating chronic stress, less sharply outlined in the course of the patient's current life may also have an adverse impact. The most frequent stresses are the minor traumata of everyday life with their often brief, transient sequelae, frequently in the form of low-grade physical symptoms.

It should be emphasized again that all stress cannot be classified as noxious. In fact, a certain amount of stimulation and excitation—of the right kind and under the right conditions—appears to be necessary for the maintenance of a healthy "psychophysical tone:" stimulating interaction with other people, physical exercise, intellectual work, and the challenge of difficult problems and new areas to be explored. In any event, while the basic composition of the human body is made up of highly sensitive and unstable material, its capacity for adapting to environmental vicissitudes is truly remarkable.

In every patient in this series, psychological stresses were found to be present in temporal relationship to the development or exacerbation of physical as well as psychological symptoms. This confirms, under more controlled conditions, what has been found in general clinical experience. However, the finding of a stress factor does not establish a sufficient explanation for the cause of the symptoms or sicknesses, somatic or mental, that are present. The presence of stress does not automatically lead to illness. The individual may adapt to stress without becoming ill—by sublimation, by accentuation of certain more or less permanent character traits, by substitute psychological formations, or by subclinical physical and psychological manifestations, transient and often overlooked. Frequently, the individual's reaction to stress may be in the form of dis-ease rather than disease. On the other hand, stress is a necessary, if not sufficient, factor in the development or exacerbation of symptoms and illness. It then acts by massively disrupting psychophysical equilibria and activating dysfunction in already sensitized (conditioned) psychological and physical systems.

In most of the cases, one particular stress situation was found. This constituted some form of loss of significant object relationship. In Schmale's (1958) medical series, there was a similar finding. However, object loss and reaction to it are highly complicated, and the mere statement that they have occurred is only a beginning step in understanding their full implications. The characteristic affective response to object loss is sadness mixed with varying degrees of guilt and feelings of helplessness and hopelessness. There are also accompanying somatic symptoms of great variety. At times these may predominate, with the emotional reactions being masked. Engel (1961) has written that "... the concepts of objects and of object loss is only meaningful in terms of the existence and operation of the mental apparatus. This means that whatever the consequences of object loss and grief may be, whether manifest ultimately in biochemical, physiological, or social terms, they must first be initiated in the central nervous system" (especially the limbic and reticular activating systems). He has emphasized the concept of grief as a disease and "in this perspective the human objects, the home, the work, the aspirations of patients cannot be neglected in our thinking about sickness ... at least not until it has been proven that the vicissitudes of object relations, including grief ... play no role in the pathogenesis of disease." It is, of course, well known that individuals may sustain object loss and not become physically or emotionally ill. Here one will find evidence that replacement of the significant object by an adequate substitute has taken place. Such substitutes may include a relative, friend, colleague, employer, teacher, family physician, nurse, and others. In addition, finances, skills, prestige, position, or other factors may change in such a favorable way that the individual's self-esteem is raised. It should be noted that recourse to alcohol and drugs as "sources of supply" to stave off the effects of object loss, particularly depression or physical sickness, may succeed temporarily in doing so, only to lead the individual back to illness through other routes.

Returning to the series, although sickness or death of the mother, a key figure in the patient's life, was found in seven instances and, in all, physical disease had developed, this particular stress alone cannot be considered to be causal in the development of organic illness. It may lead to other sequelae, to physical symptoms without organic basis, to a grief reaction without marked pathological manifestations, or to a basically psychological illness. It is of interest as a variable which can be correlated with a variety of psychophysical shifts. However, a general observation about the role of object relationships in the cases in this study may be made. In those patients that developed physical disease, stresses due to important object loss were more intense and more prevalent than stresses associated with inferiority and inadequacy feelings, especially involving competitive rivalry with parental or sibling figures. In the patients who died (Case 2 and Case 18), there was evidence that object loss in the continued absence of adequate replacement had contributed to an escalating sense of helplessness and hopelessness which reached an extreme before death. Such evidence was derived more from the content of the patient's associations than from his affective responses. It should be noted that the intense feelings themselves are not experienced directly as such by the individual. They are expressed more through somatic representations whose symbolic significance is outside his awareness. Some patients tend to associate their depressive outlook with the ongoing illness and possible fatal outcome rather than with the antecedent object loss and its meanings. Other patients deny the gravity of their condition. In careful psychotherapeutic work with seriously ill patients, it is possible, when done early enough, to help some of them achieve at least a partial affective discharge of these feelings and also gain a degree of insight into their significance. This may have a beneficial effect on the physical illness.

All stress, whether physical or psychological, causes reactions in the human organism. These reactions are directed toward maintaining an internal environment that has been variously described as "relatively constant" (Bernard, 1865) or a "steady state" (Bertalanffy, 1950). Involved is the principle of homeostasis (Cannon, 1953) which has been applied in the past principally to physiological processes and to physicochemical constancy, and has been thought of as occurring automatically. More recently, this principle has been applied to human behavior expressed through psychological systems, another basic means whereby the organism attempts to maintain a state of equilibrium in its relationship to the environment. However, factors other than homeostatic ones seem to be involved in human behavior. These factors would include forces that impel the organism toward change and toward disturbance of the status quo (heterostasis).

K. Menninger (1963) suggests that regulation of organismic functioning occurs through a complex of homeostatic agencies operating simultaneously. There is the regulated interaction between the individual and other persons, as well as the environment in which he exists. There are also different levels of internal regulation involving interrelationships between different parts of one organ system, as well as between different organ systems. Within the psychological system itself there is interaction between ego, superego, and id. The ego is considered to be the integrating and synthesizing agency of the mental apparatus, effecting through these functions a basic homeostatic influence not only on psychological, but also on somatic systems. Needs for water, certain foods, some minerals, warmth, and rest, and various other biological necessities are recognized by the individual through his ego functions, even though he may not know, for example, that measurements of his physiological functions, such as blood chemistry values or electrolytic balances, are abnormal. "We must define the steady state in a broad sense, not just as physiological constancy or just as psychological steadiness, but as the integrated operation of all constancy-maintaining partial systems of any kind comprising the total personality, and even the environment in which it moves. Changes in the balance of one partial system may reverberate throughout the system and may sometimes grossly affect the steadiness of other partial systems" (Menninger).

Psychological stress will affect both psychological and physical constancy. The primary impact on psychological equilibrium will invariably be accompanied by physiological fluctuations, but the agencies of the mental apparatus and their interrelationships within the psychological system will be the first to be involved. The strength of the instinctual drives may be increased, tensions between ego and superego heightened, mechanisms of defense realigned, and other aspects of ego functioning modified, particularly the capacity to neutralize aggressiveness. Various psychological symptoms may result, usually accompanied by some physical manifestations, if the response of the psychological systems alone has been insufficient to bind the anxiety or other affects activated by the stress. With psychological regression there is a shift to earlier levels of psychological functioning with their more primitive characteristics. The shift will be of varying kind, intensity, and duration, depending on the type, severity, and persistence of the stress, as well as on the particular psychophysical state of the individual involved. Regressive shifts are possible because in psychological development, progress to the highest levels is never complete. Earlier levels have left a varying residue of their characteristics which coexist with those of the higher levels of development. One such remainder is the tendency to discharge emotional tensions through somatic pathways. It is the most prevalent, being found even when psychological manifestations predominate. When the latter are minimal, a particular physical symptom or group of symptoms may become the most frequent and at times, the only indicator that the individual has been through a stressful experience. This is especially true in the case of everyday tensions which are far less obvious as precipitants of homeostatic shifts than major traumata.

The development of organic disease is accompanied by considerable shifts not only in physical but in psychological homeostasis. On the latter level there are both primary and secondary responses. The primary ones are part of the general psychological changes that precede the onset or exacerbation of the illness. There is regression from the usual psychological equilibrium to one in which activated libidinal and particularly aggressive excitations are largely shunted into somatic pathways of discharge. The secondary responses result from reaction to the organic disease itself. Here another regressive shift invariably occurs. It is in the direction of increased self-concern, self-preoccupation, passive dependency, and fearfulness about outcome of the illness. These manifestations in turn may evoke compensatory defensive psychological reactions of denial, rationalization, projection, and overactivity. Thus physical symptoms associated with the disease process may be more or less prominent and more or less easily tolerated. They may assume a symbolic meaning for the patient, often representing atonement for overbearing guilt feelings, or a form of secondary gain.

Physical illness may lessen in severity, but sometimes, as this occurs, increasing evidence of mental illness may then be noted. In two cases in this series (Case 6 and Case 27) such a shift occurred, and after an interval of several weeks was reversed, with the patient showing complete recovery from the psychotic episode, while his physical illness continued to improve. Although the first patient had had a massive hematemesis related to alcoholism, probable gastritis, and a diaphragmatic hernia, and the second patient was ill with thyrotoxicosis, in both instances certain general similarities could be considered in the development of the subsequent psychosis. Each patient had been exposed to continuing severe psychological stress which contributed to the disruption of the existing psychophysical equilibrium. The first shift that resulted was in the direction of a sharp somatization response. Then the physical illness itself became a further stressful situation for each patient. This additional strain evoked a second shift in equilibrium, this time primarily involving psychological systems and manifesting itself in a psychotic break. For a short time somatic and psychological dysfunction of major proportions occurred simultaneously. Then, the physical illness began to respond favorably to therapeutic measures, but the psychosis persisted. Successful treatment of the involved target organ may block it from serving as a partial outlet for continuing, severe, emotional tensions, and cause the activation of still other coping mechanisms to achieve sufficient discharge.

The interesting question here is whether under these circumstances the brain itself has become the focus of the as yet undiminished, internalized, aggressive energies, and whether this can lead to changes in its function which favor the persistence of severe psychological symptoms, or in other instances can lead to their development (when psychotic breaks occur after the initiation of successful treatment of the physical illness). In both patients a favorable shift in the functioning of psychological systems occurred after a few weeks, with restoration of reality testing, return of the previous neurotic defense mechanisms, and the persistence of some conversion reactions. This further homeostatic readjustment may have been influenced by an economic factor, i.e., a sufficient discharge of the emotional tensions through somatic and psychotic pathways.

Swartz and Semrad (1951) found in a population of 578 psychotic patients, age 16 to 60, that only 20 had so-called psychosomatic disorders such as headache, hypertension, dermatitis, asthma, peptic ulcer, etc. This incidence of 3.4 percent compared with 4.5 percent in a nonpsychotic group. They felt that in some way a psychosomatic disorder might serve as a protection against a psychotic break. They noted that psychosomatic disorders in certain patients disappeared or subsided with onset of psychotic illness, only to reappear in some instances when the psychosis lifted. However, psychosomatic conditions may be present in psychotics, and in two cases the psychosomatic symptoms were aggravated during the psychosis. Swartz and Semrad found no correlation between specific psychosomatic illness and specific psychotic disorders.

Appel and Rosen (1950), studying chronic medical disease, noted psychotic changes of great intensity in four patients. They raised the question whether some psychosomatic phenomena may be an expression of intense emotional conflict in which marked dysfunction of organ systems takes place, comparable in severity with the disorganization in psychosis— highly maladaptive. They point to the displacement of emotional conflicts onto organ systems in conversion hysteria and wonder whether such conflicts in potentially psychotic individuals can undergo parallel, though not necessarily similar, development. One of their patients with chronic rheumatoid arthritis improved under psychotherapy, becoming almost physically symptom-free, but in the course of treatment a psychotic illness emerged. They raise the question of whether removal of "this organic means of such (conflictual) expression merely exchanges an externalized symptom complex for one which may be expressed by the psychosis? Or can both reactions occur at the same time but with shifting emphasis from one to the other?" In a second case, psychosis was evident at the beginning of observation, but when the patient was threatened by intensity of homoerotic impulses, the psychotic manifestations disappeared and were replaced by symptoms of colitis.

Small and transient regressive shifts in psychophysical equilibrium leading to minor psychological and/or somatic dysfunction represent adaptive responses which may act as safety valves, serving to avert a more incapacitating buildup of emotional tensions when the individual is subject to low-grade but chronic stress. The significance of this is less well recognized in the physical than in the psychological manifestations. Both will tend to appear in patterns that are recurrent for a particular individual. A feeling of relief, even of well-being, may follow such a somatic interlude. This may be related to a temporarily sufficient discharge of accumulated instinctual drive tensions, or temporary alleviation of guilt feelings, sometimes because of the physical discomfort itself. It may be postulated that "small sicknesses" of this kind are adaptive responses which occur in the service of avoiding major shifts in psychophysical homeostasis and thus help reduce the potential for development of more serious illness.

Among the manifestations of illness, whether physical or psychological, changes and disturbances of emotional expression are always present to some extent. Yet there are difficulties inherent in any discussion of the affects. They are more easily experiencd than described, even though they are an important means of communication between persons. They also constitute a highly useful source of information about one's state of health or illness. However, the potential disposition for their development and discharge may find expression in a guise which is obscure and unfamiliar to the individual experiencing them, when they appear in the form of somatic representations. This occurs when affects are sufficiently blocked from emotional expression or from representation in thinking and behavioral processes. The data in this series indicate that intense hostile and depressive affect sources, which do not have sufficient outlet through psychological systems, are found more often in patients with organic disease than in those with nonphysical illness. On the other hand, a pre-existent potential for development of marked anxiety may have both psychological and somatic pathways of discharge but does not usually lead to organic disease, even if the soma is particularly involved.

These findings suggest that if the energies associated with potential affect development are insufficiently expressed through psychological systems, they will impinge on and influence more directly the physical functioning of the body. Under these circumstances, hostility and depression appear to play a significant role in the development or exacerbation of organic disease in general, rather than being involved in only a few frequently cited illnesses such as hypertension, peptic ulcer, arthritis, or asthma. The energies associated with hostility are impressively exhibited in a person who is in an open rage. In this release, muscular and glandular functions are considerably involved, and powerful emotional feelings are overtly expressed. However, in an individual in whom an unconscious readiness to develop this affect is activated and turned against the self, but where psychological mechanisms are blocked from sufficiently discharging the feelings, as in the form of overt depressive affect, the resultant impact on the soma seems to be greater. Although, under these circumstances, there may be relatively little or no overt emotional expression, the physical sequelae that then occur appear to be qualitatively and quantitatively different from those accompanying conscious rage. They reflect more profound, longer-lasting, local and generalized disturbances in somatic functioning, and seem to provide a particularly favorable setting for the development of physical illness.

While the forces that generate hostile and depressive emotions are importantly involved in the development or exacerbation of physical disease, their presence under these circumstances may be a relatively "silent" one, i.e., not expressed as an overt emotional response. Instead, disguised indications of their existence will be found in the patient's verbalized thoughts with links directly or indirectly to his physical symptoms, related bodily functions, or sensorimotor reaction patterns, but the patient himself will be unaware of the significance of these associations. It is from this verbal material, however, that the somatic representations of the affects may be detected by the interviewer.

It should be noted that varying emotions may manifest themselves as a consequence of the individual's response to organic illness itself. These are secondary affective reactions which will, in turn, evoke further adaptive shifts in the psychological systems. If these systems are ineffective in coping with the added strain, then it may exert an additional disorganizing impact on physical systems which already are malfunctioning and thus further unfavorably influence the course of the illness.

Severe exacerbation and fatal outcome of organic illness may more readily occur in a setting where the patient's affective state reflects pervasive feelings of helplessness and hopelessness. According to Schmale (1958) and Engel (1962), these represent the most extreme responses to stress. Helplessness is more apt to develop in individuals who basically depend on external sources of emotional supplies. Its early prototype is that of the helpless infant, whose chances for survival are slim without help from another person. It is manifest later in life in such feelings as those of being excluded, let down, and abandoned. Hopelessness tends to develop in individuals with pathologically strict superegoes. Its anlage appears to be related to primitive states of depression–withdrawal. The associated feelings in the adult are those of despair and of giving up because of the conviction that nothing can be done to alter the status quo and/or that even if help is available, the individual is unworthy of it. Under such circumstances self-integrity is threatened and in danger of dissolution.

Affects are an expression of instinctual drive activity. Elsewhere (Silverman, 1959, 1962) it has been postulated that when aggressive and libidinal drives are blocked from sufficient discharge through psychological systems, the aggressive drives will have a considerably greater disruptive effect on the physical functions of the body than the libidinal ones. The disruption may be sufficient to make the organ or physical systems involved more susceptible to the influence of noxious factors that may be incidentally or accidentally present, with the result being a setting which favors the development or exacerbation of organic disease. Libidinal drives, under similar blocking conditions, appear to have a relatively lesser impact on physical functioning. The physical symptoms appearing under these conditions are derived from minor local or systemic dysfunction, often temporary, reversible, and not leading to organic disease. It would seem that the libidinal drives have a plasticity which permits many substitute ways of gratification and avoids a deleterious effect on the individual's object relationships, whereas aggression tends to exert a destructive influence on the objects it is directed against. If not the outside world and the objects in it, then it is the self which feels the brunt of the aggressive drives, either psychologically or physically, unless their neutralization can be effected.

Freud (1938) postulated the existence of forces which he called instincts representing "somatic demands upon mental life," conservative by nature, and able to change their aim. He finally assumed the existence of only two basic instincts: *Eros* and the *destructive instinct*. The former establishes and preserves ever greater unities; it is a binding force. The latter undoes connections and appears to reduce living things to an inorganic state; it is a destructive force. Freud further hypothesized that the two basic instincts are at work in biological functions, either in opposition to or in varying combination with each other. Hartmann et al. (1949) suggested that mitigation of destructiveness in an individual is related to a "neutralizing" activity of the ego and that this deaggressivization is accomplished in a fashion similar to the desexualization of the sexual drives.

Somatic dysfunction and its manifestations may be involved in the individual's attempts to cope with and defend against activated emotional tensions. The somatic pathways of expression then become part of repetitive defensive processes directed against possible eruption of warded-off ininstinctual drives. The emotional conflicts referred to are remainders from childhood, representing instinctual impulses which have become associated with anxiety and guilt, and have then come under the influence of repressing forces. They remain outside awareness, blocked from the mitigating influence of the mature parts of the personality, and constitute a reservoir of potential emotional disturbance. When activated by events in the individual's current life, they seek any outlet for discharge, including both psychological and somatic pathways. The psychological significance of physical dysfunctions is often less easily demonstrated than their physiological or biochemical basis. Consequently, it may be difficult to view these somatic processes as being partly under the influence of the regulatory functions of the ego and associated with psychological structures in the services of coping with emotional conflicts.

Such physical dysfunction is a regression phenomenon which to some extent replaces adaptive, reality-oriented, and defensive psychological mechanisms. It has been variously called or compared with "physiologic regression" (Michaels, 1953; Grinker, 1953; Margolin, 1953), "physiologic infantilism" (Hendrick, 1952), conversion (Rangell, 1959; Deutsch, 1959), and somatization (Schur, 1955). The last two terms refer to the link between physical processes and ego function. Emotional expression and communication early in life, before the development of language and speech, is through gross affective discharge and somatic channels, both motor and visceral. Somatization, in the sense of an ego regression, represents a return to such an early phase of development. However, according to one widely held point of view, conversion as a process comes into being somewhat later, perhaps in the second year of life, when the functions of the psychic apparatus, especially those of the ego, begin to become more differentiated. During this time, the change from physical modalities of expression to increasingly greater use of psychological defenses becomes established. Conversion thus can be said to refer to the use of somatic pathways for symbolically expressing particular emotional conflicts which are repressed. This leads to the formation of physical symptoms through the interaction of a complex of defenses including identification, displacement, internalization, symbolization, turning upon the self, and especially regression (Rangell, 1959). On the other hand, Deutsch has broadened the concept of conversion to include practically all psychophysical phenomena. However, physical symptoms should not be considered invariably as specific conversions of emotional conflicts into specific body language. Psychological disturbances may also affect body functions without the altered physiological or biochemical process having specific symbolic meaning.

Various psychological mechanisms of defense are found in characteristic patterns of alignment in any given individual, but some element of physical dysfunction related to emotional disturbance is invariably present also, though its activity may range from occasional and transient to prolonged and intense. Its persisting prominence in the defensive alignment will depend on many factors, both constitutional and developmental, but particularly on the strength of the aggressive drives, the capacity of the ego to neutralize them, and the extent to which primarily psychological systems, especially through defensive alignments, are blocked from adequately coping with these activated drives.

In this series of cases, no specific constellations of psychological mechanisms of defense could be correlated with particular illnesses, although some manifestation of overactivity and denial was present more often in organic disease, and the mechanisms of projection and rationalization appeared prominently in nonphysical sickness. It should be noted that not all over-activity or other aspects of behavior are linked with psychological conflict (such as defense against marked passive–dependency needs). Certain aspects of behavior are conflict-free.

Emotional conflicts with marked pregenital elements originating in early disturbance of psychological development were found frequently in the cases with organic illness. There appeared to be an admixture of such premorbid personality components and of regressive by-products of the patient's reaction to the disease process itself. However, it should be noted that other individuals with basically similar pregenital features in their personality makeup may develop severe psychological rather than physical illness. The prominent presence of pregenital factors in some individuals suggests only a vulnerability to the development of rather severe illness, either emotional or somatic, but in others this predisposition is neutralized or modified by certain psychological and environmental influences, and such people appear to function relatively well and without grossly apparent incapacity.

Elements of somatic identification were noted in all but one patient in this series, irrespective of the final diagnosis, although all had been hospitalized because of physical symptoms. Since in this series each psychiatric interview was conducted after the patient's illness had begun, it might be maintained that the somatic identification elicited had been derived post hoc, i.e., that the patient, having experienced certain physical sensations first, would then recall associatively in the interview that one or another key figure in his life had had related physical manifestations. However, other indicators of identification in addition to the physical ones were noted in the anamnestic material and obviously had existed prior to the onset of the patient's sickness. These included resemblance in appearance, mannerisms, behavior, various interests, outlook on life, and so on. It has been demonstrated also that at the time when key figures become ill, die, or are lost in some other way, the individual sustaining the loss tends to react to it by regressing from the more mature forms of psychological relationship with these objects to a process of identification with them. It has been repeatedly observed that not only mourners, but all individuals who experience considerable disappointment, may begin thereafter to resemble the lost object in a physical and/or psychological way (Fenichel, 1945). The identification may be temporary or may remain indefinitely. In the detailed clinical observations made in psychoanalytically treated patients, it is possible to note more specifically the time relationships involved in somatic identification. The reference in the patient's associations to physical manifestations in the emotionally significant object will precede the appearance of similar symptoms and/or sensations in the patient by a variable period of time, ranging from hours to a week or more.

For example, one patient, a middle-aged man with initially observed passive–dependent tendencies, had entered a phase in his analysis in which there appeared increasing evidence of his highly ambivalent relationship with his wife, a phallic, domineering woman. Partly he was afraid of her devaluations, partly he felt very angry with her, and partly he identified with certain of her attitudes and mannerisms. One morning he was notified by her physician that in her annual physical checkup she had been X-rayed, and the preliminary evaluation of the chest film revealed a suspicious coin-shaped area of infiltration in the left upper lung field. The patient, who had already had his analytic hour, became preoccupied with thoughts that his wife might die very shortly. He noticed himself becoming increasingly anxious. This feeling intensified when, some hours later on the same day, he also heard from his wife that his only son, to whom he was very much attached, had developed a severe cough which sounded to her as if it might be whooping cough. That night the patient slept poorly and the next day he felt physically below par and began to cough. He thought he was coming down with a severe cold. During the analytic hour that day his associations turned to his reaction to his mother's death some months before. He had seen her, too, as dominating him, had been very ambivalent toward her, and in his childhood had developed a strong feminine identification with her. Many years later she had become ill with cervical carcinoma which had metastasized to the lungs. In his depression following her death he had often wondered if he, too, would develop cancer of the lungs, and bitterly thought "it would serve me right" for having been so hostile toward her. Now he became aware that he was having similar thoughts in connection with his wife, and that his youngster represented an extension of himself. That evening his cough lessened. The next day further tests revealed that neither his wife nor child had any organic disease. His own symptoms disappeared shortly thereafter.

Only a few hours elapsed between the patient's hearing the stressful news, his becoming concerned with it, and the development of the physical symptom which represented an identification with his wife and child. This "latent period," before the manifestation of the somatic identification, varies considerably in duration. In another patient a week elapsed. He had been troubled by homosexual fantasies and had experienced strong castration fears for some time before his daughter, aged four, was examined, and found to have enlarged adenoids blocking the internal auditory canals and causing hearing difficulty. She was scheduled for surgery, and this concerned the patient for several days. He became preoccupied with the matter of body mutilation and irreparable loss of function in both his child and himself until he was finally able "to put the whole situation out of my mind." A few days later he developed a rather severe cold and was told by his internist that it was due to a virus infection. The principal manifestations were laryngitis, tinnitus, and severe otitic pain. The patient did not recall the occurrence of any ear trouble during the colds he had had since childhood. Within a few days after his daughter was operated on, his symptoms subsided.

The phenomenon of fascination seems to be a precursor of identification. Early efforts by the infant to master incoming stimuli may be by imitation of that which is perceived. A regression to this primitive level was observed by Goldstein (quoted in Fenichel, 1945) in brain-injured patients with alexia. They attempted to make up for their inability to read by compensatory movements of the head. Their awareness of the resultant kinesthetic and proprioceptive sensory perceptions made it possible for them to "read" in this way. There is another very early reaction to objects that can be noted in the infant's attempts to mouth them (Fenichel). These primitive psychophysical mechanisms of oral introjection and imitation are reactions which stand in close relationship to each other: Object, motor response to external stimulus, and perception appear as one. Thus the early forms of identification have basic somatic components which will reappear as regressive manifestations such as have been described in hysterical and in all disappointed and depressed individuals.

When a relationship with an emotionally significant object undergoes a regressive modification, elements of somatic identification should be looked for, even if they are not quickly apparent. Somatic identification appears as a manifestation of reactions in the physical systems especially to the impact of losses, deprivations, and disappointments experienced by the individual. It represents an attempt to compensate for the loss. There are also hysterical identifications in which somatic manifestations represent a response to guilt over wishes to replace a competitor who is envied by the individual. Most often, hysterical identification involves a person to whom the individual relates more because of the need for similar gratification which the other has experienced than on the basis of a real object relationship.

Sensorimotor data are a valuable source of information about the interrelationships between physical symptoms and bodily functions, affective responses, behavior, and reactions to significant figures and events in the past and present. Such data was obtained in all cases in this series. For example, in Case 1, there were presenting stomach symptoms. In the associative material, interoceptive percepts were elicited which were linked to affects of anxiety and hostility, and to deeply rooted oral needs associated with eating problems and stomach symptoms, now and in childhood. These were considered to represent a very early psychophysical expression of one particular aspect of the patient's relationship with his mother. In Case 4, pain sensations were linked by the patient with having many sore throats as a child, then with being hospitalized for a tonsillectomy and experiencing feelings of loneliness and fear at being left by his mother, misinterpreted as a desertion. Motor referents involved walking, and were connected with loss of breath, chest colds, and long-standing anxiety about assuming the erect position, symbolizing manliness. The patient in Case 31 had a chief complaint of hazy vision and the associations to this contained visual, pain, and interoceptive percepts connected with father's illness and death during the patient's childhood, and a lingering concern that such a fate might await him. Motor configurations featured activity of various kinds, linked with inability to relax, to sleep, to breathe right, and serving as a defense against passive–feminine attitudes, especially in relation to mother. These sensorimotor patterns are not just simple bodily responses, but may be subject to or exert psychological influence.

In psychophysical development, sensorimotor-visceral reactions and gross emotional discharge reflect the individual's response to his external environment and internal milieu before language and speech make verbal communication possible. The ego is thought to have a bodily origin: Its primitive nucleus develops from the sensory perceptions—particularly the external tactile and internal kinesthetic—of the body. These sensations in turn appear to be closely related to almost immediate motor discharge. They are the early means of sensing and initiating reactions to objects. As the ego develops, some aspects of its functioning are influenced by emotional conflict in relation to these objects, while other aspects remain conflict-free. From the beginning, each individual has a different somatic reactivity. This encompasses acuity of vision and hearing, temperature responses, pain threshold, kinesthetic reaction, motor coordination together with muscle development and strength, visceral function, and its relation particularly to the autonomic nervous system. Sensory impressions derived from the earliest years of life are not present in simple constellations, but have been formed into hierarchical groups. Synesthesia is a fundamental principle governing perception (Schilder, 1950). With the differentiation of thinking processes from their archaic beginnings and the acquisition of the faculty of speech, psychological systems become more and more involved in the interreactions of the individual with the objects around him, while somatic aspects appear less prominently. Yet the latter, especially in the form of sensorimotor patterns never disappear entirely, and at times become significant, if disguised, indicators of object relationships. Such physical connections appear to be less variable and less easily substituted for than the psychological.

The increase in self-interest and self-observation with concomitant decrease of interest in the outside world may be noted not only in people ill with a psychosis but also in those who have an organic illness, or have been through one. The intrapsychic representation of the body and its various parts has derivations from complex memory residues of many interrelated internal physical sensations fused with perceptions of the outside world and its objects. In this way, a body image has been built up which is not, however, necessarily the same as the real body. Sensations referable to an extremity may continue to exist long after the particular member has been amputated. Other preceptions associated with certain functions of an organ may persist after it has been removed or been bypassed by surgery, e.g., defecatory sensations in the rectal area after surgical resection and colostomy. Various articles of clothing and other objects such as motorcycles or automobiles, seen as extensions of the self, may also be included in the body image. The intrapsychic representations of body parts are mental configurations which, under certain circumstances such as loss, may become the target of energies diverted from investment in external objects. These body areas may already have a symbolic meaning related to such figures. Instead of the lost object, the involved body parts then appear more prominently in the individual's thinking, this being manifested through an increased awareness of and preoccupation with associated physical sensations from that area. There is concomitantly an absent or diminished interest in the external objects or situations. If the physical sensations reach sufficient intensity, defensive or coping reactions may be activated which result in a denial of the perceptions or even of the existence of the body part. A patient whose attention is basically focused on his physical symptoms and sensations is difficult to interview. There may also be an accompanying anxiety which interferes with the ability to communicate freely. The patient "gets stuck" on the sensations, tending to mention them over and over again.

Deutsch (1959) suggests that an unfavorable physical outcome is more likely when destructive impulses are blocked from outward expression and redirected against an organ which has become involved in the symbolic representation of people toward whom the patient's hatred has been activated. The concept of a death instinct is applied here, and it is postulated that this instinct finds discharge via the organ which has become sensitized or conditioned by symbolization.

Interoceptive stimuli have received special attention from Soviet investigators in conditioning experiments. Razran (1961) cites experiments in which inflatable rubber balloons containing three-pronged electrodes were swallowed by humans and positioned by fluoroscopy. Distention of the stomach and electrical stimulation were thus possible. A discriminatory analysis of direct visceral stimulus and sensation could be carried out with increasing intensity of stimulation. Vague general sensations in the area were noted first; these proceeded to simple discrete sensations which could be localized between two points, and finally localization of two successive stimuli to two distinct loci was possible. In this way it seemed that conscious reactivity could be separated from unconscious reactivity. It was possible in another experiment to develop a "vascular neurosis" by disrupting a conditioned reflex stereotype: A flash of blue light or words that a blue light was being flashed preceded warming of the epigastrium (vasodilatation) on odd trials and cooling of gastric mucosa (vasoconstriction) on even trials. When the trial sequence was not followed and the blue or red light flashed indiscriminately, wholly irregular and conflicting vasomotor responses occurred, accompanied by vomiting, sensory disturbance, and headache. It seems that (1) interoceptive stimulation is followed by unconscious reactions, (2) interoceptive conditioning itself is largely unconscious, (3) interoceptive conditioning is an inherent response which is constantly being activated, (4) interoceptive conditioning is slower, but more fixed, with greater tendency to irreversibility and more dominant than exteroceptive conditioning, (5) if interoceptive and exteroceptive stimuli in the same conditioned reaction are juxtaposed, a certain degree of conflict and disturbance of the conditioning process may be noted

Razran believes that eventual material validation of Freudian dynamics will come from studies of interoception and interoceptive conditioning. He considers that experimental evidence from studies of interoceptive conditioning suggests not only that anxiety feelings or their unconscious visceral equivalents may become conditioned stimuli for organ dysfunction, but also that sensations derived from malfunctioning organs may be conditioned to produce anxiety or result in other disturbances of psychophysical homeostasis.

What leads a patient with uncomfortable or disagreeable physical sensations to seek medical attention is multidetermined. The timing of such a move is a particularly complicated matter. The somatic factors are, to be sure, closely linked with the disease process, but become manifest to the patient in the form of symptoms, which in turn can be quite variable and not necessarily reflecting for him the actual organ system involved. This is due to the many different ways that the sensorimotor components from which symptoms are formed are capable of being assembled in the individual's thinking processes. Anxiety, denial, rationalization, activated symbolic potential of the area involved, secondary gain, and other psychological

elements play a role in determining the patient's degree and kind of awareness of his physical dysfunction, the discomfort he experiences, and what
he does about it. He may not actually know or may only guess from his
physical sensations what organ is involved. Sometimes he may have been
told. Not infrequently, the presenting symptom and accompanying physical
sensations bear for the patient no apparent relationship to the actual organ
which is malfunctioning. Backache, for example, may be attributed by him
to muscle strain and yet may be due to a kidney involvement. Headache
may be the chief symptom of a disease elsewhere than in the head, and so
on. The patient's associations may thus not necessarily lead directly to the
involved organ, but may come to it by a circuitous route. In the process of associating, there may be references to past physical illness, symptoms, or
troublesome sensations, not necessarily concerned only with the currently
malfunctioning organ, but with other body areas, and not only in himself,
but in other persons. In addition, the past emotional setting in which these
physical responses occurred may also be elicited, and can provide useful
and relevant information.

In this series, pain was the symptom and sensation most often presented by the patients. Despite its prevalence in illness in general, it has
until recently received relatively little attention from a psychoanalytic point
of view. In 1957, Szasz wrote comprehensively on the subject. He considered pain from three levels of symbolizations: (1) It can be conceived
of as a signal warning of danger to the integrity of the body and can be
registered by the perceptive functions of the ego. This is a concept which
refers to "the biologically given meaning of pain." It is acquired independently of cultural determinants and is applicable to animals. It is a
phenomenon involving only the affected individual. (2) Pain can be conceived of as a basic method of asking for help. Two or more individuals are
involved, and when the pain experience is communicated from one to the
other, problems arise in terms of validation and the possible differences in
the meaning of "body" to the participants in the interchange. (3) From
the standpoint of communication, pain may have various symbolic meanings. Rather than a reference to the body it may be a disguised plea for
help, a symbol of feared attack or anticipated punishment, or a repressed
aggressive impulse against an external object. If the body, as an object of
the ego, acquires special meaning because of psychological transference to
it of feelings and attitudes originally directed to other people, pain then
may serve as an affect, warning the ego of possible loss of the external
objects, as well as part or all of the body.

Engel (1959) has referred to "pain-prone" patients as those who are
in good physical health when life situations are adverse, but then become
ill with accompanying pain when these change for the better. He com-

mented (1961) on the need to suffer experienced by many individuals, and how illness, especially when pain is a major symptom, becomes a means of atonement for guilt and a way of self-punishment. He presents a case in which a glomus tumor of the toe and a peptic ulcer were sources of considerable pain to a patient for over 25 years. During this time, however, the sufferer had great success in business. Following surgical treatment and cure of these illnesses, together with cessation of the pain, the individual began to experience reverses both in his general condition and in his fortunes. When circumstances made further medical assistance impossible and ended his success in business, an extended phase of peace and tranquility set in for both the patient and his family.

Schneider (1962) emphasizes the anticipatory function of pain. Pain immediately experienced leads to immediate avoidance of the noxious stimulus, thus becoming a warning of further possible trauma. The question is raised, however, whether pain or anxiety warn the ego about "anticipated danger of body injury." This would appear to be a function of anxiety, but both pain and anxiety are so closely interwoven that it may be very difficult to distinguish between them at times. Schneider postulates that indifference to pain (confined to body surface) may have its origins in childhood (oedipal) attempts to ward off danger, specifically the threat of castration. He feels that the ego response is characterized by reactivation of the very early defense of denial, and the ego state resembles that seen in depersonalization.

Perceptions in general may be blocked from an individual's awareness, as already indicated. To extend consideration of this matter further, it may be noted that a physical illness (such as the lung disease in Case 4) may go through a "silent phase" when a physical symptom is not evident as such. This time interval is one in which bodily changes triggered by shifts in the individual's psychophysical equilibrium are taking place without any overt manifestations. However, during this period, indirect and less specific indications of such ongoing physical dysfunction may be found in the associative responses of the patient, though their significance is outside his awareness. They would be derived from internal stimuli developing as a result of the early effects of the disease process on a particular organ system or body area. These excitations in the form of sensory clusters and/or motor-visceral referents then may become linked with associative chains or previous experiences involving the integrity of the particular body area. In this way, a combination of past and current references to the involved area may appear in disguised form in the individual's consciousness. As the illness develops, these combinations may be replaced by more discrete sensations and overt physical symptoms in the individual's awareness, though in certain instances this replacement may be long delayed.

The point at which symptoms become consciously perceived depends on anatomic, physiologic, and biochemical factors, but not altogether. Powerful psychological forces may prevent or delay various body perceptions from entering consciousness.

Prominent among these is the process of denial, already mentioned. The form which denial takes as a psychological mechanism of defense varies from simple to complicated. Simple denial is involved when a patient, asked about a symptom of his, may respond by saying that he has no symptom. When reminded of his recurrent headache, he asks, "Do you consider headache to be a symptom?" Seidenberg (1963) has noted that some patients may interpret the presence of psychological elements in the total clinical picture as being an indication that hidden powers may be brought into play against actual physical disease. Focus on emotional aspects may then be used by the patient to deny the existence of a feared organic illness. Such patients seem only too willing to furnish an overabundance of psychological data with which investigators may become more or less exclusively absorbed. The physical symptom often is referred to as a neurotic manifestation, when it is actually organic.

La belle indifférence is a frequent response to physical manifestations in hysterics who admit the presence of somatic symptoms but do not permit themselves to be affected by them in any way. Physical symptoms may continue to be minimized even when they persist or become more intense. Many forms of denial have an early origin. Parental attitudes which incorporate some element of denial are communicated to children and influence their responses to physical symptoms and illness.

Another variable noted in this study is pathological superego formation and function, especially in conjunction with powerful aggressive impulses turned inward. This combination can be found in persons who develop either serious mental or physical illness. It has been postulated that formation of the superego results in the fixation of large quantities of aggressive instinct in the ego which then may operate in a self-destructive way, more or less. Freud (1939) stated: "This is one of the dangers to health to which mankind became subject on the path to cultural development. The holding back of aggressiveness is in general unhealthy and leads to illness. Some portion of self-destructiveness remains permanently within, until at length it succeeds in doing the individual to death, not perhaps until his libido has been used up or has become fixated in some disadvantageous way."

Age is another variable to be considered in the complex of psychophysical factors that produce symptoms of bodily dysfunction. Infancy presents its own special background because physical and psychological states are more primitive, yet at the same time are beginning to undergo significant changes. Homeostatic regulators are relatively unstable. Immunity is undeveloped and there may be, concomitantly, frequent exposure to infectious agents. The child is relatively more dependent and helpless than it will be later on. Bowel and bladder control, locomotion, speech, and language are all in process of development. This is the period when sensori-motor patterns, symbolization of body parts, and reactions to emotionally significant figures in both health and illness, will become interrelated to form psychophysical prototypes which may emerge later in time of stress to influence the kind of symptoms and degree of physical dysfunction that will develop. Latency with its relative quiescence, and puberty and adolescence with their resurgence of psychophysical developmental activity and their reactivation of earlier emotional conflicts, provide a different setting for the development of physical symptoms. The long period of adulthood is characterized by a relative stabilization of psychophysical development. The patients seen in this series belong to this age group. When the involutional period sets in, once again the potential for greater psychophysical fluctuations and regressions is reinforced by actual psychophysical changes which occur in all individuals during this period. These involutional processes which may involve perceptual and motor apparatuses deepen in the aging individual, and his more rigid psychological reactions are also subject to the influence of an inexorable reality that less and less living time can be anticipated.

Accidental and incidental factors play a role in illness but are difficult to predict in advance, and involve, to a certain extent, the element of chance. This qualification is made because, at times, what on the surface appears to be due to chance, can be found to have been basically determined by the individual's current emotional state which led him to act in a way harmful to his physical health, e.g., accident proneness, alcoholism and drug addiction, unnecessary exposure, and the like. Most often, the accidental and incidental factors in the individual's environment are thought of in terms of their noxious effect: bacteria, viruses, toxins, allergens, injurious physical and chemical agents of all kinds, realistically difficult interpersonal relationships, and socioeconomic insults. Insufficiently considered are those aspects of the environment, whether they be physico-chemical, socioeconomic, or psychological, which influence a *favorable* shift in the individual's psychophysical equilibrium. Though it appears at first glance paradoxical, physical sickness, like other misfortune which entails a certain degree of suffering, may symbolically represent punishment and atonement, relieving the pressures of guilt feelings. Other life experiences, such as a new benevolent or loving personal relationship, the achievement of a position of power or prestige, or oppositely, changes in external circumstances which decrease one's responsibilities, may all act to reassure the individual, relieve his guilt, and decrease his anxiety or depression. However, favorable environmental events do not in themselves necessarily guarantee improvement. The individual's internal psychophysical state and, in particular, his current adaptational capacities will determine more basically which way the equilibrium will shift.

Theoretical Implications

The manifestations of illness as expressed in the form of physical symptoms have been studied in this presentation from a psychodynamic point of view. The focus has been on a number of psychological variables: (1) overt and more subtle indicators of psychological stress; (2) shifts in psychological equilibrium; (3) affective responses; (4) psychological mechanisms of defense; (5) processes of somatic identification (and related psychological sensitization or conditioning of organ systems); (6) recurrent sensorimotor patterns; (7) other factors, including superego-ego tensions and preexisting pregenital elements of emotional conflict.

While a detailed study of each of these factors is essential for a better understanding of physical symptoms accompanying illness, no one of them alone or in combination with others can be said to represent the necessary *and* sufficient condition for the development of such manifestations. Recently, workers in this area have referred increasingly to the multifactorial causation of disease, and the present study, while focusing on psychological factors, reemphasizes such a concept. It should be noted, however, that not only physical symptoms and illnesses are related to multiple systems—the psychological and the somatic (including constitutional influences) in the individual, the social, the economic, and the physicochemical in his environment—but that there are also multiple factors in each system. This makes for a considerable variety of causal combinations, hierarchical levels, transactional and interactional patterns related to the development of somatic dysfunction in different individuals, and in the same individual at different times.

The development of physical symptoms, whether or not they are due to organic disease, is related to an insufficiency of the psychological systems for handling the stimulus influx mobilized by stress. Ideational, affective, or behavioral responses, singly or in combination, cannot fully discharge these excitations, though in some individuals the capacity to do so is greater than in others. Furthermore, in any given person this capacity may

414

vary from time to time, though within certain limits. The matter cannot be explained simply on the basis of quantities of psychological energy and their displaceability. As yet, even this concept is limited by the inaccessibility to measurement of psychological energies. The concept has usefulness when one contrasts the primitive, compelling tendencies toward reduction of activated drives by immediate, direct somatic discharge with the binding of such energies through the development of pathways and structures which postpone and reroute their discharge. However, psychological systems are so highly complex that additional psychoanalytic points of view about these systems need to be mentioned. Both heredity and development influence psychological functioning. The dynamic point of view suggests that there are basic instinctual drives, derivative drives, and drive objects in the environment, as well as psychological defense and control systems, some of them automatized, but all of them forces which motivate and influence psychological response. The topographic point of view postulates not only that a certain amount of mental activity and functioning occurs outside the awareness of the individual, but also that these unconscious processes have different characteristics than those that are conscious. Psychological systems are also considered to have structure; the id, ego, and superego represent the basic organizations. These provide a certain degree of stability to psychological response. There are also autonomous and acquired structures. The role of the ego in dealing with internal and external stimuli is, of course, a central one. Finally, the adaptive point of view suggests that the environment is not necessarily a source of conflict for the individual but may provide a setting which both facilitates and evokes adaptation. Thus, the shunting of reactions from psychological to physical systems that takes place under the influence of stress is most complicated, even when this situation is considered from a study of the psychological phenomena alone.

In *nonphysical illness*, somatic dysfunction is not limited in location or duration, but is limited in terms of physicochemical change, which is often modifiable and responsive to psychotherapeutic intervention. However, chronicity, severe psychopathology, and secondary gain may present considerable interference in the treatment and resolution of the underlying emotional problems. In those instances where physical innervations are used for symbolic expression of both the repressed, forbidden, predominantly libidinal instinctual drive and defense against its direct discharge, a conversion process may be said to be in effect, extending through the whole range of psychopathology. Nonspecific physical sequelae of emotional tensions, undischarged affects, and generally what has been called the chronic, dammed-up state constitute a less well-defined area of somatic dysfunction on the borderline of organic disease, with its still more complex relationships of psychological and physical factors.

Are there any common psychological denominators which are involved in the development of *organic illness* in general, its symptoms, onset, progression, improvement, exacerbation, and final outcome? What factors play a role in determining the kind of physical disease that occurs in different individuals? These are complicated and difficult questions. As a result of the findings in this study, the following formulations are proposed, principally from the standpoint of the psychological factors which are necessary, but by themselves are not sufficient to cause somatic illness: Stress always precedes the onset of physical disease, but stress does not inevitably lead to it. Other outcomes may result, such as: primarily psychological illness with or without somatic manifestations; no clearly definable sickness but a condition of dis-ease; or little if any perceptible disturbance. The most frequent psychological stress preceding the development of organic disease is actual, threatened, or symbolic loss of objects which have *basic* importance for the individual, occurring in the absence of adequate substitutes and associated with overwhelming, continuing, unrelieved frustration in attempting to cope with and resolve the impact of such loss. These objects, originally human, may have other representations and connections, animate or inanimate, involving job, money, physical or intellectual capacities, reputation, familiar surroundings, hobbies, food, alcohol or drug gratifications, and the like. Further findings in individuals who develop physical disease are the presence of psychopathological remainders from childhood, characterized by predominance of pregenital elements and considerable ego-superego tensions. The impact of stress will first affect psychological systems in which these elements are prominent. Shifts in equilibrium will occur. Psychological coping mechanisms, frequently including those of denial and overactivity, but essentially nonspecific for any given physical disease, will then be activated. Libidinal energies will tend to be regressively redirected more and more to the self, while the ego function of neutralization will be increasingly impaired. Thus the stage will be set for an upsurge of intense, unmodified aggressiveness. If such destructive energies accumulate and their discharge through affective, ideational, and behavioral pathways becomes increasingly insufficient, a point will be reached where critical shunting of such discharge to physical systems occur. *Major* somatic dysfunction will then be triggered off. Limited capacities for handling marked emotional stress through psychological systems are found in those who develop organic disease. These reactive limits may represent a specific, inherited characteristic of the individual's adaptive abilities.

In the physical systems there are one or more potential target areas or organs which have a special responsiveness to the impact of stress. These have been determined by multiple factors, especially heredity, which creates potentials for such reactivity and for utilization of particular physical mechanisms through which the somatic compliance is effected. Sensitization or conditioning of particular somatic systems is further affected by the vicissitudes of development. Infectious disease in early life may cause not only specific organ involvement but also secondary physical complications. The accompanying sensations and symptoms occurring at this time, when both physical and psychological systems of the individual are relatively unstable, may become associated with antecedent and accompanying emotional disturbances, especially those involving the individual's relationship to the key figures around him at the time. Complex, conditioned psychophysical responses could thus be established, which later, activated under critical stress, may manifest themselves in combinations of particular psychological and physical symptoms—the latter from the sensitized and conditioned body areas, which have become established as such for the individual. Physical symptoms in related important persons early in the individual's life may reactivate and reinforce still earlier sensorimotor links to these figures. Any consequent somatic identification also seems to play a role in determining which body parts are sensitized to respond to later stress, and are thus more apt to become involved in physical processes.

While all these psychological factors are of importance in organic illness, their relationship to the individual's age and to the incidental and accidental physicochemical stresses to which he is exposed must also be taken into consideration. Early in life, psychophysical structures, organizations, and mechanisms are in the process of development, and at puberty they are subject to further internal changes. Their relative stability during adulthood is again affected by the involutional phase and by the processes of aging. In addition, the cumulative effect of life experiences will be different at different age periods. Thus, the individual's adaptive powers will vary both qualitatively and quantitatively, depending on which period in his life is exposed to critical stress. Though emotional factors (often largely outside the individual's awareness) may play a role in exposing him to noxious environmental stimuli, such exposure may occur at times on the basis of chance and may thus be simply unavoidable.

The course of physical disease and its manifestations, while dependent on multiple causes, including the extent and reversibility of structural changes and physicochemical malfunction, is, from the psychological standpoint, particularly influenced by quantitative factors. Among these are the kind, duration, and intensity of the psychological stress, which can be both primary and secondary. The former may be acute and self-limited, relentlessly intensifying, or chronic, with the individual "locked into" it. Secondary stress reflects the individual's reaction to the physical disease, also invoking a wide range of responses and putting a further strain on the psychophysical equilibrium. Increase in total stress tends to favor exacerbation, decrease tends to favor remission of the somatic illness and its manifestations. Persistence of stress and underlying emotional conflicts may influence a relative fixation of the involved physical systems as principal adaptive responses. The effectiveness of medical or surgical intervention must be considered not only in terms of reversing, modifying, or mitigating the somatic dysfunction, but also in connection with its impact on the individual's psychic economy, which may be influenced favorably or unfavorably. Relief of physical symptoms and illness, in the presence of persisting, sufficiently high-level emotional tension, may lead to unexpected complications. The successful medical or surgical intervention may have blocked the originally involved physical systems as pathways of discharge for emotional conflict, requiring further adaptive shifts and possibly other physical or psychological outlets for this purpose. New symptoms and another kind of illness may be the outcome.

The individual's reactions to physical illness and associated symptoms may range from denial of varying degree to marked panic, depending on what kind of psychological coping devices are activated and how effective they are. One particular response—that of secondary gain—requires special attention. Although the physical manifestations of illness are generally unpleasant and disagreeable, the individual's adaptation to them often contains elements of secondary gain. While financial compensation appears as a frequent advantage thus derived, the real basis of secondary gain is the presence of strong, chronic, unsatisfied, repressed, infantile needs for emotional supplies. These are represented by attention, pity, comfort, and reassurance which are used to ward off fears of being left alone and helpless. This childhood need to be taken care of may be powerfully reactivated in time of crisis, and illness—whether emotional or physical—is this type of stressful situation. The attention the individual requires may not always be from other people. Mitigation of ego–superego tensions is a less obvious kind of secondary gain which the suffering from illness affords. Another aspect of secondary gain which is frequently overlooked is that, when physical illness develops, the presence of psychological difficulties in general can be and often is denied. When these various advantages, one or several in combination, become associated with organic disease, the tendency toward chronicity becomes greatly enhanced.

Some Clinical Observations

INTERVIEWING

Regrettably, many nonpsychiatric physicians do not look for or pay attention to those determinants in the case history which have a bearing on the patient's psychological state. This seems to be due either to lack of information, training, experience, conviction, aptitude, or a combination of these factors. Much information which is of immediate clinical pertinence or would provide invaluable research material is just not collected, or at least never gets into the record. There is need for training and experience in interviewing techniques which can be used by all physicians for eliciting data about psychological disturbance, irrespective of the presenting symptoms and signs. The associative anamnesis or various modifications of it represent an example of such a technique. Unfortunately, such interviewing techniques, insofar as they might be applied to the comprehensive examination of medical or surgical cases, are not usually taught in medical schools, or, if they are presented at all, the opportunities to use these "instruments" are limited. By the time the student is graduated and enters internship and residency training, he is caught up in the hustle and bustle of his work, often with almost exclusive emphasis on the physical aspects of his cases. There are, of course, exceptions to this trend in medical school and postgraduate curricula. Some attempts have been made to increase the awareness of the practicing nonpsychiatric physician about the presence of emotional factors in every case he sees. These efforts are in the form of seminars, review conferences, or special courses; but even here, the exposure is limited, superimposed as it were, and cannot really make up for what belongs in medical school and internship programs. Such courses are best taught early, when they have the greatest chance of taking hold, and in conjunction with comprehensive exercises in physical diagnosis, in fact as an integral part of the interviewing of somatically ill patients done at that time.

In interviewing a patient with physical complaints, it is possible that

419

different examiners will not elicit the same chief symptoms (Case 3). This may be due to a number of reasons: The training and experience of interviewers may differ considerably, or interviewing techniques may vary from strictly superficial to complexly dynamic. Particularly important are the patient's initial transference reactions which may range from strongly positive to strongly negative, making it possible for some physical symptoms and related associations to be easily elicited by one interviewer and suppressed or even repressed in the presence of another.

Several rather striking examples of medical patients' responses to an associative anamnestic interview (in the presence of a small group of interns and residents) will be briefly cited. The first of these patients, an adolescent of 19, was admitted to the medical service with the chief complaint of difficulty in swallowing. He had been carefully worked up and no organic basis for this symptom had been elicited. The intern, who had some interest in the relationship of psychological factors to illness, previously had attempted unsuccessfully to learn about possible emotional difficulties which might be related to the patient's complaints. The interview held in front of the group was remarkable in that the patient acted as if only he and the senior interviewer were there. He brought up another, previously unmentioned symptom, dysuria, which in turn was related to compulsive masturbation. He confessed, as it were, to preoccupation with fellatio fantasies during masturbatory activity. Positive transference elements, quickly developed, had led the patient to see the interviewing psychiatrist as a kindly authority figure who understood and forgave the sexual activity. The figure of the past represented by the interviewer was an uncle, living with the family, who had intervened to protect him against his parents' brutal physical punishments for minor childish misdeeds. So powerful was the influence of the transference elements, that the presence of the group had been blocked out, and the patient could abreact with considerable relief of tension, followed by diminution of both dysuria (without organic basis) and dysphagia (which turned out to be globus hystericus).

Another patient, in his thirties, reacting negatively, did not mention his chief complaint of dyspnea in an interview with the psychiatrist, although he had described it in great detail to the medical student who had taken the original history. He had entered the hospital because of mild congestive failure associated with rheumatic heart disease. Actually, this had been quickly brought under control, but in the psychiatric interview, as the patient talked particularly about his boss (toward whom he had a strongly negative father transference) and tensions at work, he breathed heavily without being aware of it. He also moved his chair back a little at a time during the interview so that by the time it was over, the chair was four feet further away, having been finally brought to a halt by a nearby wall. The patient had not been aware of this movement which had rather dramatically opened up so much space between him and the interviewer (also seen as a potentially hostile father figure).

Usually, while different symptoms and their connections may be traced down different associative pathways, if they are pursued far enough they will lead to the core emotional conflicts of the individual patient. Different interviewers with competent training thus should be able to gain at least a generally similar understanding of a given patient's basic emotional difficulties, even though the physical symptoms elicited initially may not always be the same. Generally, psychiatric interviewing tends to focus on ideas and affects, and overlooks sensorimotor patterns or the extraordinary variety of related concomitant physical manifestations that can be observed if one is looking for them. Such data are a rich source of information about the individual's particular psychophysical responses and should not be disregarded, whether interviewing is done for purely clinical reasons or to collect research data. Interviews should be so structured as to make it possible to elicit the associations which reveal the presence of such long-standing psychophysical configurations which otherwise might be bypassed all too easily.

Sensorimotor patterns are also a valuable source of information about the individual's early perceptions of emotionally significant persons in terms of their symbolic somatic representation. Often such patterns will appear in associative chains linked to the symptoms of physical disease; they may be considered to be of little value and thus not get the attention they deserve. It is through the associative connections derived from physical symptoms and, in particular, their sensorimotor patterns, that the particular illness may be more fully understood in terms of earlier psychological and somatic interrelationships. It should be emphasized, however, that in an interview, the patient communicates not only verbally, but by facial expression, emotional or affective discharge, postural patterns, other motor activity, vasomotor responses, and still other ways which may be perceived by the interviewer through visual, auditory, or olfactory channels. All these methods of communication and their interconnections should be carefully noted.

Sensory perceptions may have other significance outside the individual's awareness. When they are derived from the rapidly developing bodily changes associated with the prodromata of an acute organic illness and connected with the patient's perceptions and emotional reactions to current events, the combination may reveal indirectly the presence of the disease process. The following case strikingly illustrates this. A single, female nursery worker in her early twenties had been in analysis for a year when she and her boyfriend broke up. She reacted to this with some overt depression and but little evident hostility. The content of her associations, however, suggested a very sensitive reaction to rejection and loss, with considerable negative impact on her narcissistic feelings. In the following week she mentioned that an "epidemic" of illness had been causing much absenteeism among the children. She did not, however, make any further, more specific comment about this event. Several days later she reported a dream: She and an uncle were riding in a red convertible in the back seat of which was a barking German police dog. The associations to this dream suggested a preoccupation with her appearance and how she would look to others. She also was reminded of her aunt's illness and death, and was concerned about her own physical integrity. In addition, there were associative references to being hurt from behind, with description of the accompanying sensations of pain that might be experienced. A variation of this general theme expressed on a different level was the frequent expectation of being criticized by the analyst. The next day the patient came for her interview, but this time was quite preoccupied with complaints of malaise, a reddish rash on her chest and arms, and painful "lumps" behind her ears, these having developed a few hours previously. She had come down with German measles. Sensory perceptions derived from the rapidly developing bodily changes associated with the prodromata of the disease had apparently combined with certain perceptions about the prevalence of sickness at the nursery school. This combination occurred against a background of recently activated feelings of rejection and deprivation which had deep infantile roots. The working over of this in the patient's unconscious resulted in the dream. The subsequent associations pointed in the direction of a preoccupation with the possibilities of illness which actually had already begun.

PSYCHOTHERAPY

In Case 2, the patient (with Hodgkin's disease) had had no psychotherapy during his hospitalization or subsequently. Although his physical history contained some references to situational factors and their possible connection with the recurrence of illness, the internist had taken no further cognizance of these psychological elements. Such a reaction may occur frequently, if an organic illness is suspected or its diagnosis is confirmed. It is as if, then, the usefulness of psychological data is considered to be minimal, and all attention may be focused on the organic therapies. This is understandable in a life-threatening situation, but such instances are relatively infrequent, compared with the many illnesses in which there is no immediate danger. Patients in whom a diagnosis of physical disease is made have not only the emotional problems which existed prior to the onset of illness, but also psychological reactions secondarily related to the disease itself. These complicate the course of the illness. Under their influence, patients exhibit a varying psychological regression, which in some individuals may be considerable, in the form of infantile attitudes and behavior, more labile affective responses, and thinking which borders on the unreal or even becomes psychotic. Awareness and understanding of the meaning of these primary and secondary emotional responses is necessary for a truly comprehensive treatment approach.

In another patient with lymphoma, not in this series, the principal physical manifestation in the irregularly recurrent episodes of illness was pain from shifting regional adenopathy, usually cervical, axillary, or inguinal. Fever was either minimal or absent. This individual was seen in psychotherapy over a period of years, and detailed observations could be made about the psychophysical aspects of his sickness. In his case also, there was a buildup of emotional stress before physical symptoms and signs of a relapse manifested themselves. Tensions were related principally to chronic marital crises. Conflict with a phallic, castrating wife resulted in mobilization of intense hostility which was only partially and occasionally discharged through a rage reaction, culminating in things being thrown by the patient at his wife. Such reactions were quite out of character for him, who, most of the time, was an extremely polite, soft-spoken, gentle, shy person. Marked sensitivity to rejection, particularly by his wife, and somewhat less prominent anxiety about his ability to compete with other men in his field were the principal areas of psychological difficulty in this passive–feminine man. There was an underlying intense sense of guilt, often outside awareness, which derived from his accumulated hostility and also from episodic heterosexual adventures. This acting out was multidetermined, but an important aspect was that the affairs were selected (unconsciously) in such a way as to needlessly put his reputation in jeopardy. As he came close on several occasions to being caught and exposed, the purpose this served as a potential punishment became quite clear. While this patient received courses of X-ray therapy for each physical exacerbation, his psychotherapeutic treatment afforded ego support, opportunities for recognition and ventilation of feelings, particularly hostility, modification of his acting out, and a limited development of insight. An improvement in psychological as well as physical well-being occurred, following the combined treatment approach, and the interval between relapses became longer. He has been maintained in this way for a period of over 10 years.

In Case 7, the patient, whose leg pain represented a conversion reaction, was referred to a mental hygiene clinic for psychiatric treatment. Here was an instance where the physician in charge of the case had recognized the major role played in it by emotional factors and had recommended specialized therapy. Unfortunately, all too often, such recommendations are not followed, or if treatment is actually begun, it soon founders. This is due to a number of circumstances. The patient's preparation for psychotherapy may be inadequate. The attitude of the general practitioner, internist, or other specialist who does the referring, the tact with which the referral is made, the recognition and careful handling of the patient's anxieties, negativism, or other manifestations of resistance can be crucial in making it possible for the patient to undertake this new experience. Should any of these aspects be improperly handled, then in all likelihood the patient's reluctance or outright refusal may only be reinforced. It is helpful to be aware, even if only on a superficial basis, of the individual patient's specific concerns.

Motivation for treatment will vary from individual to individual. The trained physician will be able to distinguish rational readiness for treatment from neurotic motives and at least roughly estimate the proportion of each. Neurotic motivation reflects the patient's infantile needs and expectation of their gratification from treatment. In some patients, motives will be more reality-oriented, and the individual will be more apt to recognize and undertake to deal with his illness accordingly. Environmental factors, particularly the positive or negative advice and/or pressures from relatives, friends, or others close to the patient cannot be disregarded. The patient's suffering, as associated with his symptoms, whether physical, psychological, or both, will exert a causal effect in motivating the patient to seek out treatment, but not always. Under certain conditions, when a high degree of masochism is present, suffering may serve the gratification of this neurotic tendency. There are those patients who seemingly live on their physical or emotional discomfort as experienced through their symptomatology. They find this very difficult to give up, because through illness they can get attention, pity, and various material and emotional supplies from the world around them. Here, suffering, in the service of secondary gain from illness, will not help to motivate a patient to seek psychiatric help. The more chronic and "frozen" the emotional disturbance, the greater will be the patient's resistance toward entering treatment, or, if already in it, toward continuing.

The patient whose case was described above actually went for only one visit to the mental hygiene clinic where he had been referred. Despite the suffering which he emphasized he was experiencing, the secondary-gain element interfered significantly with his motivation for treatment and he did not return again to the clinic.

In chronic illness, secondary-gain aspects may assume special importance (Case 10). If secondary gain becomes established as a complicating factor in such illness, recovery—from a psychophysical standpoint—will be impeded. Simply stated, under these circumstances, sickness is used to gain something for the individual from the outside world. Often it appears as if what is gained is attention. Such attention, however, has a more significant and complex underlying meaning which can be related to a persisting infantile need for love, reassurance, and most deeply—evidence of parental affection and acceptance. This aspect of secondary gain involves the use of the chronic illness by the individual patient to manipulate relationships with the people who are emotionally important to him. Such needs can be noted in those individuals who have sustained severe emotional trauma in childhood, associated with strong feelings of deprivation, loss of love, and in turn disturbed relationships with family figures, subsequently reactivated and reinforced by the vicissitudes of life. It has been shown repeatedly that the insistence on and fight for financial compensation in connection with illness may be due basically to the symbolic meanings (just described) which the pension or other monetary return has for the individual involved. Certain patients with intense guilt feelings may derive secondary gain from their chronic suffering through the diminution of superego–ego tensions. Physically ill patients may also be able to point to their symptoms or illness as adequate reason for not being able to assume certain responsibilities.

Chronic illness with increasingly greater secondary-gain elements may become the principal way of life for individuals so afflicted. Consequently, such patients may be said in fact to live on their illnesses. Psychotherapy as a supplement to any medical (or related) procedures in such cases will meet with the greatest difficulties. Thus, if early estimates can be made about the possibility of chronicity in any given patient with physical symptoms and/or illness, psychotherapeutic intervention, if indicated, should be instituted as soon as possible. A prompt combined treatment approach prevents the development of secondary-gain factors which, if not confronted early enough, would complicate the condition once they had become established.

In another case, not in this series, both recent and remote trauma played a significant role in disruption of the patient's psychophysical equilibrium. However, it was possible to favorably influence the course of the illness with a combined approach of carefully worked-out medical regimen and psychotherapeutic intervention.

The patient, a pharmacist in his early sixties, originally came for psychiatric consultation because of deepening depression. At that time he presented no physical symptoms, though he revealed that 10 years before, after experiencing rather prolonged easy fatigability, he had been examined by a physician who found "high blood pressure." Subsequent checkups revealed pressures in the range of 170 to 180/80 to 90. The patient was reassured by his physician and thereafter had no further physical complaints.

He was the older of two siblings, his brother, now a successful lawyer, having been born when the patient was 14 years old. For a long time the patient was an only child but, because parents were both busy in the family business, he was looked after by his maternal grandmother who spoiled him a great deal and would also frighten him with ghost stories and tales about his grandfather's death. He grew up to be a rather shy individual, sensitive, easily upset by losses, but a hard worker who put himself through pharmacy school and then went into business for himself. When he was not working, he would read extensively. He was married and had two grown sons.

The patient's depression clearly coincided with the finalization of plans for urban renewal which involved the area in which his pharmacy had been located for over 30 years. This had been his little "domain" where he ruled as a "benevolent neighborhood despot," being looked up to and admired for his considerate attitude toward his customers and for his obviously superior intellect. The early interviews were filled with many references to the traumatic effect the forced giving up of his business was having on him. It had also activated the involutional process and this became part of his depressive tendencies. He thought that "everything" was over, that he could not get started again, and that he had made many terrible mistakes in the past. It was felt that a supportive approach was indicated in the treatment. This was done in the form of sympathetic listening, reassurance, exploration of the more optimistic possibilities in his reality situation, and emphasis on the positives in his past. This, together with the patient's ability to ventilate some of his more immediate hostile feelings, resulted in a lessening of the depression. At this point, the therapist had to be away for a month, and treatment was interrupted. Subsequently, the patient did not resume treatment, but called to say that he continued to feel less depressed. Several months later, he arranged to come in for a "checkup," but arrived at the wrong time, waited an hour, and then left. A new appointment several weeks later was kept. At that time, he stated that his improvement was being maintained and that he had undertaken to start a new pharmacy in another section of the city. He indicated he was experiencing some somatic reactions: "butterflies in the stomach and slight vertigo." He ascribed this to nervous tension at the prospect of "starting from scratch all over again after so many years." He did not return for further interviews, but about a month later, after finalizing rental and renovation plans for his new store, he had increasing symptoms of vertigo and then an episode of Stokes-Adams syncope. He was hospitalized and a heart block with pulse rate of 30 to 32 per minute was discovered. On returning home, he had a number of syncopal attacks resulting in minor head injuries, despite a carefully worked out medical regimen, including increased doses of ephedrine. For a while he was restricted in his activities to a bed-chair area.

Psychotherapy was resumed at this time. Depressive manifestations could again be noted, but this time they appeared in part to be secondary to the physical illness. The patient described himself as an "empty shell" with no future. His long-standing inferiority feelings, long defended against by his position as "king" in the old store, had been greatly activated by the uncertainties of his new venture, and now by the physical difficulties he had been experiencing. Confidence was at a low ebb, and there was marked anxiety. Superego reactions to all this were in the form of much self-blame, devaluation, and guilt. The traumatic effect of his being dislocated from his old business had been reinforced by a second "shock wave"—the reality of having to start afresh in a new and strange setting. Once again, in the presence of an ambivalent but more positively weighted transference, a supportive approach was intensively employed. A more extensive airing of hostile thoughts and impulses was possible. Then after a month, the patient brought up highly traumatic childhood memories: When he was about six he had tried to get closer to his father, to have him show more affection. Time and again his father rudely and abruptly pushed him away, until the patient felt that he was not wanted or liked by his father. The rec-ollections, many years repressed in this man of over 60, were related with great emotion, and accompanied by bitter crying. Following these abreactive episodes he said: "I feel free, as if a burden had dropped off. I had been carrying this hate for so many years and now I feel as if I had made my peace with father." Following this, there was definite and increasing physi-cal improvement. The patient was able to increase his activities and had no further syncopal attacks. His pulse rate became stabilized in the forties. There was renewed self-confidence, manifested by a growing interest and participation in the late-stage planning and developments in the new store. Further psychotherapeutic work was in the direction of developing some further but limited insights into his basic emotional problems.

Some five years later, the patient had continued to feel well physically and had made his new store into a highly successful venture. He had been able to resume his formerly active life.

Meinhardt (1962) reports the case of a 28-year-old male whose only demonstrable cardiac pathology was manifested in intermittent episodes of Stokes-Adams syndrome. It was possible to correlate preceding expres-sions of intense grief and resentment over frustrated dependency feelings with the occurrence of episodes. A hypothesis is advanced that rage and fear, which ordinarily cause sympathetic physiologic discharge, are shifted by inhibition of the fight-flight response (anger might cause an intolerable loss of significant object) to intense vagal stimulation which precipitates heart block. Psychological defenses of repression, denial, and rationalization were noted.

Marked self-preoccupation with symptoms may be modified by tactful persistent diversion of the patient's attention to stimuli other than those originating in his body, and by searching out other interests of his and engaging him in these within the limits of his incapacity. An opposite emotional response to organic disease, as already noted in a number of cases in this series, occurs when the patient uses the mechanism of denial extensively. This may lead to irrational attitudes and behavior in the patient, but not necessarily. At times it may serve as a useful and not unhealthy form of psychological defense, enabling the patient to avoid being overwhelmed by the emotional impact of his illness. The defense of denial should, therefore, be carefully evaluated before any modifications of its influence are attempted.

PATIENTS' REACTIONS TO LABORATORY PROCEDURES

Obviously every clinical and laboratory procedure cannot and need not be evaluated routinely for its particular symbolic meaning for the patient. However, in certain instances, patients are resistive to these procedures, or else overreact to them. When this resistance is openly and dramatically manifested through fright, tearfulness, negativism, or other disturbed behavior, the consequences will vary depending on how the situation is handled by the patient's physician. Sometimes the individual can be forced into having the procedure done, but on other occasions crude pressure may result in the patient's leaving. If the patient's emotional reactions are clearly out of proportion to the reality aspects of the intended procedure, various approaches could be tried. If the situation is urgent, tactful firmness may be indicated. If feasible, however, some attempt could be made to inquire into the nature of the resistance in order to learn something of its cause. Even a partial understanding of the irrational components of the patient's reaction will be helpful in dealing with the situation and may determine what kind of approach is best suited to overcome the emotional resistance. Simple reassurance, suggestion, and explanation are supportive measures which may be useful as a kind of first-aid psychotherapy.

A patient's neurotic reactions to clinical and laboratory procedures are, of course, multidetermined. Some of the factors involved are the patient's current psychophysical state, the particular symbolic meanings a given procedure may have for him, his general reaction to being hospitalized, his transference responses to hospital personnel, the current attitudes of doctors, nurses, family figures, and the exposure to and familiarity with the intended procedure (or lack of it). Previous traumatic experiences in connection with doctors, examinations, and hospitalization may also influence the patient's reactions. The symbolic significance of what the patient is exposed to in medical (or surgical) treatment, whether at home, in the clinic or hospital, should neither be under- or overrated. A practical understanding of the emotional components involved, where indicated, can spare the patient much discomfort or suffering, and make diagnosis and treatment much more effective.

HOSPITALIZATION

Being in the hospital itself removes a patient from actual contact with disturbing situations and the immediate stimuli and excitations they arouse. Of course, this does not necessarily prevent him from thinking and reacting emotionally to the troublesome events. However, even some diminution in intensity of these activating situations—such as is possible through physical separation—can be useful. The hospital may be seen as a place where regressive psychophysical states are both tolerated and cared for. However, emotional disturbances, at times reinforced by actual or distorted previous unpleasant hospital experience, may cast an anxious pall over what the patient expects will happen to him there. This fearful expectancy may begin long before the individual actually is hospitalized. Admission to a hospital may at times be a hurried, even emergent matter. More often, it is not so urgent as to preclude the possibility of some preparation, even a brief one, by the referring physician. This is especially indicated when it is the individual's first hospital experience. Admission procedure itself at the receiving point in the hospital does not ordinarily have to be rushed and mechanical. Admitting personnel, whether they be nurses, social workers, or aides, as well as doctors, need to have some awareness of and experience in dealing with the special aspects of a patient's emotional reactions to entering the hospital. Psychiatric specialists are not necessary to do this kind of work or to handle most emotional reactions that patients exhibit once they are hospitalized.

In Case 17 (stomach pain, no ulcer found), the nursing personnel and the physician in charge gave the patient enough attention and support to at least partially satisfy his activated oral-dependent needs, and thus modify to some extent his feelings of deprivation. As his frustrations and concomitant hostility were lessened, he also could experience some relief of guilt feelings. The fact that his emotional upset was relatively recent also made possible a quicker and more favorable shift in psychophysical equilibrium, so that conversion symptoms were less prominent in the defensive realignments that were taking place. In more chronic and complicated cases such favorable changes do not occur so easily and may require the consultative help of the psychiatrist.

*   *   *

These brief clinical observations indicate that the data collected in this study can be usefully applied in understanding and treating physically sick patients. More psychophysical data about every conceivable kind of somatic illness needs to be collected. Its integration with related social and economic factors would contribute significantly to our concepts about health, disease, and dis-ease, enabling the clinical approach to the physically sick patient to become truly comprehensive.

Bibliography

Adamson, J. D., and Schmale, A. H., Jr. Object loss, giving up, and the onset of psychiatric disease. Psychosom. Med., 27:557, 1965.

Alexander, F. Psychosomatic Medicine. New York, W. W. Norton & Co., 1950.

———— The development of psychosomatic medicine. Psychosom. Med., 24:13, 1962.

———— Flagg, G. W., Foster, S., Clemen, T., and Bland, W. Experimental studies of emotional stress: I. Hyperthyroidism. Psychosom. Med., 23:104, 1961.

Alexander, R. P. Contribution to the psychological understanding of pruritus ani: Report of a case. Psychosom. Med., 21:182, 1959.

Alkan, L. Anatomische Organkrankheiten aus Seelischer Ursache. Stuttgart, Hippokrates-Verlag, 1930.

Appel, J., and Rosen, S. R. Psychotic Factors in Psychosomatic Illness. Psychosom. Med., 12:236, 1950.

Bacon, C. L., Renneker, R., and Cutler, M. A psychosomatic survey of cancer of the breast. Psychosom. Med., 14:453, 1952.

Benedek, T. Toward the Biology of the Depressive Constellation. Presented at Chicago Psychoanalytic Society, February, 1953.

Bernard, C. An Introduction to the Study of Experimental Medicine (1865). New York, Macmillan, 1927.

Bertalanffy, L. von. An outline of general systems theory. Brit. J. Phil. Sci., 1:134, 1950.

Browning, J. S., and Houseworth, J. H. Development of new symptoms following medical and surgical treatment for duodenal ulcer. Psychosom. Med., 15:328, 1953.

Calden, C., Dupertuis, C. S., Hokanson, J. E., and Lewis, W. C. Psychosomatic factors in the rate of recovery from tuberculosis. Psychosom. Med., 22:345, 1960.

Cannon, W. B. The Wisdom of the Body. New York, W. W. Norton & Co., Inc., 1932 (1939).

———— Bodily Changes in Pain, Hunger, Fear and Rage. Boston, Charles T. Branford Company, 1953.

Chafetz, M. E., and Schwab, R. S. Psychological factors involved in bizarre seizures: Report of four cases. Psychosom. Med., 21:96, 1959.

Chambers, W. N., and Reiser, M. F. Emotional stress in the precipitation of congestive heart failure. Psychosom. Med., 15:38, 1953.

Cleveland, S. E., and Fisher, S. A comparison of psychological characteristics and physiological reactivity in ulcer and rheumatoid arthritis groups. I. Psychological measures. Psychosom. Med., 22:283, 1960.

Day, G. P.P.S.: Pneuma, Psyche and Soma. Lancet, 2:691, 1952.

Deutsch, F. Psychoanalyse und Innere Medizin. Speech delivered at the Second Congress for Psychotherapy in Bad Nauheim, 1927.

—————— The associative anamnesis. Psychoanal. Quart., 8:354, 1939.

—————— Analytic synesthesiology. Int. P. Psychoanal., 35:293, 1954.

—————— ed. On the Mysterious Leap from the Mind to the Body. New York, International Universities Press, Inc., 1959.

—————— and Murphy, W. F. The Clinical Interview. New York, International Universities Press, Inc., 1955, Vol. 1.

Dunbar, H. F. Psychosomatic Diagnosis. New York, Hoeber, 1943.

—————— Emotions and Bodily Changes. 4th ed. New York, Columbia University Press, 1954 (First Edition, 1935).

Duncan, C. H., Stevenson, I. P., and Ripley, H. S. Life situations, emotions and paroxysmal auricular arrhythmias. Psychosom. Med., 12:23, 1950.

Engel, G. L. Studies of ulcerative colitis: III. The nature of the psychologic processes. Amer. J. Med., 19:231, 1955.

—————— Psychogenic pain and the pain-prone patient. Amer. J. Med., 26:899, 1959.

—————— Is grief a disease? Psychosom. Med., 23:18, 1961.

—————— Guilt, pain, and success. Psychosom. Med., 24:37, 1962a.

—————— Psychological Development in Health and Disease. Philadelphia, W. B. Saunders Co., 1962b.

Epstein, A. W., and Ervin, F. Psychodynamic significance of seizure content in psychomotor epilepsy. Psychosom. Med., 18:43, 1956.

Fechner, G. T. Einige Ideen zur Schöpfungs und Entwickelungsgeschichte der Organismen. Leipzig, Breitkopf und Härtel, 1873.

Fenichel, O. The Psychoanalytic Theory of Neurosis. New York, W. W. Norton & Co., 1945.

Féré, Ch. The Pathology of Emotions (trans. by Robert Park). London, The University Press, Ltd., 1899.

Ferenczi, S. The phenomena of hysterical materialization (1919). In Further Contributions to the Theory and Technique of Psychoanalysis. London: The Hogarth Press, 1950, pp. 89-104

Fox, H. M. Some recent trends in psychophysiological research. The Medical Clinics of North America, 44:1341, 1960.

French, T. M. Psychogenic factors in asthma. Amer. J. Psychiat., 96:87, 1939.

—————— and Alexander, F. Psychogenic Factors in Bronchial Asthma. Psychosom. Med. Monographs 4. Washington, D.C., National Research Council, 1941.

Freud, A. The Ego and the Mechanisms of Defense. New York, International Universities Press, Inc., 1946.

Freud, S. Psychogenic visual disturbances according to psychoanalytical conceptions. In Collected Papers, II. London, Hogarth Press, 1924, pp. 105-112.

—————— The Problem of Anxiety. New York, W. W. Norton & Co., 1936 (1926).

—————— An Outline of Psychoanalysis. New York, W. W. Norton & Co., 1949 (1938).

Freud, S. The Origins of Psychoanalysis. Letters, Drafts and Notes to Wilhelm Fliess (1887-1902). Project for a Scientific Psychology (1895). New York, Basic Books, 1954.

Garma, A. Internalized mother as harmful food in peptic ulcer patients. Int. J. Psychoanal., 34:102, 1953.

Gibson, J. G. Emotions and the thyroid gland: A critical appraisal. J. Psychosom. Res., 6:93, 1962.

Gottschalk, L. A., Serota, H. M., and Shapiro, L. B. Psychologic conflict and neuromuscular tension: I. Preliminary report on a method as applied to rheumatoid arthritis. Psychosom. Med., 12:314, 1950.

Greene, W. A., Jr. Psychological factors and reticuloendothelial disease. I. Preliminary observations on a group of males with lymphomas and leukemias. Psychosom. Med., 16:220, 1954.

———— Role of a vicarious object in the adaptation to object loss: I. Use of a vicarious object as a means of adjustment to separation from a significant person. Psychosom. Med., 20:344, 1958.

———— Role of a vicarious object in the adaptation to object loss: II. Vicissitudes in the role of the vicarious object. Psychosom. Med., 21:438, 1959.

———— and Miller, G. Psychological factors and reticuloendothelial disease: IV. Observations on a group of children and adolescents with leukemia: An Interpretation of Disease Development in Terms of the Mother-Child Unit. Psychosom. Med., 20:124, 1958.

———— Young, L. E., and Swisher, S. N. Psychological factors and reticuloendothelial disease: II. Observations on a group of women with lymphomas and leukemias. Psychosom. Med., 18:284, 1956.

Grinker, R. R. Some current trends and hypotheses of psychosomatic research. In The Psychosomatic Concept in Psychoanalysis, Deutsch, F., ed. New York, International Universities Press, Inc., 1953, pp. 37-62.

———— and Robbins, F. P. Psychosomatic Case Book. New York, The Blakiston Company, Inc., 1954.

Groddeck, G. Die Psychische Bedingtheit und Psychoanalytische Behandlung Organischer Krankheiten. Berlin, S. Hirzel, 1917.

———— The Book of IT. New York and Washington, N.M.D. Pub. Co., 1928.

Ham, G. C., Alexander, F., and Carmichael, H. T. A psychosomatic theory of thyrotoxicosis. Psychosom. Med., 13:18, 1951.

Hamburger, W. W. Emotional aspects of obesity. Med. Clin. N. A., 35:483, 1951.

Hartmann, H., Kris, E., and Lowenstein, R. M. Notes on the theory of aggression. Psychoanal. Stud. Child, 3:9, 4:36, 1949.

Hebb, D. O. The Organization of Thought. New York, John Wiley & Sons, 1949.

Heiman, M. The role of stress situations and psychological factors in functional uterine bleeding. J. Mount Sinai Hosp. N.Y., 23:775, 1956.

Hendrick, I. Instinct and ego during infancy. Psychoanal. Quart., 11:33, 1942.

———— Early development of the ego: Identification in infancy. Psychoanal. Quart., 20:44, 1951.

———— Physiologic infantilism and psychosomatic disease: An Hypothesis. Paper read before the Boston Psychoanalytic Society, February, 1952.

Hinkle, L. E., Jr., Christenson, W. N., Kane, F. D., Ostfeld, A., Thetford, W. H., and Wolff, H. G. An investigation of the relation between life experience personality characteristics, and general susceptibility to illness. Psychosom. Med., 20:278, 1958.

Hinkle, L. E., Jr., Evans, F. M., and Wolf, S. Studies in diabetes mellitus: III. Life history of three persons with labile diabetes, and relation of significant experiences in their lives to the onset and course of the disease. Psychosom. Med., 13:160, 1951a.

────── Evans, F. M., and Wolf, S. Studies in diabetes mellitus: IV. Life history of three persons with relatively mild, stable diabetes, and relation of significant experiences in their lives to the onset and course of the disease. Psychosom. Med., 13:184, 1951b.

Holmes, T. H., Treuting, T., and Wolff, H. G. Life situations, emotions, and nasal disease: Evidence on summative effects exhibited in patients with hay "fever." Psychosom. Med., 13:71, 1951.

────── and Wolff, H. G. Life situations, emotions, and backache. Psychosom. Med., 14:18, 1952.

Imboden, J. B., Canter, A., and Cluff, L. Separation experiences and health records in a group of normal adults. Psychosom. Med., 25:433, 1963.

Kaplan, S. M. Psychological aspects of cardiac disease: A study of patients experiencing mitral commissurotomy. Psychosom. Med., 18:220, 1956.

────── and Gottschalk, L. A. Modifications of the oropharyngeal bacteria with changes in the psychodynamic state: II. A validation study. Psychosom. Med., 20:314, 1958.

────── and Hetrick, E. S. Thyrotoxicosis, traumatic neurosis, and the dangerous environment. Psychosom. Med., 24:240, 1962.

Kepecs, J. G., Robin, M., and Brunner, M. Relationship between certain emotional states and exudation into the skin. Psychosom. Med., 13:10, 1951.

────── Rabin, A., and Robin, M. Atopic dermatitis: A clinical psychiatric study. Psychosom. Med., 13:1, 1951.

Kissen, D. M. Specific Psychological Factors in Pulmonary Tuberculosis. Health Bulletin. Issued by the Chief Medical Officer of the Department of Health for Scotland, 1956, Vol. 14.

Kowal, S. J. Emotions as a cause of cancer. Psychoanal. Rev., 42:217, 1955.

Langheinrich, O. Psychische Einflüsse auf die Secretionstätigkeit des Magens und des Duodenums. München. Med. Wschr., 69:527, 1922.

LeChatelier, H. L. Recherches expérimentales et théoriques sur les équilibres chimiques. Paris, Dunod, 1888.

Libow, L. S., and Durell, J. Clinical studies on the relationship between psychosis and the regulation of thyroid gland activity: I. Periodic psychosis with coupled change in thyroid function: report of a case. Psychosom. Med., 27:369, 1965a.

────── and Durell, J. Clinical studies on the relationship between psychosis and the regulation of thyroid gland activity: II. Psychotic symptoms and thyroid regulation in a case of post-thyroidectomy depressive psychosis. Psychosom. Med., 27:377, 1965b.

Liddell, D. W. Observations on epileptic automatism in a mental hospital population. J. Ment. Sc., 99:732, 1953.

Lidz, T. Emotional factors in the etiology of hyperthyroidism. Psychosom. Med., 11:2, 1949.

────── and Whitehorn, J. S. Life situations, emotions, and Grave's disease. Psychosom. Med., 12:184, 1950.

Lilly, J. S. Mental effects of reduction of ordinary levels of physical stimuli on intact, healthy persons. Psychiat. Res. Reports, 5:1, 1956.

Lindemann, E. Psychiatric problems in conservative treatment of ulcerative colitis. Arch. Neurol. Psychiat., 53:322, 1945.

Ludwig, A. O. Psychogenic factors in rheumatic disease. Bull. Rheum. Dis., 2:33, 1952.

———— Rheumatoid arthritis. In Recent Developments in Psychosomatic Medicine, Wittkower, E., and Cleghorn, R. A., eds. Philadelphia, Lippincott, 1954.

Macalpine, I. Pruritus ani: A psychiatric study. Psychosom. Med., 15:499, 1953.

Margette, E. The Early History of the Word "Psychosomatic." Canad. Med. Ass. J., 63:402, 1950.

Margolin, S. G. The behavior of the stomach during psychoanalysis. Psychoanal. Quart., 20:349, 1951.

———— Genetic and dynamic psychophysiological determinants of pathophysiological processes. In The Psychosomatic Concept in Psychoanalysis, Deutsch, F., ed. New York, International Universities Press, Inc., 1953, pp. 3-36.

McLary, A. R., Meyer, E., and Weitzman, E. L. Observations on the role of the mechanism of depression in some patients with disseminated lupus erythematosus. Psychosom. Med., 17:311, 1955.

Meinhardt, K., and Robinson, H. A. Stokes-Adams Syndrome precipitated by emotional stress. Psychosom. Med., 24:325, 1962.

Menninger, K. The Vital Balance. New York, Viking, 1963.

Meyer, A. The role of the mental factors in psychiatry. In Collected Papers of Adolf Meyer, II. Baltimore, Johns Hopkins Press, 1951.

Meyer, Albrecht, Bollmeier, L. N., and Alexander, F. Correlation between emotions and carbohydrate metabolism in two cases of diabetes mellitus. Psychosom. Med., 7:335, 1945.

Meyer, B. C., Blacher, R. S., and Brown, F. A clinical study of psychiatric and psychological aspects of mitral surgery. Psychosom. Med., 23:194, 1961.

Michaels, J. J. Discussion. In The Psychosomatic Concept in Psychoanalysis, Deutsch, F., ed. New York, International Universities Press, Inc., 1953, pp. 144-149.

Millet, J. A. P., Lief, H., and Mittelmann, B. Raynaud's Disease. Psychogenic factors and psychotherapy. Psychosom. Med., 15:61, 1953.

Mirsky, I. A. Emotional hyperglycemia. Proc. Cent. Soc. Clin. Res., 19:74, 1946.

Mittelmann, B. Psychogenic factors and psychotherapy in hyperthyreosis and rapid heart imbalance. J. Nerv. Ment. Dis., 77:465, 1933.

Mohr, F. Psychophysische Behandlungsmethoden. Leipzig, Hirzel, 1925.

Moos, R. H. Personality factors associated with rheumatoid arthritis: A review. J. Chronic Dis., 17:41, 1964.

———— and Solomon, G. F. Psychologic comparisons between women with rheumatoid arthritis and their nonarthritic sisters: I. Personality test and interview rating data. Psychosom. Med., 27:135, 1965a.

———— and Solomon, G. F. Psychologic comparisons between women with rheumatoid arthritis and their nonarthritic sisters: II. Content analysis of interviews. Psychosom. Med., 27:150, 1965b.

Paneth, H. G. Some observations on the relation of psychotic states to psychosomatic disorders. Psychosom. Med., 21:106, 1959.

Papper, S., and Handy, J. Observations in a "control" group of patients in psychosomatic investigation. New Eng. J. Med., 255:1067, 1956.

Piney, A. Recent Advances in Hematology. London, J. and A. Churchill, Ltd., 1927.

Rangell, L. Psychiatric aspects of pain. Psychosom. Med., 15:22, 1953.

――― The nature of conversion. J. Amer. Psychoanal. Ass., 7:632, 1959.

Razran, G. The observable unconscious and the inferable conscious in current Soviet psychophysiology. Psychol. Rev., 68 (No. 2):81, March, 1961.

Reiser, M. F., Brust, A. A., and Ferris, E. B. Life situations, emotions, and the course of patients with arterial hypertension. Psychosom. Med., 13:133, 1951a.

――― Rosenbaum, M., and Ferris, E. B., Psychologic mechanisms in malignant hypertension. Psychosom. Med., 3:147, 1951b.

Renneker, R. E., Cutler, R., Hora, J., Bacon, C., Bradley, G., Kearney, J., and Cutler, M. Psychoanalytic explorations of emotional correlates of cancer of the breast. Psychosom. Med., 25:106, 1963.

Richter, C. P. Hormones and rhythms in man and animals. Recent Progr. Hormone Res., 13:105, 1957.

Ripley, H. S., and Wolff, H. G. Life Situations, Emotions, and Glaucoma, Psychosom. Med., 12:215, 1950.

Rubin, J., Nagler, R., Spiro, H. M., and Pilot, M. L. Measuring the effect of emotions on esophageal motility. Psychosom. Med., 24:170, 1962.

Saul, L. J., and Bernstein, C. The emotional settings of some attacks of urticaria. Psychosom. Med., 3:349, 1941.

Schilder, P. The Image and Appearance of the Human Body. New York, International Universities Press, Inc., 1950.

Schindler, R. Die Psychoneurosen des Verdauungstraktes, Differentialdiagnose, Psychogenese und Psychotherapie. Ber üb D. II Allg. Artzl. Kong. F. Psychotherapie, pp. 184-194, Leipzig, Hirzel, 1924.

Schmale, A. H., Jr. Relationship of separation and depression to disease: I. A report on a hospitalized medical population. Psychosom. Med., 20:259, 1958.

Schneider, S. F. A psychological basis for indifference to pain. Psychosom. Med., 24:119, 1962.

Schur, M. Comments on the metapsychology of somatization. In The Psychoanalytic Study of the Child. New York, International Universities Press, Inc., 1955, Chap. 10, pp. 119-164.

Seidenberg, R. Omnipotence, denial, and psychosomatic medicine. Psychosom. Med., 25:31, 1963.

Seitz, P. F. D. Experiments in the substitution of symptoms by hypnosis II. Psychosom. Med., 15:405, 1953.

Selye, H. The general adaptation syndrome and the disease of adaptation. J. Clin. Endocrinol., 6:117, 1946.

――― and Fortier, C. Adaptive reaction to stress. In Life Stress and Bodily Disease. Baltimore, The Williams and Wilkins Co., 1950, Chap. 1.

Silverman, S. The role of the aggressive drives in the conversion process. In On the Mysterious Leap from the Mind to the Body, Deutsch, F., ed. New York, International Universities Press, Inc., 1959, pp. 111-130.

――― Ego functions and bodily reactions. J. Am. Psychoanal. Assoc., 10:538, 1962.

Solomon, G. F., and Moos, R. H. Emotions, immunity and disease: A speculative theoretical integration. Arch. Gen. Pychiat., 11:657, 1964.

————— and Moos, R. H. The relationship of personality to the presence of rheumatoid factor in asymptomatic relatives of patients with rheumatoid arthritis. Psychosom. Med., 27:350, 1965.

Stainbrook, E. Psychosomatic medicine in the nineteenth century. Psychosom. Med., 14:24, 1952.

Swartz, J., and Semrad, E. Psychosomatic disorders in psychosis. Psychosom. Med., 13:314, 1951.

Szasz, T. S. Pain and Pleasure. London, Tavistock Publications Limited, 1957.

Waelder, R. Basic Theory of Psychoanalyis. New York, International Universities Press, Inc., 1960.

Weisman, A. D. A study of the psychodynamics of duodenal ulcer exacerbations: With special reference to treatment and the problem of specificity. Psychosom. Med., 18:2, 1956.

Wittkower, E. Ueber den Einfluss der Affekte auf den Gallefluss, Klin. Wschr., 7:2193, 1928.

————— A Psychiatrist Looks at Tuberculosis. London, National Association for the Prevention of Tuberculosis, 1949.

————— and Russell, B. Emotional Factors in Skin Disease. New York, Hoeber, 1953.

Wolff, H. G. Life stress and bodily disease—A formulation. Proc. Ass. Res. Nerv. Ment. Dis., 29:1059, 1950.

————— Stress and Disease. Springfield, Ill., Charles C Thomas, 1953.

Indexes

Indexes

Author Index

Adamson, J. D., 167, 431
Alexander, F., 5, 11, 13, 14, 16, 20, 191, 251, 291, 431, 433, 435
Alexander, R. P., 64, 431
Alkan, L., 345, 431
Appel, J., 398, 431

Bacon, C. L., 27, 431, 436
Benedek, T., 58, 431
Bernard, C., 18, 395, 431
Bernstein, C., 126, 436
Bertalanffy, L. von, 18, 395, 431
Blacher, R. S., 321, 435
Bland, W., 431
Bollmeier, L. N., 11, 435
Bradley, G., 436
Brown, F., 321, 435
Browning, J. S., 72, 163, 431
Bruch, H., 11
Brunner, M., 126, 434
Brust, A. A., 10, 136, 436

Calden, C., 76, 431
Cannon, W. B., 16, 18, 395, 431
Canter, A., 29, 30, 434
Carmichael, H. T., 433
Chafetz, M. E., 93, 431
Chambers, W. N., 27, 174, 267, 272, 431
Christenson, W. N., 433
Cleghorn, R. A., 435
Clemen, T., 431
Cleveland, S. E., 210, 432
Cluff, L., 29, 30, 434
Cullen, W., 7
Cutler, M., 27, 431, 436
Cutler, R., 436

Daniels, G. E., 11
Day, G., 27, 432
Descartes, R., 6, 7
Deutsch, F., 9, 18, 32, 45, 402, 407, 432, 435, 436
Dolger, H., 11
Dunbar, H. F., 9, 10, 11, 345-346
Duncan, C. H., 11, 148, 432
Dupertuis, C. S., 76, 431
Durrell, J., 238, 434

Engel, G. L., 20-22, 27, 29, 392, 394, 400, 409-410, 432
Epstein, A. W., 93, 432
Ervin, F., 93, 432
Evans, F. M., 434

Fechner, G. T., 18, 432
Fenichel, O., 9, 53, 384, 403, 405, 432
Féré, Ch., 6-7, 432
Ferenczi, S., 8-9, 432
Ferris, E. B., 10, 136, 436
Fischer, A. E., 11
Fisher, S., 210, 432
Flagg, G. W., 431
Fortier, C., 436
Foster, S., 431
Fox, H. M., 22, 432
French, T. M., 14, 27, 432
Freud, A., 432
Freud, S., 8, 9, 45, 401, 411, 432-433

Garma, A., 191, 433
Gibson, J. G., 238
Goldstein, K., 405
Gottschalk, L. A., 210, 277, 433, 434
Greene, W. A., Jr., 28, 29, 53, 57, 58, 433

441

Griesinger, W., 6
Grinker, R. R., 15, 16, 20, 191, 402, 433
Groddeck, G., 9, 433

Halliday, J. L., 11
Ham, G. C., 251, 433
Hamburger, W. W., 27, 433
Handy, J., 27, 436
Hartmann, H., 17, 401, 433
Harvey, W., 5
Hebb, D. O., 22, 433
Heiman, M., 27, 433
Heinroth, J. C., 6
Hendrick, I., 45, 402, 433
Hetrick, E. S., 251, 252, 434
Hinkle, L. E., Jr., 11, 12, 433-434
Hokanson, J. E., 76, 431
Holmes, T. H., 10, 12
Hora, J., 436
Houseworth, J. H., 72, 163, 431

Imboden, J. B., 29, 30, 434

Kane, F. D., 433
Kaplan, S. M., 251, 252, 277, 320, 434
Kearney, J., 436
Kepecs, J. G., 126, 434
Kissen, D. M., 27, 434
Kowal, S. J., 27, 434
Kraepelin, E., 6
Kris, E., 17, 401, 433

Langheinrich, O., 345, 434
Le Chatelier, H. L., 18, 434
Lewis, W. C., 76, 431
Libow, L. S., 238, 434
Liddell, L. S., 93, 434
Lidz, T., 11, 251, 434
Lief, H., 27, 435
Lilly, J. S., 22, 435
Lindemann, E., 27, 435
Lowenstein, R. M., 17, 401, 433
Ludwig, A. O., 27, 82, 435

Macalpine, I., 64, 435
Margette, E., 6, 435
Margolin, S. G., 155-156, 402, 435
Maupertius, 18
McLary, A. R., 27, 435
Meinhardt, K., 427, 435

Menninger, K., 16-18, 22, 395-396
Menninger, W. C., 11
Meyer, A., 9, 10, 435
Meyer, Albrecht, 11, 435
Meyer, B. C., 321, 435
Meyer, E., 27, 435
Michaels, J. J., 402, 435
Miller, G., 58, 433
Millet, J. A. P., 27, 435
Mirsky, I. A., 11, 435
Mittelmann, B., 27, 435
Mohr, F., 345, 435
Moleschott, J., 6
Moos, R. H., 13, 82, 435, 437
Murphy, W. F., 32, 432

Nagler, R., 358, 436

Ostfeld, A., 433

Paneth, H. G., 230, 435
Papper, S., 27, 436
Parry, C. H., 251
Pilot, M. L., 358, 436
Piney, A., 57, 436

Rabin, A., 126, 434
Rangell, L., 19-20, 101, 402, 436
Razran, G., 407-408, 436
Reiser, M. F., 10, 27, 136, 174, 267, 272, 431, 436
Renneker, R. E., 27, 431, 436
Richter, C. P., 238, 436
Ripley, H. S., 11-12, 148, 432, 436
Robbins, F. P., 15-16, 20, 191, 433
Robin, M., 126, 434
Robinson, H. A., 427, 435
Rosen, S. R., 11, 398, 431
Rosenbaum, M., 436
Rubin, J., 358, 436
Russell, B., 64, 437

Saul, L. J., 126, 436
Schilder, P., 406, 436
Schindler, R., 345, 436
Schmale, A. H., Jr., 27, 28, 29, 167, 394, 400, 431, 436
Schneider, S. F., 410, 436
Schur, M., 16, 17, 20, 191, 402, 436
Schwab, R. S., 93, 431

Seidenberg, R., 411, 436
Seitz, P. F. D., 108, 436
Selye, H., 17, 436
Semrad, E., 398, 437
Serota, H. M., 210, 277, 433
Shapiro, L. B., 210, 277, 433
Silverman, S., 400, 436
Solomon, G. F., 13, 82, 435, 437
Spinoza, 6
Spiro, H. M., 358, 436
Stainbrook, E., 6, 437
Stevenson, I. P., 11, 148, 432
Swartz, J., 398, 437
Swisher, S. N., 433
Sydenham, T., 5
Szasz, T. S., 409, 437

Thetford, W. H., 433
Treuting, T., 434

Waelder, R., 38, 437
Weir, J., 7
Weisman, A. D., 119, 120, 437
Weitzman, E. L., 27, 435
Whitehorn, J. S., 11, 251, 434
Willis, T., 11
Wittkower, E., 27, 64, 76, 345, 435, 437
Wolf, S., 434
Wolff, H. G., 12, 433, 434, 436, 437

Young, L. E., 433

Subject Index *

Abdominal pain
  and marital crisis, 366-373
  and somatic identification, 333-339
Accident, and emotional factors, 331
Accident proneness, 282, 283, 361-365
Adaptation, 17
  in chronic illness, 121-127
  failures of, 11
  and minor psychophysical dysfunction,
    398-399
  shifts in, 93
Addictive tendencies, 217
Addicts, motivation of, 217
Affect. See also Pathways of expression.
  development of, 399
  and drive activity, 400-401
  intensity of, 37
  somatic equivalents of, 111-120
Affect block, 243, 249
Affective responses, 3, 382t, 383t, 384
  secondary, 400
Age, and symptom production, 411-412
Aggression, 38
  and brain, 397-398
  deflections of, onto organs, 115
Alcoholism, 213-219
  and dependency, 256
  and secondary gain, 128-137
Ambivalence, 43, 45, 50, 235, 256
  toward excrement, 291
  toward mother, 282
Amenorrhea, 7
Anality, 62, 64, 89
Anamnesis, associative, 32, 34-35, 419-420
Anniversary stress, 144-150, 159, 201
Anorexia, 51
  and psychophysical instability, 227-231

Anxiety, 37, 41, 43, 45, 72, 80, 146, 382t
  and cardiac arrhythmia, 148-149
  chronic, 358
  defenses against, 99
  as ego function, 17
  equivalents of, 350
  and gut reaction, 291
  intractable, 261
  and lymphoma and leukemia, 58
  about medical procedures, 302-309
  and pain, 410
  pathways of expression, 384t
  severe, 260
  somatization of, 115-116, 353
Appendectomy, 69
Appendicitis, 56
Arthritis
  and object loss, 27
  psychological aspects of, 82, 209-210
  and stress, 13-14, 77-84, 210
Asthma, 72
  and object loss, 27
  and stress, 14
Avoidance, 43, 99

Back pain
  in accident-prone patient, 361-365
  following hematemesis and psychosis,
    87-88
  and medical procedures, 302-309
  psychological aspects of, 280-286
  and somatic identification, 287-295, 333-
    339
  and stress, 12, 205-212
Basic anamnestic excerpts, definition of, 34
Biliary symptoms, and stress, 340-347

* Page numbers entered in italics refer to extended case material or discussion in the text. Entries followed by a lowercase t refer to tabular material.

445

Body image, and chronic illness, 125
Body organ language, 358, 402
Body organ, symbolization of, 159-163, 407
Body, preoccupation with, 146
Bowel activity, and psychological factors, 291
Brain, as focus of aggression, 397-398
Brucellosis, and psychological factors, 392-332

Cancer, and object loss, 27
Cardiac arrhythmia, psychological factors, 11, 148-149
Cardiac decompensation, and emotions, 271-272
Cardiovascular system, as target organ, 350
Castration fantasies, 221
Castration fear, 61, 70, 79, 90, 108, 124, 142, 146, 207, 248-249, 274, 312, 335, 342
Castration themes, 235
Causality, multiple, 15
Central nervous system, 15
Cerebral embolism, 158
Chest pain, 213-219
    and narcissism, 310-315
    psychological and bacteriological factors, 273-279
Chief presenting symptom, definition of, 34
Chills and fever, in neurotic patient, 254-261
Chronicity
    adaptation to, 121-127
    and body image, 125
    in organic disease, 17
    and passivity, 125
    psychological results of, 125-126
    and secondary gain, 418, 422-425
Claustrophobia, 114
Clinical procedures, psychological aspects of, 151-157, 302-309, 428-429
Coitus interruptus, 284
Colic, and emotions, 7
Comment section of cases, description of, 35
Compensation, in stress, 23
Compulsiveness
    and cardiac arrhythmia, 149
    and dermatitis, 123
Conditioning. See also Target organ.
    interoceptive, 407-408
Conflict
    and effects of medication, 346
    and endocrine dysfunction, 247-253

Conflict (cont.)
    instinctual, and physical illness, 53
    masculinity, and indigestion, 140
    pregenital, and organic illness, 403
    and space motility, 210
    and sympathetic nervous system, 14
Congestive heart failure, 177, 271-272
    emotional factors in, 174-175, 267
    and object loss, 27
Constant milieu, theories of, 18
Constipation, and somatic identification, 287-295
Conversion hysteria, 19, 398
Conversion reactions, 8, 9, 18-20, 23, 99, 100-101, 115-116, 141-142, 166, 217, 261, 379, 382, 402
    chronic, 284
    differentiated from organ neuroses, 20
    origin of, 402
    and sexual impulses, 25
Convulsion, and emotions, 7
Cornell Medical Index, 29
Cough, and depression, 104-110
Crises, physical, and stress, 262-272

Daydreams, and traumatic neurosis, 393
Death, fear of, 350-351
Death instinct, 407
Decompensation, 189, 201
    physical, 26
    psychophysical, 50
Defense. See also Denial, Intellectualization, Overactivity, Projection, Reaction formation.
    mechanisms of, 3, 387-388, 402-403
    shifting, and pain remission, 193-197
Defensive patterns, in arthritic patient, 210
Defensiveness, 256
    and hospitalization, 207
Delirium tremens, 132, 134, 136
Denial, 23, 69, 114, 146, 166, 387-388
    of chronic illness, 125
    counterphobic, 251
    of dependency, 152
    of emotional problems, 43
    of grief, 28
    of hostility, 255, 270
    of pain, 411
    to perpetuate symptoms, 245
    of symptoms, 196
    of tension, 256
    usefulness of, 428
Dependency, 15, 130, 152, 258, 263
    and arthritis, 82

Dependency (cont.)
and asthma, 14
needs, 182, 188, 230, 249, 256, 282, 290
and stress, 165
Depletion, 41, 43
Depression, 37-38, 57-58, 104-110, 383t
agitated, 282
masked, 70, 265, 365
and object loss, 27
pathways of expression, 386t
and rheumatic heart disease, 320
as setting of disease, 28
and somatic illness, 108
and stomach pain, 164-168
and tuberculosis, 76
and ulcer, 120, 230
Deprivation, 50, 69
oral, 282
sensory, 22-23
syndrome, 22-23
Dermatitis, as adaptation, 121-127
Dermatoses, 7, 17
Desomatization of reactions, 17
Destructive instinct, 401
Destructiveness
essential, 38
mitigation of, 17
Diabetes
and emotions, 7
and life situation, 11
Diagnosis, and interviewing techniques, 419-422
Diagnostic terms, used by patients, 200, 207, 307
Diarrhea, 51, 56
and emotions, 7
Differentiation, self-object, 36
Discharge
of affect, 249, 305
pathways of. See Pathways of expression.
Disease
contagious, and emotions, 7, 277-278
defined, 20
factors, 21-22
Displacement, onto organ systems, 398
Doctor-patient relationship, in heart cases, 267, 272
Drive discharge, and bodily function, 400-401
Dysfunction, parasympathetic, 15
Dysfunction, somatic
and emotional tension, 401-402
in nonphysical illness, 415
Dyspnea, 171
and stress, 144-150, 316-322

Eating, emotional connotations of, 243, 325
Economic factors, and regression, 93
Ego
and cognition of objects, 45
development of, 36
as regulative agency, 16-18
and secondary thought process, 17
as synthesizing agency, 396
Ego function
and physical processes, 402
and specificity hypothesis, 191
and traumatic neurosis, 393
Elimination, 14
Emotional conflict
and effects of medication, 346
and endocrine dysfunction, 247-253
and pathogenesis of infection, 277-278
and sympathetic nervous system, 14
Emotions, and somatic disease, 11-14
Endocrine dysfunction
and emotional conflict, 247-253
and psychotic episode, 232-240
Endocrine system, as target organ, 238
Epigastric distress
chronic, 186-192
surgery and chronic neurosis, 241-246
symbolic aspects of, 138-143
Epilepsy, 92
psychological factors in, 93-94
and stress, 344-345
Equilibrium, psychophysical
and illness, 136
shifts in, 3, 106, 230, 237, 344-345, 373, 379-382
and stress, 396
Eros, 401
Esophageal motor function, and emotions, 358
Etiology, factors in, 21-22
Exhaustion, 43-44
Exhibitionistic tendencies, 61
Eye trouble, and psychotic episode, 232-240

Fascination, phenomenon of, 405
Fear, and hyperthyroidism, 251
Fever
and emotional factors, 329-332
and environmental factors, 329-332
in a markedly neurotic patient, 254-261
and object loss, 48-58
Field theory, in psychosomatic medicine, 15-16
Fluid shifts, and psychological state, 266

Followup data, definition of, 36
Food, symbolic meaning of, 243, 325
Frustration, 15

Gallbladder disease, and stress, 340-347
Gastrointestinal complaints, 198-204. See also Stomach pain.
  and loss, 180-185
  and tension, 67-76
  and vertigo, 111-120
Gastrointestinal and respiratory symptoms, 67-76
Gastrointestinal system, as target organ, 369, 371
Gastrostomy, symbolic meaning of, 155-156
Genitalization, 8
"Giving up," preceding psychiatric illness, 167
Glaucoma, and stress, 12
Globus hystericus, 284. See also Conversion reactions.
  and sexual repression, 8-9
Glycosuria, precipitation of, 11
Gout, and emotions, 7
Grief
  denial of, 28
  as disease, 394
Guilt, 223, 225
  and somatic identification, 337
Gut reaction, and anxiety, 291

Hair loss, and emotions, 7
Hallucination
  auditory, 87
  and discharge of hostility, 87
  and sensory deprivation, 23
  and superego pathology, 93
  visual, 87, 236
Headache, environmental factors in, 329-332
Health, defined, 20
Heart disease, rheumatic, 177
Heat-regulating mechanisms, and disturbed emotions, 54
Helplessness, 28, 50, 57, 104, 179, 395
  and exacerbation of illness, 400
  and ulcer, 119
Hematemesis, 117
  and psychotic episode, 85-95
Hepatitis, infectious, and loss, 27
Heredity
  and etiology of disease, 21
  and psychosomatic illness, 16
  and susceptibility to epilepsy, 94

Heterostasis
  definition of, 18
  further considerations of, 395
Hodgkin's disease, 53, 57
Homeostasis, 18
  agencies of, 395-396
  behavioral, 395
  shifts in, 38, 93, 379-380, 381t, 382
Homosexuality, and pruritis ani, 64
Hopelessness, 28, 395
  and exacerbation of illness, 400
Hospitalization, patient's reaction to, 429
Hostility, 16, 37, 42-43, 45, 54, 62, 80, 106, 115, 130, 140-141, 153, 171, 195, 223, 235, 243, 249, 342, 369, 383t
  and cardiac arrhythmia, 149
  denial of, 255, 270
  energies associated with, 399
  pathways of expression, 385t
  and somatic illness, 16
  and tuberculosis, 76
  turned inward, 37, 57
Hyperactivity. See Overactivity.
Hyperemia, and stress, 16
Hyperglycemia, precipitation of, 11
Hypermotility, and stress, 16
Hypersecretion, and stress, 16
Hypertension, 72
  and stress, 10-11, 14, 136
Hyperthyroidism, emotional factors in, 11, 250-252
Hypnosis, and symptom substitution, 108
Hypochondriasis, 64
Hysteria, 8-9
  conversion, 19, 398
  and pain, 101, 411

Icterus, and psychological factors, 345
Identification, 50, 229
  body image, 123
  feminine, 89, 183, 297, 300, 312, 320, 327
  hysterical, 405
  with lost object, 28
  multiple, 80
  passive, 243
  process of, 300
  somatic, 3, 36, 50-51, 70, 90, 99, 105-106, 113, 130, 140, 146, 166-167, 171, 181, 188, 222, 249, 274, 289, 292, 295, 305, 314, 319, 336-337, 339, 342, 344, 351, 365, 369, 388, 389t, 403-405
    and abdominal pain, 333-339

Identification (cont.)
  somatic (cont.)
    and back pain, 287-295, 333-339
    and constipation, 287-295
    and dyspnea, 316-322
    and guilt, 337
    manifestation of, 404-405
Illness
  accidental and incidental factors, 412-413
  multifactorial approach to, 20-21
  nonphysical, theoretical considerations, 415
  organic, psychological factors, 277-278, 416-417
  as punishment, 53
Immunological dysfunction, and life situation, 13
Indigestion, symbolic aspects, 138-143
Infantilism, physiologic, 402
Infection, emotional influences on, 7, 277-278
Innervation, concommitant, 13-14
Insomnia, and traumatic neurosis, 393
Instability, and anorexia, 227-231
Instinctual conflicts, and physical illness, 53
Instinctual drives, somatic origin, 8
Intellectualization, 23, 201
Interoception, 407-408
Interviewing, techniques of, 33, 419-422.
  See also Anamnesis, associative.
Introjection, 37, 191, 405
Isolation, and stress, 23
Itching, 296-301
  and adaptation, 121-127
  anal, 59-66

Journal of Psychosomatic Medicine, 9

Laboratory procedures, and patients' reactions, 151-157, 302-309, 428-429
Lactation, and emotions, 7
Leukemia, 28, 53, 58
  and object loss, 28-29
  and vicarious object, 28-29
Life situation, and somatic disease, 10-14
Loss
  of body parts, 171
  and gastrointestinal symptoms, 180-185
  of objects, 50
    and asthma, 27
    and bodily representation, 161

Loss (cont.)
  of objects (cont.)
    and cancer, 27
    and conversion, 19
    and depressive-like reactions prior to onset of medical disease, 27
    and fever, 48-58
    and obesity, 27
    somatic response to, 27-30, 53, 57, 69, 119, 123, 169-179, 289, 394-395, 416
    and stress, 379
    sudden, 230
"Lowered resistance," and psychological state, 108
Lupus erythematosus, and object loss, 27
Lymphoma, 28, 51, 53, 57-58, 422-423

Malaise, generalized, 296-301
Marital crisis, and abdominal cramps, 366-373
Masculinity conflicts, and indigestion, 140
Masochism
  and arthritis, 82
  and medical instructions, 225
Material used in this study, 31-38
Materialization phenomenon, 9
Medical advice, difficulty in following, 220-226
Medical procedures, psychological effect of, 151-157, 302-309, 428-429
Medication, and blocking of emotional discharge, 300, 345-346
Mesmerism, 6
Methodology, of present study, 31-38
Migraine, following gastrectomy, 162
Mind-body relationship, 5-21
Minnesota Multiphasic Personality Inventory, 29
Mitral surgery, and emotions, 321
Motor referents, 80, 183, 390t
Mourning
  pathological, 179
  preceding death, 167
  and stress, 24
Mouth lesions, 59-66
Musculoskeletal system, as target organ, 364

Narcissism, 146, 298
  and chest pain, 310-315
Nausea, 296-301
  and psychological loss, 169-179
Nervousness, and stomach pain, 41

Neurodermatitis, and stress, 14
Neurosis
    combat, 261
    and epigastric distress, *241-246*
    organ, 9, 14, 20
    persistent, 258
    traumatic, 393
    and weakness, *348-354*
Neutralization, 17
Nightmares, and traumatic neurosis, 393

Obesity, and object loss, 27
Object loss. See Loss.
Object omission, 179
Object relation, and sensory development, 45
Oral needs, 59, 62, 89, 105-106, 114, 130, 153, 171, 179, 195, 264, 282, 312, 325, 342
    and peptic ulcer, 191
    and smoking, 320
Organ neuroses, definition, 9, 20
Organ system, sensitized, 36
Organ, target. See Target organ.
Organic diagnosis, patient's need for, *198-204*
Organic heart disease, situational factors, 319-321
Organic illness, psychological factors, 416-417
Organic vulnerability, and X-factor, 14
Overactivity, 34, 49, 64
    compensatory, 114, 135, 249, 270
    compulsive, 50
    counterphobic, 237, 282
    defensive, 119, 130, 132, 152, 207, 264, 387t

Pain
*   anticipatory function of, 410
    denial of, 411
    and dependency needs, 101
    determinants of, 304-305
    epigastric, and symbolic aspects of, *138-143*
    lower extremity, psychological factors, *96-103*
    and masochism, 101
¦   without organic disease, 101
    in relation to psychological and bacterio-
¦   logical factors, 273-279
    remission of, *193-199*
    and superego pathology, 411
*   symbolic meanings of, 409
    threshold of, 101

Painful joints, and stress, *77-84*
"Pain-prone" patients, 409-410
Panic state, 87
Parallelism, doctrine of, 6
Paranoid symptoms, 236
Passivity, 43, 79-80, 130, 215
    in chronic illness, 125
    and ulcer, 119
Pathways of expression, 236-237, 243, 331, 384-386t, 387, 398-399
    affective, 195, 201
    somatic, 93, 108, 115, 120, 136, 142, 188, 190, 223, 235, 284, 345-346, 396
Patient-physician relationship, 267
Patients in this study, 31
Peptic ulcer. See Ulcer.
Perception. See also Sensorimotor config-
    urations.
    and disease process, 421-422
    of objects, 45
Personality profile, 10
Personification, of body parts, 189
Phagocytism, and emotions, 7-8
Phantom organ, 245
Phobic reaction, and stress, 23
Physical data, compilation of, 33, 35
Physical symptoms, alternating with psy-
    chosis, 230, 397-398
Poisoning, delusions of, 230
Pregnancy fantasy, 70, 243, 327
Premature birth, and emotions, 7
Projection, 43, 79, 90, 166, 195, 388
    of significance of loss object, 28
Pruritis, 134, *296-301*
    and adaptation, *121-127*
    ani, *59-66*
Psychoanalysis
    and organic disease, 9
    and psychosomatic medicine, 8
    and somatic disease, 13-14
Psychobiology, 9-10
Psychodynamic impressions, definition of, 35
Psychodynamic patterns in gastric hyper-
    function, 191
Psychopaths, motivation of, 217
Psychosis, and thyroid function, 238
Psychosomatic medicine, 5-6
    introduction of term, 9
    in nineteenth century, 6-8
Psychosomatic processes, implications of, 45
Psychotherapy
    in comprehensive treatment approach, 422-428

Psychotherapy (cont.)
  motivation for, 424
  resistance to, 213-219
  and secondary gain, 424-425
Psychotic break, and psychosomatic disorder, 398
Punishment, illness as, 53

Rationalization, 79, 99, 166, 388
  of symptoms, 196
Raynaud's disease, and object loss, 27
Reaction formation, 123
Reality event, and improvement in somatic illness, 137
Reality testing, 23, 87
Reception, 14
Regression, 15, 16, 36, 53, 61, 234-235, 396
  narcissistic, 161
  in organic illness, 422-423
  "physiologic," 402
  from psychological equilibrium, 396-397
  psychophysical, 80, 179
Rejection, 54
Remission, of pain, 193-197
Repression
  of passive-dependent tendencies, 387
  and somatic disease, 13-16
Resistance, to psychotherapy, 213-219
Resomatization, of responses, 17
Respiration, and emotion, 7
Respiratory system, and tension, 67-76
Retaliation fantasies, 221
Retention, 14
Reticuloendothelial disease, and emotions, 57-58
Retrojection, and conversion, 19
Rheumatic heart disease, and depression, 320
Rheumatoid arthritis. See Arthritis.

Screen memory, 64, 221
Scurvy, and emotions, 7
Secondary gain, 53, 61, 99, 116, 207, 215, 217, 225, 256, 258, 284, 314, 321, 418, 424-425
  and alcoholism, 128-137
Sensorimotor configurations, 3, 390t, 406-409, 421
Separation, 30, 58. See also Loss.
  compared with non-separation, prior to somatic manifestations, 29
  and leukemia, 58
  in normal adults, 29

Separation anxiety, and passive needs, 215
Sexualization
  of activities, 235
  of body areas, 62, 64
  of chest pain, 215
  of heart, 146
  of medical procedures, 89-90, 333-335
Sibling reaction, to parental illness, 339
Sibling rivalry, 188, 293, 331
  and hyperthyroidism, 188
"Silent" affects, 400
"Silent phase," 72
Skeletal structure, and psychosomatic disease, 20
Skin disorders, and emotions, 7, 17
Somatic equivalent, 115, 146, 201, 384, 393
Somatic identification. See Identification, somatic.
Somatic representation, 384, 395
Somatization, 20, 397, 402
Sore throat, 159-163
  and stress, 323-328
"Sources of supply," 394, 400
Space motility, and conflict, 210
Specificity hypothesis, 14, 191
  and psychosomatic problems, 15
Stereotypy, and psychosomatic medicine, 15
Stimuli, interoceptive, 407-408
Stokes-Adams syndrome, 426-427
Stomach pain, 41-47
  and depression, 164-168
  and emotional tension, 355-360
  psychological aspects, 151-157
  remission of, with shifting defenses, 193-197
Stress, physical, 22-23
Stress, psychological, 22-24, 37, 58, 378-379, 395. See also Tension.
  anniversary, 24-25, 144-150, 159, 201
  anticipation of, 25-26
  and arthritis, 13-14, 77-84
  and asthma, 14
  and back pain, 205-212
  and biliary symptoms, 340-347
  and cardiac function, 11, 148-149, 271-272
  compensation in, 23
  concepts of, 391-413
  definitions of, 22
  disguised, 77-84
  dynamics of, 22-24, 380t
  and dyspnea, 144-150, 316-322
  and epilepsy, 344-345

Stress (cont.)
  and everyday events, 25
  and glaucoma, 12
  intensity of, 26
  and local tissue changes, 371
  and loss of object, 27-30, 394-395
  and medical procedures, 302-309
  and mourning, 24
  and national events, 24
  neutralization of, 26
  origins of, 392
  and painful joints, 77-84
  psychophysical response, 45, 396
  recurrent, and physical crises, 262-272
  and serum sickness, 296-301
  and sexual impulse, 25
  somatic responses to, 16, 22-30, 35, 53
  and sore throat, 323-328
  and success, 26
  and syncope, 350
  and traumatic events, 24
  and ulcer, 222
  varieties of, 25-26
Structure-function, and field theory, 15
Sublimation, 20
Success, and stress, 26
Suffering, and secondary gain, 424
Superego activity, 44
  and hopelessness, 400
  and pain, 411
  pathological, 93, 217, 411
Superego-ego tensions, 391, 392t
Surgery, psychophysical complications of, 245, 321
Symbolism, of clinical procedures, 151-157
Symbolization
  of body organs, 159-163, 407
  and conversion, 19
Sympathectomy, 269, 271, 273
Symptom awareness, psychological determinants, 174-175
Symptom substitution, 108
Symptoms
  and age, 411-412
  hysterical, 5
  physical, relation to psychological systems, 414-415
  redistribution of, 72
Syncope, 350
  and stress, 340-347
Synesthesia, 406

Target organ, 6-7, 36, 69, 120, 136, 146, 153, 163, 190, 200, 230, 416-417

Target organ (cont.)
  cardiovascular system as, 350
  gastrointestinal system as, 186-192, 369, 371
  musculoskeletal system as, 364
  peripheral nerves as, 136
  stomach as, 223
  thyroid as, 238
Tension. See also Stress.
  and cardiac dysfunction, 175
  defined, 22
  and rheumatoid arthritis, 210
  and shifting symptoms, 67-76
  superego-ego, 391, 392t
  symbolic expressions of, 355-360
  and throat symptoms, 355-360
Theoretical implications, of present study, 414-418
Threshold, of pain, 101
Throat symptoms, and emotional tensions, 355-360
Thyroid, as target organ, 238
Thyrotoxicosis
  emotional factors, 251
  and object loss, 27
  and psychotic manifestations, 235-236
  and stress, 14
  and traumatic neurosis, 251-252
Tiredness, 41
Total-field theory, 16
Transference
  and elicitation of symptoms, 420-421
  father, 57
  negative, 293
  positive, 76
Traumatic event. See also Neurosis, traumatic.
  as chronic psychological irritant, 353
  delayed response to, 24
  and somatic responses, 393
Tuberculosis, 72-75
  emotional factors, 76
  and object loss, 27

Ulcer, 20, 21
  and aggression, 115
  and depression, 120
  emotional factors, 119-120, 151-157, 161-162
  and oral needs, 191
  and passivity, 119
  and psychosis, 230
  and stress, 14
  symptoms of, 72, 220-226

Ulcer patient
  and arthritic patient, compared, 210-211
  and need for organic diagnosis, 202
Ulcerative colitis
  and object loss, 27
  and stress, 14
Unconscious, the, and bodily function, 8
Urethral fantasies, 264
Urinary secretion, and emotions, 7
Urticaria, and emotions, 126
Uterine bleeding, and object loss, 27

Variables
  affects: intensity and pathways of ex-
    pression, 37-38
  definition of, 36-38
  homeostatic shifts, 38
  other factors, 38

Variables (cont.)
  psychological defenses, 38
  role of, 4
  sensitized organ system, 36-37
  sensorimotor configurations, 36
  somatic identification, 36
  stress: dynamic significance, 37
  stress: surface meaning, 37
  systematic consideration of, 376-392
Vector concept, and organic neurosis, 14
Vertigo, 72
  in gastrointestinal disease, *111-120*
Vicarious object, 28-29
Voyeuristic tendencies, 61
Vulnerability, organic, 14

Weakness, and neurosis, *348-354*
"Weeping" lesions, 123-126

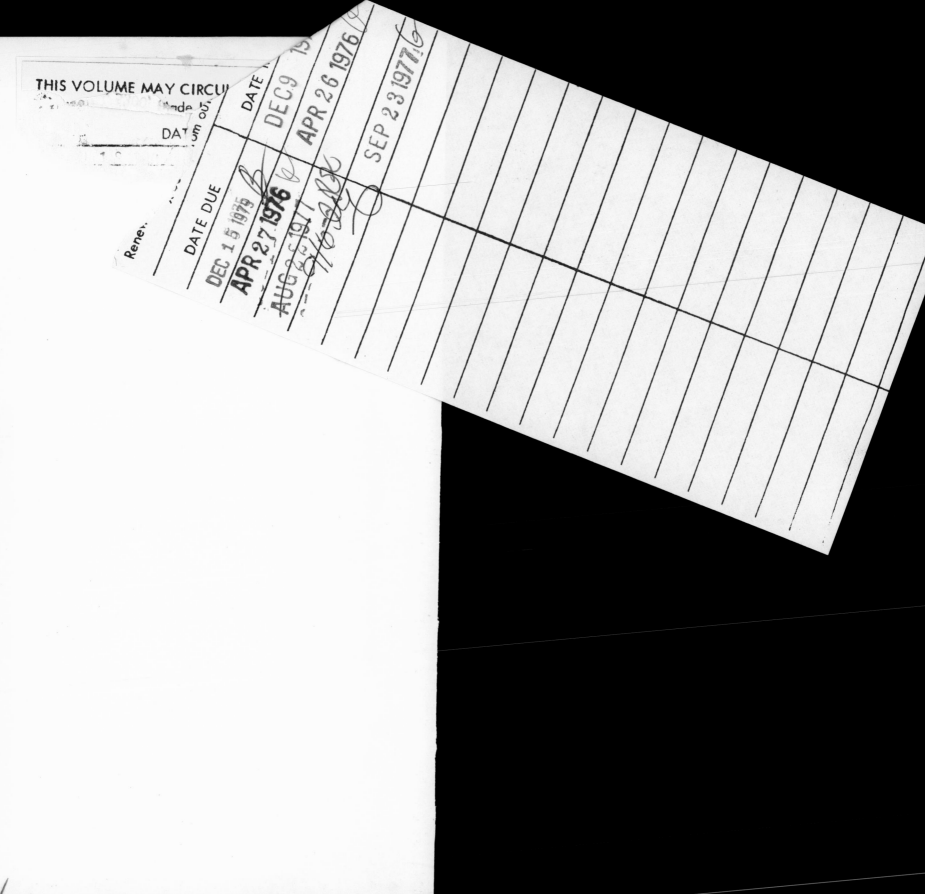